PC PLUS MODEM AND COMMUNICATIONS GUIDE BOOK
Sue Schofield

PC PLUS
MODEM AND COMMUNICATIONS GUIDE BOOK
Sue Schofield

Future Business Books
Future Publishing Ltd
Seven Dials
Saw Close
Bath BA1 1EN

Future Business Books
Future Publishing Ltd
Seven Dials
Saw Close
Bath BA1 1EN

ISBN 1 85870 000 0

British Library Cataloguing in Publication Data

A CIP catalogue record for this book is available from the British Library

Commissioned by Graham Douglas
Cover design by Steve Chard
Typeset by Barbara McGavin
Printed and bound by Beshara Press, Cheltenham.

'Speak English!' said the Eaglet. 'I don't know the meaning of half those long words, and, what's more, I don't believe you do either!'

Lewis Carrol
Alice's Adventures in Wonderland

For Charles, who ended up aiding and abetting

Contents

7   Going on-line

8   Inter-species file transfer

15   CompuServe

Appendices

This is a book about personal data-communications and how to make them work for you. It's a book that needed writing – there are few objective and useful books on the subject and the ones that are available usually seem to carry the indelible stamp of some manufacturer or other, or are filled with endless reviews of comms packages and equipment.

You won't find any product reviews in this book. That's a function best left to the dozens of computer magazines on the market. Nor will you find any recommendations as to specific equipment – this isn't a book for the equipment junkie, although it could very easily have been. But what I hope you will find is enough information to get you going with a modem and your computer. Having some basic telecommunications skills will soon become almost mandatory for users of personal computers, just as a driving license is essential to contemporary life in the UK. This book will help you achieve those skills.

Like many modern books this one was produced entirely on the sort of personal computer which can be bought in any High Street electronic store. But unlike many books this one was also researched electronically by using some of the vast knowledge resources available through the telephone modem. Virtually all of the mail and research for this book was sent and received through the excellent CompuServe Information Service (CIS). This eventually included dozens of megabytes of ASCII text research material, and several megabytes of E-mail. Even paper mail was sent to the USA by sending ASCII text to CompuServe, whose computers then printed it out, put it in an envelope, and somehow licked and posted the result.

The section on Integrated Services Digital Network (ISDN) was written after a startling demonstration by British Telecom's ISDN marketing supremo. Over a mug of stout brown tea and a plateful of BT biscuits, Andrew Stansfield calmly switched on his PC which then connected him through ISDN to a remote Novell network. He didn't touch the keyboard during the process. The connection was almost instantaneous, without any of the usual fighting with modem connect strings, or reading of the inch thick technical manuals that normally accompany the process. It was enough to convince me that the days of the dial-up analogue modem are numbered.

When ISDN equipment prices drop, as they are bound to do, we shall sit around the log fire on cold winter nights regaling each other with sagas about just how difficult analogue modems were to use. Sadly, our children will not believe us as they flit instantly around the world on error-free digital lines. So keep that 'old' V32bis modem. It will make a useful conversation piece for your grandchildren.

Equipment used

The book was written on a Mac Classic with the 'Nisus' word processor. Mobile computing and comms was via Amstrad NC100 and Atari Portfolio computers, and a Viva 2400 pocket 'rocket' modem. An Amiga 600HD and 'Deluxe Paint' was used to generate the line art objects, which were then transported, collated and integrated into 'Ami-Pro 3' on a 33MHz PC. The line art files were then transported to the Mac for eventual integration with the text in 'Quark XPress'.

A Bernoulli 90 Mbyte Transportable Drive provided backup for the Mac, and a Logitech Hand Scanner was used for image scanning on the PC. The PC, MAC, and Amiga were all used with the Hayes 'Optima 144' sextuple-standard, and 'Smartmodem 9600 + Quad' modems to connect to the services listed. Session logs and drafts were printed on Hewlett Packard 'Deskjet' and Apple 'Stylewriter' printers. Screen grabs from the PC were converted to PCX files and transferred to the Mac using the techniques described in the book.

The Comms packages used were: 'Hayes Smartcom Exec', 'Hayes Smartcom EZ' for the Mac, 'Term24' for the Amiga, 'ACOM' for the Atari Portfolio, and the inbuilt terminal emulator on the Amstrad NC100. The PC package 'Rencom Plus' from Dortec was used to rummage around the European dial-up services. 'Odyssey' and 'Deputy' for the PC were used for miscellaneous screen shots, and to prove to the world that Shareware works.

Windows 'Terminal' provided many other screen shots, to show that you don't need to spend much money to get going, as did 'Microlink', a Shareware comms programme for Windows. CompuServe Information Manager (CIM) was used in its DOS, Windows 3.1 and MAC versions for EMAIL and file transfer through CIS, and a Panasonic UF121 fax machine squirted faxes around the world. Technical references were checked on-line with CompuServe's Grolier Encyclopedia.

The book was deliberately written using as many different computing platforms as possible, to put to bed the myth that one computer type is really any better than any other for basic telecomms. Most computers can now handle telecomms with ease, some have more or less facilities, but you don't need the worlds largest and fastest PC or Mac to get started. So if some propeller-head on a bulletin board tells you that you his £10,000 set-up is any better for basic personal comms, tell him to go take a jump. At the end of the day, personal computer communications are about people, not computer equipment.

My thanks to

Sylvia Thornley and the Crew at CIX who helped out at short notice with accounts and access to that service. Also a 'thank-you' to Martin Turner and his staff at CompuServe, and to all at Hayes UK for their encouragement. And to Charles Schofield, who produced the technical illustrations and soothed the fevered brow of the Author on occasions too many to count.

The quotations at the start of each chapter are taken from the similarly numbered texts of the I CHING, the 'Book of Changes', a book describing personal and social inter-communications. It was written 4000 years BC. (Before Computers)

About the Author

Sue Schofield was born and raised in England, educated in France, and ran a successful specialised data-comms and communications business until 1991. She now writes extensively about personal computers and is the author of several books on personal communications and computer related issues.

Sue lives in Sussex, with a miscellany of felines, and husband Charles, all of whom like to sleep upside down in dark corners. Her leisure interests include fending off a passion for Italian food, and not having to wear shoes. She is a member of the Society of Authors, the Scientific and Technical Authors Group (STAG), and was born in the Year of the Cat.

Sue can be contacted directly on 100113.2132 @ compuserve.com – and on CIX as S_SCO.

My thanks to the following people:

Sue Starie and Bill Pechey, Hayes Microcomputer Products UK

Martin Turner, CompuServe UK

Andrew Stansfield and Andrew Kenyan, BT ISDN Marketing

Barry Cartman, BABT

Don Milne, author of *Odyssey*

Denis Dornoy and Todd Currie of Dortec, Copenhagen

Sylvia Thornley, Compulink Information Exchange (CIX)

Mike Large, British Telecom Canterbury Press Office

Mike Shoenbach, New York

Peter Ellefsen, Pan Technology UK

Michael Spalter, S/E/G/ Communications Ltd and co-author of *Deputy*

West Sussex County Council Trading Standards Officers

Minitel Communications Ltd., Dublin

AT&T Istel UK

Demon Internet Services Ltd UK

Transpac UK

British Telecom

Mercury Communications Ltd

CompuServe Information Services UK

Why this book?

If you have picked up this book in a bookshop or library you may well have wondered how it's possible for anyone to write getting on for a hundred thousand words on the subject of modems. It's a bit like those ghastly Sales Meetings, where you have to stand up and talk for five minutes without repetition, hesitation, or boring the pants off your fellow delegates, only longer.

This book contains so much information, not because authors are paid by the word but because we now live in the Computer Age. Sooner or later, your boss, your customer, or your wife is going to ask you to "send it over by EMAIL" – and where will you be then if you don't know your ASCII from your elbow? If we are to get anywhere in the 21st Century then we have to communicate with our fellow human beings. Nowadays, most of them seem to be permanently attached to personal computers of one sort or another.

The mass acceptance of computer equipment into the home and work environment has changed our perceptions of communication. It used to be that a phone call which ended with the phrase "I'll put it in the post tonight" was all that was needed to clinch a deal or seal an agreement – now we must all have fax machines and electronic mail to be able to keep up with the competition, the Joneses, or the demands of our computer-hungry children. But how can we possibly keep up with the relentless march of technology? And more to the point, why should we? Your grandfather certainly didn't need a computer or modem to go about his daily work, as, quite probably neither did your father. But if we cannot use a computer or a modem, then we are looked upon as being slightly backwards (and less employable) by those others in our peer group.

So this is a 'get-smart' book. It tells you all you need to know to get even with your fifteen year old who's been using modems and computers since Junior School and seems to understand them instinctively. The book has purposely been written in a conversational style to encourage you to read it, rather than in the breathless "Gosh – Look at the size of these download statistics" approach which seems to be the norm for books about comms these days. Its aim is to simply make you as knowledgeable about comms as the next man (or woman) in the street, and perhaps a bit more so.

So take heart. There is a secret to be gleaned within. Comms is easier to learn then you might think, and much of the technical hype that surrounds the subject is inaccurate and designed to confuse. Ignore it. After all, you don't need to know about gearbox and final drive ratios to take your Fiat Uno down to the shops, and you don't need to know too much about comms to get up and running with the rest of us. Your modem and software should be able to do it all for you.

If you are slightly cheered up by this fact then you should now be able to proceed to Chapter 1 with a small glow of anticipation – because in all truth using a personal computer and a modem is not as hard as it looks at first sight. And being able to use personal comms will open up a thousand doors to you, in your professional and social life.

In the true spirit of personal data-comms this book comes with as much on-line support as you can absorb. You can contact any number of people for help on virtually every bulletin board in the world, and most all of them will give you a helping hand. But if that fails then you can contact the Author on CompuServe 100113,2132, or as S_SCO on CIX, the numbers are provided. The only catch is that you will need to take the first step by hooking your computer or terminal up to a modem, and making that first call.

Finally, whatever machine you have you will find that comms is an absorbing pastime once you have conquered the basic methods needed to get you on-line, not just because the technology is interesting for its own sake, but because there are some wonderful people out there.

Have fun.

Sue Schofield
September 1993

1
A BRIEF HISTORY OF COMMUNICATIONS
"All things appear in their developed form"

1.1 Early days

The year is 1850. You are standing in the general store of a small town in America's mid-west, wondering pensively what you should buy as a present for your mother-in-law's birthday. The choice is a jar of molasses or a warm beaver pelt. Suddenly you hear a rapid clicking noise from behind the counter. A minute later the telegraph operator comes to you with a handwritten message. Your mother-in-law, who was to arrive on tomorrow's train, will not be coming after all due to a slight cold. You thank the telegraph operator, and reluctantly spend the money earmarked for the birthday present on a large cigar.

The railway telegraph, invented in England in 1837 by Cooke and Wheatstone, brought the first mass implementation of electrically driven communications. The range over which mankind could previously communicate in real-time was limited to line of sight signals, such as the smoke signals used by American Indians, or communication systems such as the talking drum. In today's jargon the telegraph was the first carrier of real-time, binary encoded, electrically driven digital data comms.

The first trans-oceanic telegraph cable was laid in 1858, expanding the possible communication range of a single person to many continents.

The rate at which data could be encoded and transmitted was limited only by the skill of the telegraph operator and the hand-operated equipment he used to 'key' the data. This was around 100 words a minute or 10 characters a second at the fastest speeds possible. A binary encoding system invented by Samuel Morse was used, which encoded electrical pulses into a digital representation of the letters of the alphabet. This was enough for many purposes, but the equipment could only be used by skilled operators. An enhancement, the recording telegraph printer made marks on a moving piece of paper as the code was received, enabling unattended reception of telegraphs. Morse successfully demonstrated the system in 1844 by sending the message "What God hath wrought" from Baltimore to Washington.

The invention of the telephone in 1876 by Alexander Graham Bell was the next communication breakthrough. The human voice was converted into an electrical signal, which could be sent over reasonably long distances to a receiver where it was re-converted into noise. Anyone could use the system with little or no training and the transmission rate was limited only by the speed of the spoken word The transmission medium, the cables which carried the electrical signals, could carry speech at a greater rate than one person could speak or understand it. However, as with the telegraph, a continuous cable needed to be attached to the telephony equipment at both ends.

Digital coding

As more and more people became attached to the growing telephone network some means of switching between the hundreds of installed telephone cables became necessary. The first telephone 'switches' (exchanges) were operated by human beings – telephone operators physically connected subscribers to others by plugging phone cables into a patch-box system.

Eventual automation of these switches was implemented by one Almon Brown Strowger, an undertaker in Kansas City. There was such competition between the town's undertakers that telephone operators were often bribed to divert requests for undertaker services. An incensed Strowger devised the world's first telephone automatic telephone switchboard, which used electromagnetic relays to select numbers automatically from a remote telephone dial which generated the control pulses. The number of pulses sent to the switch directly operated the Strowger relays, at a rate of ten pulses per second. Strowger's ideas were adopted by AT&T and dial-phones were eventually released to the public in 1919. The basic theory of the Strowger system and its near cousin the Crossbar system is still used in many countries today, although switching using digital processing is now becoming commonplace. But modern digital exchanges still recognise pulses sent from dials originally designed for Strowger exchanges.

The 'Wireless'

Radio telegraphy arrived in 1897 courtesy of Guglielmo Marconi and was later enhanced by invention of the thermionic vacuum tube ('valve' in the UK) by Lee De Forest in 1907. Wireless telegraphy allowed pieces of equipment not physically attached by wires to communicate electronically. Wireless telegraphy worked by transmitting a carrier signal, which was modulated by another wave-form consisting of the information to be transmitted, and worked with voice (telephony) or digital codes (telegraphy).

As vacuum tube technology progressed it become possible to transmit signals around the earth by bouncing signals from the moon and the ionosphere. Global communications had arrived. Real-time transmission and reception were possible almost anywhere in the world where there was suitable equipment and a power supply. With the development of the thermionic vacuum tube came electronics, first as a science, and later as a series of technology derived products. The vacuum tube could amplify, switch and invert electronic signals, and automatic coding of such signals become possible. Arrays of valves could be used to simulate logic operations, and became the pre-cursors of modern digital computers.

The first generation of electronic binary computers was born from the advances made possible by electronic communications technology, although mechanical computing devices had been made much earlier. With electronic computing came a need for electronic man-to-machine communication.

Talking to computers

The first real electrical computers communicated with human beings in a variety of ways. Flashing lights were useful as they readily indicated an ON or OFF from the computer. Simple banks of switches served as the 'store' of instructions to be passed to the computer. Large numbers of instructions were fed to computers by setting these arrays of switches or by plugging cables into sockets ('patch-boxes') to make a 'program'. The patch-boxes had the huge disadvantages of slowness and inaccuracy, but allowed relatively easy storage and revision of the program. (One oddball computer design used the dials from Strowger/Crossbar based telephones to send a sequence of pulses to the computer). Punched cards, although not a new idea since Jacquard had used them many years earlier to program machinery, were thought a great advance and used as the primary program storage method for many years.

Electro-mechanics were gradually added to punch card systems and greatly added to the commercial viability of early computing systems. Electromagnetically operated typewriters eventually became available and electrically driven printers were developed from them. These could directly reproduce alpha-numeric characters generated by the computer. The punch-card readers ('input devices') were subsequently replaced by arrays of key driven switches, and computer keyboards were purpose built. In the late 1930s Howard Aitken built the Harvard Mk1 out of components rescued from IBM's electromagnetic parts bins. The computer was controlled from punched paper tape, itself a development from punched cards and output was to an electrically operated typewriter. A single multiplication took around three seconds and the machine could run automatically under program control.

Huge advances in cathode ray tube (CRT) technology soon brought screens which displayed data instead of printing it on paper and the screen and the keyboard were eventually combined to provide a 'terminal'. This was essentially a single device which could accept data from a human being, and output data in a human readable form. Early terminals which used a printer as the output device were closely related to the teleprinters then being used to send typewritten copy by electrical signals (Tele-Type) and terminals which used CRTs as the output device were nicknamed 'Glass Teletypes'. Computer Luddites have always existed – even as late as the early 1970s CRT equipped terminals were regarded as expensive toys by data processing diehards.

Early standards

The American and UK military were much in evidence during the early stages of development of computing standards and some early automated computing devices were used to replace rooms full of human operators. These 'battery farms' of human beings consisted mainly of women who computed artillery trajectory tables by hand. Standardised electronic coding systems were needed when electronics took the job over and, after a period of gestation, the American Standard Code for Information Interchange (ASCII) became a de-facto standard for translating binary signals into alpha-numeric characters. Seven bit ASCII replaced the previous BAUDOT code, a five bit code used mainly in telexes and radio traffic.

IBM, at that time the world's largest computer innovator and designer chose to stick with EBCDIC the 'Extended Binary Coded Decimal Interchange Code' for most of its mainframe operations, although EBCDIC coding was to lose ground in later years. ASCII allowed the use of 128 characters. This was more than enough to send full alpha-numerics to terminals, and have space left over for printer control codes such as BEL (bell) and FF (Formfeed). ASCII eventually became enshrined as International Alphabet No. 5, and gained an extra parity bit in the process. It is now used almost exclusively by modems and terminals throughout the world.

When the first IBM personal computers (PCs) hit the market there were few computing communication standards for small computers other than those already mentioned. IBM used the ASCII alphabet for the machine but used an eight-bit word length which allowed for up to 256 characters.

Printing of computer text received a boost when IBM used the 'Centronic' standard to equip the PC with a port which could send data down eight wires at once instead of one (parallel transfer). Printing had previously been carried out by squirting one bit at a time down slow serial ports. This wasn't a case of IBM showing massive foresight: the PC design team was given just three months to design the computer from scratch as IBM had no faith in making computers for personal use. Why on earth would anyone want a computer in their house? Most of the technology, including the Centronics port, was bought in because of the fast-track nature of the project.

1.2 The RS232

The connection for connecting terminals to computers was eventually standardised (in the States) on an 'Electrical Industries of America RS232' standard to allow manufacturers to produce compatible terminal and comms equipment. EIA RS232 was (and is) an electrical specification for voltages and bi-directional connections between communicating equipment. RS232 stands for Recommended Standard number 232 and it was created in 1969. RS232 recognised Data Terminal Equipment (DTE) – screens, printers and keyboards – and Data Communications Equipment (DCE) – modems, radio equipment etc. Electrically speaking, one was the complement of the other so, in theory, any DTE and any DCE could be plugged together and would 'talk', as long as they were both fully RS232 compliant.

The original RS232 specifications called for a voltage of nominally plus or minus 12-15 volts DC which was easily obtained from power supplies for the vacuum tubes. It provided connections for the input device (keyboard) and the output device (screen). Twenty five connections were provided, although later intelligent computer terminals could use as few as three for bi-directional input and output (I/O).

In Europe the RS232 was ratified into the V24 port. The CCITT V24 recommendation describes the physical connections between equipment. V24 became synonymous with RS232, and RS232 became RS232/V24 in some circles. The interface is still with us today, in its extended RS232-E revision and is used on the most modern personal computers for data communications. The nominal voltage levels have been altered to accept plus or minus 3 to 25 volts to co-exist with the power supplies used for solid state technology and RS232C is now utterly synonymous with personal computer communications. The RS232C is the most widely used data communications standard we have today, although purists will say that it's a standard for electrical connections, not communications.

RS232 and its derivatives will accept modems, printers, computer mice, digital samplers, musical keyboards and I/O from other computers. The serial port is the 'ear' of the communicating computer. Recent attempts to improve RS232 have been doomed to failure, simply because so much of todays installed equipment base has the capability to talk only via the original specification or its later revisions.

Modems

One of the first appearances of the modem as we know it today was in 1958 when

AT&T produced a value added service called Dataphone. The service was used to connect remote terminals to large computers over the American phone network and was an immediate success. Dataphone ran at 300bps which was adequate for driving the slow electromechanical terminals of the time and the communications standard used was Bell 103. Faster devices followed and the Bell 212a modem, developed by AT&T gave a working speed of 1200bps. A 212A modem made by Racal-Vadic was introduced shortly afterwards. Although it used the same standard it could not communicate with the AT&T 212A modems. A precedent for implementing non-workable 'standards' had been set, and continues to this day.

Modem speeds started to climb and 2400bps modems were introduced around 1983/84. The CCITT introduced a standard for 9600bps working as long ago as 1984 but American modem manufacturers decided not to make a commitment to the 'foreign' standard and marketed proprietary modems instead. Naturally these modems could only communicate at high speeds with a second identical modem. Some famous early American 9600bps modems were the Telebit Trailblazer, the Hayes Smartmodem 9600, and the US Robotics Courier HST. Many of these modems also carried both Bell and CCITT lower speed modes, the Courier HST became the de-facto 'standard' fast modem in the UK, and the Hayes Smartmodem 9600 was supreme in the USA for some years.

Some of the very first modems designed for personal (as opposed to corporate) use were designed by Dale Heatherington in the late 1970s and marketed by Dennis C Hayes through the Hayes Microcomputer Products Co. The Hayes Smartmodem 9600 sold well to US corporations and the fast protocols used then are still present in Hayes V-Series modems today. In the early 1990s we now have compliance to CCITT standards by virtually every modem manufacturer in the world.

1.3   The future

There is a dire need for change in the way that computers communicate. The RS232 interface can only transmit data one piece at a time and this limits the theoretical maximum data transfer rate to the bandwidth of the cables which link the devices together. Recent 'blitzkrieg' modems from Motorola Codex go so fast that special low capacitance serial cables between the modem and the computer are needed to pass data at high speed. The limit of the RS232 serial interface has been reached.

Attempts have been made to use other standards such as RS422 for personal computers, but these have not generally succeeded (other than for networking Apple Macs together), possibly because up until recently the limiting factor in telephonic computer communications was the telephone system itself. This was never designed for fast data transfer, and a great deal of research has to go into each new advance in modem technology.

Digital telephone switches (exchanges) now offer the opportunity to bypass the serial port altogether and move towards something more exciting. A standard for connecting disks to computers (the Small Computer Systems Interface – SCSI, pronounced to rhyme with Fuzzy) looked useful for fast communications but one manufacturer's SCSI is not guaranteed to work with another's SCSI device, despite this being an agreed 'standard.' So much for proprietary standards. As yet there are no SCSI modems on the market, which is a pity as SCSI can handle large amounts of data quickly.

PCMCIA

A second 'standard' set by manufacturers, the Personal Computer Memory Card International Association Type 2 (PCMCIA 2) slot looks more promising. This is a small, machine independent interface which can be used to connect memory devices, hard disks or modems to computers. PCMCIA came out of the 88 pin Japan Electronic Industry Standard (JEIDA) card used for add-in memory cards and is becoming a rapidly accepted standard. PCMCIA modems are already here, but still use a serial method to handle data. This may change to faster parallel transfer methods as ISDN becomes more widespread. PCMCIA devices will need special software to recognise them or a 'patch' to configure existing software although this is only a small matter and cannot be regarded as an obstacle.

PCMCIA cards are already being fitted to new laptops and it shouldn't be too long before card adapters become available for desktop machines. The forward-looking Commodore Amiga 600, launched in mid-1992 was one of the first computers to come already equipped with a type 2 PCMCIA slot and a fast serial port.

ISDN

Most promising of all, a new standard for connecting computers to telephone lines is now with us. This is ISDN, or Integrated Services Data Network. Adapters for the service plug directly into the motherboard of modern PCs to give a fast throughput, or into existing RS232 ports. RS232-based ISDN is currently limited to around 58-

60kbps transfer, whilst internal ISDN devices can achieve 128Kbps and probably more than that with proprietary data compression methods.

ISDN is as yet far too expensive for mass market acceptance or for recreational work. It offers data transfer rates up to 64,000 bits per second per channel and can handle two channels at once. Voice and data can be combined on the one line and the service offers sufficient bandwidth for a new generation of real-time video-phones. Bus-driven ISDN looks set to eventually replace the RS232 interface for fast computer to computer communications through telephone lines, although the 25 pin D type socket and its nine pin variant will be with us for many years yet.

It's clear that modern data communications are a huge growth area and in real terms we are still only at the beginning of the revolution in communications technology that started in 1844. Data communications used to be the province of the specialist, first the telegraph operator, then the phone operator, and then the men in the white coats who operated the first mainframe computers. The consumer market, with its vast reserves of disposable income is the next target of the marketers.

'Personal' data communications are now with us, and are set to become the target of a huge marketing blitz aimed at the man in the street. Portable book-size computers with built-in radio modems link are already here.

Oddly enough, the latest all-singing, all-dancing models still communicate at slow speeds through RS232 ports.

2. COMMUNICATIONS BASICS – THE RS232

"Supreme success through steadfast acceptance"

2.1 RS232 jargon

We have already been introduced to the RS232 interface via the history lesson in the previous section and now it's time to get down to basics. Here we will look at the RS232 interface, and the language that goes with it. Even if you don't learn the technical bits you should still try to pick up some of the jargon – acronyms such as DTE and DCD liberally pepper modem and terminal manuals, and cannot really be avoided. Once you have a basic insight into the RS232 standard you will probably find that the information is valuable when you hit your first comms problem.

ARMED WITH A BASIC KNOWLEDGE OF THE RS232 YOU CAN

- ELECTRICALLY CONNECT MOST COMPUTERS TO MOST OTHER COMPUTERS, REGARDLESS OF SIZE.

- HOOK UP YOUR PERSONAL COMPUTER TO MODEMS, PRINTERS, PERSONAL ORGANISERS, OFFICE PCS AND SOME DISK DRIVES.

- TRANSFER FILES AND DATA BETWEEN 'INCOMPATIBLE' HARDWARE.

- NETWORK A SERIES OF COMPUTERS TOGETHER.

- ATTACH YOUR COMPUTER TO HUNDREDS OF THOUSANDS OF OTHER INDIVIDUAL COMPUTERS AND COMPUTER SYSTEMS ALL OVER THE WORLD, USING A TELEPHONE MODEM.

- MAKE A NUISANCE OF YOURSELF IN RESTAURANTS BY TALKING LOUDLY ABOUT HARD HANDSHAKING, DTE/DCE INTERFACES, AND PATCH-BOXES.

Here's a view of the cut-down version that inhabits the back of many PCs and other computers and peeks out on to the world via a DB25 or DB9 male connector. The first thing to remember is that there's no such thing as a standard 'standard' in the computer world and that the RS232 socket on the back of your computer may have nine or 25 pins. This isn't the full story, many of the pins have a CCITT label too. The CCITT number RS232 pins from 100 to 125, but you won't need to know this unless you buy an ancient ex-PTT modem or terminal device, or a new ISDN adapter from a European PTT (Post, Telegraph, Telecommunications authority). The real comms world still uses RS232 mnemonics.

Some devices have a 25 way D type socket labelled 'V24' on them. This is also an RS232 socket – V24 is a specification for 'interchange circuits' used by the CCITT and V24 is almost identical to RS232. The US Department of Defence has its own version too. It's called MIL-STD-188C. Feel free to invent your own standard and add it to the list. The International Standards Organisation (ISO) has already used 'ISO-2110'.

FIGURE **2.1**

RS232 Pinouts

PIN	NAME	MNEMONIC
1	Frame Ground	FG
2	Transmit Data	TD
3	Receive Data	RD
4	Request To Send	RTS
5	Clear To Send	CTS
6	Data Set Ready	DSR
7	Signal Ground	SG
8	Data Carrier Detect	DCD
20	Data Terminal Ready	DTR
22	Ring Indicator	RI

Once explained the RS232 is very simple, a long as you know a little about electrical (not electronic) matters. The pins in FIGURE 2.1 are the only pins in the RS232 interface we need to know about in the first instance, since these are the only pins that are commonly used in the sort of data communications we are going to be looking at. All the others are either never used at all on personal computers for basic communications, or are occasionally used for more sophisticated comms.

The phrase 'serial data' is used a lot in this section. It means 'send or receive data a single piece at a time', a little like the telegraph systems of 1844. Before we move ahead it's important to remember that the RS232 interface uses a low voltage direct current (DC) signal of around 12 volts or less. If you are moved to experiment with that old computer you found in the office, don't attempt to try anything that involves mains electricity. The results tend to be black and charred and expensive.

2.2 The Black Art of Telecomms

To make anything 'talk' we need something for it to talk to. The only language computers have is an electronic one and, following the simple rules of electricity, we need a single wire to connect A to B and a return (or 'ground') to complete the circuit. The 'ground' is sometimes called 'earth' in the UK. On the RS232 these pins are pin

2 -'Transmit Data' and pin 7- 'Signal Ground'. The return goes along a cable called 'ground' or 'earth' because the return paths in the early telegraph systems were connected to the physical ground with copper spikes to save the cost of a long return cable. In dry climates these spikes had to be watered to maximise the conductivity but modern technology saves us from this chore.

FIGURE **2.2**

Simple signal paths

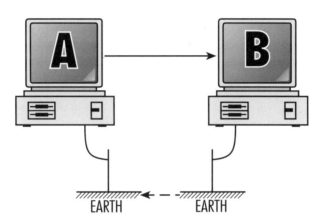

Now A can signal B and there's a return path (ground) from B. The RS232 also has a pin 1 (FG – Frame Ground), but this is used for connecting the metal cases or frames of larger computers together for safety reasons and is not much used on personal computers these day. Sometimes the outside metal braid of RS232 cables is connected to Frame Ground at both ends to maximise safety and electrical screening properties. It follows that, if both A and B are equipped with RS232 adapters, that data coming into B cannot go into the Transmit Data pin (pin 2) if only because computers listen on RS232 pin 3 Receive Data. Pin 2 on the transmitting computer is therefore connected to pin 3 on the receiving computer, and of course we need a ground to complete the circuit. (Only one signal ground wire is needed for all the RS232 signals).

A fully working, simple RS232 comms link between two computers is shown in FIGURE 2.3. This is known to comms engineers as a three-wire link, and is in some cases, all you need to hook up two computers physically, or a computer to a printer equipped with RS232.

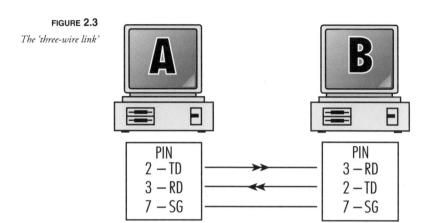

FIGURE **2.3**

The 'three-wire link'

DTE/DTC jargon

The physical layout of the RS232 socket needs some explanation. As we can see, at some point we need to make a cross-over in the TD and RD lines to enable listening and 'speaking' at both ends of the link between our two computers. Pin 2, Transmit Data, has to be connected to pin 3, Receive Data, to enable one way communication and then this is repeated for the other side of the link. This can be done either by fighting with a soldering iron to make a reversed cable, or by using an RS232 convention called...

The DTE/DCE convention

The DTE/DCE convention defines how the two pieces of equipment should have their RS232 connectors wired. A computer or other 'intelligent device' is known as a Data Terminal Equipment (DTE). It transmits data on pin 2 and receives data on pin 3. A modem or 'non-intelligent device' is known as a Data Communications Equipment (DCE). It receives data on pin 2 and transmits on pin 3. Many of the other RS232 pins have functions which are mirrored between DTEs and DCEs

THE IMPORTANT THINGS TO REMEMBER ARE:

■ A DCE (OR MODEM) HAS ITS PINS WIRED UP AS COMPLEMENTS OF THOSE ON A DTE, SO THAT A STRAIGHT-THROUGH CABLE CAN BE USED TO CONNECT THEM.

■ CONNECTING TWO DTES TOGETHER MEANS THAT CONNECTIONS HAVE TO BE CROSSED OVER SO A SPECIAL

CABLE MUST BE USED TO CONNECT THEM. (THE CROSS-OVER CABLES ARE OFTEN CALLED A 'NULL MODEM' CABLE BY THE TRADE, FOR NO REAL GOOD REASON OTHER THAN TO DEMORALISE WOULD-BE COMMS ENGINEERS).

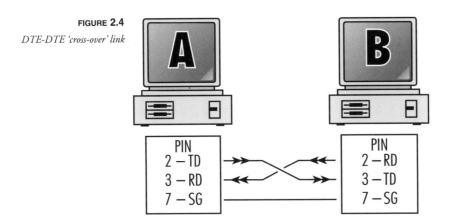

FIGURE 2.4

DTE-DTE 'cross-over' link

Pins 2 and 3 are crossed to enable the Transmit Data line on each DTE to couple to the Receive Data line of the other. A simplified wiring diagram for connecting a computer to a modem looks like FIGURE 2.5

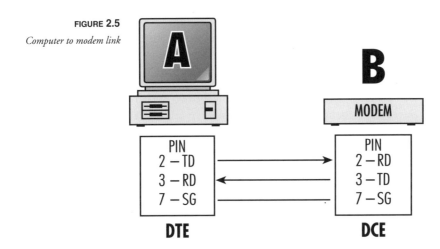

FIGURE 2.5

Computer to modem link

As pin 2 on the DCE is Receive Data and pin 3 is Transmit Data a straight cable can be used. If you forget everything else in this book remember that 'DTE devices are wired to each other with a cross-over cable.' It will save you hours of trouble. The three-wire link is the basis of all computer RS232 connections. In fact many comms engineers use nothing else for temporary lash-ups or permanent hook-ups. The only disadvantage with it is that it has no 'hard-handshaking.'

Flow control

Having read through the above and decided that making two computers talk to each other is only slightly less difficult than planning the next Mars landing, you may be wondering what the rest of the RS232 connections are for. We've looked already at pins 1, 2, 3, and 7, and know that these are Frame Ground, Transmit Data, Receive Data, and Signal Ground, when looking at the DTE end of a comms link. All these wires (except Frame Ground) are there for signal transmission and return. The rest of the ten wires are there for 'handshaking' a process which prevents one computer sending data at the wrong time or in the wrong quantity to the other.

Handshaking

If you have a large bucket full of water, and a small one which is empty you may wish to fill the small one from the large one. Pouring all the water from the large one into the small one will result in overflow, unless there is some feedback mechanism in place to warn you of an impending watery disaster.

In human terms this mechanism is sometimes provided by nerves in the feet, which sense a superfluity of water and transmit this information to the brain. In many intelligent humans this information transfer causes an immediate cessation of water flow and a muffled curse. In others nothing happens until a large degree of flooding has occurred and both feet are wet.

In data-comms a similar contrivance, called 'flow control' or 'overrun control' is used, where, if one device squirts data too quickly to another it is told by the receiver to stop transmitting until the received data can be dealt with. This is accomplished by either using the wires and pins of the RS232 or by a system of software codes.

The act of one device signalling flow control information to another with is called 'handshaking' or, in the case of our water bucket analogy, 'footshaking'.

Hard handshaking

If the hardware (RS232) method of flow control is used this is denoted as 'hard hand-shaking', and if software is used this is called 'soft handshaking'. Soft handshaking will be covered in a later section. Virtually all RS232 hook-ups will require either hard or soft shaking before they will transfer data correctly at high speeds.

There are two main sets of handshake lines in our sub-set of the RS232 interface.

These are: **RTS/CTS (pins 4 and 5)** and **DCD/DTR (pins 8 and 20)**

FIGURE **2.6**

RTS/CTS handshaking

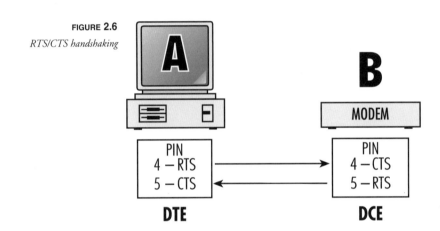

The first, RTS/CTS handshaking is quite straightforward although not easily explainable on paper. Remember that terms like DTE (computer, terminal or printer) and DCE (modem) are used in modem manuals and connection diagrams, so it pays to learn them if you can.

RTS means Ready To Send. RTS is an output signal from the DTE to the DCE to 'flow control' data coming from the DCE. If the DTE cannot handle data from the DCE (buffer full, equipment not turned on, mouse gnawed through cable etc) the RTS line will be held low to prevent data transfer from the DCE.

CTS is Clear To Send – an output signal from the DCE to control the data coming from the DTE. If the DCE cannot handle data (buffer full, line dropped, etc.) it will drop the voltage on its CTS line to signal to the DTE that no more data should be sent.

In operation the RTS/CTS lines tend to flip high and low alternatively, as buffers at each end of the link fill and empty, although in some cases of low speed comms they are not used at all. For DTE to DTE links, as in the case of two computers linked together, a cross-over cable must be used to wire the RTS line of one computer to the CTS line of the other, and vice versa.

For DTE-DCE links a straight-through cable would normally be used. The convention for cross-over cables on DTE-DTE links should be observed if your link is to work at all.

RTS/CTS handshaking fell out of favour during the mid to late 1980s as software handshaking became the norm. However, the new breeds of fast modems need RTS/CTS handshaking to maximise throughput rates, for reasons that will be explained later.

DTR/DCR handshaking

Data Terminal Ready (DTR) is a signal output from computers, terminals and printers to say "I am present." It comes from pin 20 of the RS232 interface and is almost always implemented.

DTR is often used to inform a modem that it has something intelligent attached to it, and that the modem may go about its normal business when this line is high (On). Modems can be set to drop the phone line if DTR is interrupted for any reason and modem control software often makes use of this feature to make sure that the modem disconnects on a hang-up command from the user.

FIGURE 2.8

DTR handshaking

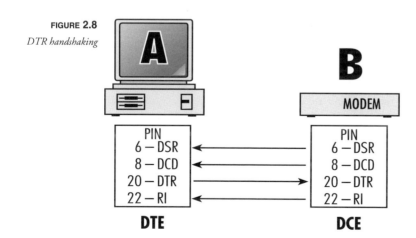

DTR usage can be controlled by internal settings on most DCEs so that if it is not present the DCE will still function.

DCD, Data Carrier Detect, is an output from the modem on pin 8, which says that "I have locked on to carrier from a remote device". Again DCD is useful in modem control where loss of carrier can be mirrored by loss of the DCD signal. The connected DTE can then ensure an orderly disconnection of the modem from the line.

Other control line signals

RING INDICATOR (RI)

This is an easy one to understand. Pin 22 of the DCE RS232 will pulse high and low in sympathy with the ring signal from the telephone line, if the DCE is a modem. This tells the DTE that there is an incoming call, leaving the DTE to decide whether or not to answer it. Quite often DTR is raised from the DTE on receipt of a ring indicator to tell the modem to go on-line.

DATA SET READY (DSR)

The only line we haven't covered is pin 6: – DSR – Data Set Ready. Data Set Ready was originally used as a signal from a DCE to a DTR to inform it that it was ready to accept data. 'Data Set' is an archaic term for modem. Most modern modems don't use DSR and simply keep it high all the time. However, the serial interface of the IBM PC often expects DSR to be present, even if its signals are ignored by software. If in doubt keep DSR high at all times.

PC handshaking

It's invidious that IBM, having launched the definitive personal computer, then goes and spoils everything by using at least three different RS232 configurations. The original machine had a perfectly normal 25-way connector, the AT range came with a nine pin adapter. Later machines in the PS/2 range came with a miniature round socket for serial mice although this is not strictly speaking an RS232 socket. The 25-way and the nine-way sockets both carry our required sub-set of nine lines from the full RS232 set.

Before communications software became commonplace it was usual to hardwire pins

8, 20 and 4, 5, 6 of the IBM PC COM port together to get it talk to anything and this is still a good tip today. However, most commercial software and modems 'know' about the oddities of the IBM COM port and will work out of the box, without resorting to a soldering iron.

2.3 Asynchronous/synchronous systems

If you intend to inflict your newly found comms knowledge on something and try to get two PCs talking, then start with a three-wire link. This goes for many other personal computer hook-ups, too. Once they are 'talking' you can try hard handshaking methods, but before that you should break with a lifetime's tradition and read the friendly manual (RTFM) first. Most manufacturers describe equipment handshaking methods in their manuals and this knowledge can save you hours of bad-tempered cussing.

2.4 General comments

You will sometimes hear the term 'asynchronous or asynch' applied to RS232 communications. Asynchronous simply means 'without timing' and an asynch comms link is indeed free from timing control signals. A synchronous link needs timing information to be sent from one or both ends of the link and uses more of the pins and handshake lines of the RS232 interface to transfer this information. Virtually all of today's commonly encountered personal computer data-comms are asynchronous, and work with the three or nine wire implementation of RS232.

RS232 connections are easier to practise than to read about. In these days of consumer convenience most off-the-shelf packages will be set up correctly for you, and will 'plug and go'. It often surprises modem buyers that RS232 cables are never supplied with the product, but then, what is a correct RS232 cable? In the real world comms engineers still use small boxes with red and green lights connected to the main nine lines to determine handshake and DTE or DCE status. The lights flash and twinkle as data passes through the TD/RD lines and flash on and off as the handshake lines go high and low.

Sometimes it becomes impossible to determine the handshaking needs of various devices (especially serial printers) and then the comms engineer will resort to a 'data-faker' – a small patch-box which allows any handshake line to be connected to any other until the two devices are forced into amicable discourse. These devices, the patch-box, the RS232 tester with its lights and a hot soldering iron, are the tools of the trade of exasperated and prematurely balding comms engineers.

2.5 Summary

Connecting two personal computers together regardless of shape or size

YOU WILL NEED

■ A DTE TO DTE (CROSS-OVER OR NULL-MODEM) LEAD.

■ COMMUNICATIONS SOFTWARE FOR EACH OF THE COMPUTERS

■ DATA THAT IS READABLE OR TRANSFERABLE BETWEEN THE TWO SYSTEMS.

First, make sure that all power is turned off on each of the computers and on any peripherals such as printers that may be connected. Connect the RS232 cross-over lead to each of the two serial ports, and power up. You will need to install the communications software on each computer, and set the transmission speeds and parameters to the same at each end of the link. If in doubt try 9600bps, 8 data bits, 1 stop bit, no parity (explained later) as a starting point.

Set both computers into terminal mode and type at the keyboard on one of them. If you see garbage on the screen of the other then you probably have one machine set to a wrong parameter. If you see nothing then you may be talking to the wrong serial port on one of the computers, especially if the machine is fitted with more than one. PCs often have up to four ports called COM 1 through COM 4 and it can be difficult to identify which is which. The only real way is by trial and error.

Once you have legible text appearing on the other screen you can use a File Transfer Protocol such as KERMIT or ZMODEM to transfer the file(s). If you are transferring only ASCII text you can use the ASCII text upload feature found in most comms packages. ZMODEM is good for file transfer between two directly connected machines as an incoming ZMODEM transfer is automatically detected in most cases, leaving you with only one keyboard to manipulate. If your file transfers go well at 9600bps you can try upping the transfer rate to 19,200 or even 38,400bps. The results you get will depend on all sorts of factors such as the type of machine, and even the type of comms software you use, so again, trial and error is the best approach. If none of this means anything to you then read the chapter on communication software before you start.

If you have a true multi-tasking multi-user computer you will find that you can access your computer's operating system via a second computer of almost any type, acting as a terminal. This is useful for sorting or deleting files, or for general DOS housekeeping work. The Amiga works well in this way. You hook up a second computer or terminal through a null-modem adapter, set the parameters to the same on both sides of the link and type on the Amiga: NEWSHELL AUX: This tells the Amiga to open a new command line interface through the serial port (AUX). All the DOS output is textual and this will appear on the screen of your terminal while the Amiga gets on with zapping aliens.

Connecting a serial printer

YOU WILL NEED

■ THE CORRECT LEAD TO FIT BETWEEN THE COMPUTER AND PRINTER.
In virtually all cases this will be a cross-over lead, as serial printers are wired as DTEs – a hangover from the days of teletypes.

■ THE HANDBOOK FOR THE PRINTER

■ THE CORRECT PRINTER DRIVER SOFTWARE FOR THE PACKAGE YOU ARE USING.

■ LOTS OF PATIENCE

FIGURE **2.8**
printer settings

PRINTER SETTINGS

Printer Type	⟶	HP Deskjet
Serial Port	⟶	COM2
Speed	⟶	9600
Data Bits	⟶	8
Stop Bits	⟶	1
Parity	⟶	None
Handshake	⟶	RTS / CTS

You should ask your dealer for the specific cable for your printer and computer combination. Many serial printers use non-standard hard handshaking methods and not all serial cables work with all printers. Check that the printer driver you are using within your software package knows about serial printers (some don't). If in doubt look in the manual or on the Help Screen for information on setting up printers.

You should be able to find a set-up screen for the printer which looks something like FIGURE 2.8.

You should then check your printer's manual to find out how to set your printer to the above settings. In the case of the HP Deskjet and many other printers there are a series of Dual In-line Package (DIP) switches on the rear of the printer. These set the various parameters. Other printers, including most laser printers, have a series of scrolling menu options available on the front panel. You set up the parameters by selecting options, usually with an up or down key.

9600bps is a good starting point. If you set a speed higher than this you may find that your printer doesn't seem to go any faster. You should also try to use RTS/CTS hard handshaking where possible to help speed things up.

If you have a Mac or an Amiga then your printer will work for screen-dumps outside of an application. Only one setting-up operation is needed. If you have a PC the screen-dump operation, accessed with the PrtSc key, expects to find a printer connected to LPT1:. Your serial printer will be connected to one of the COM ports and won't see the screen-dump from plain DOS mode without being redirected by software.

You therefore have to re-assign the LPT port to the COM port with a MODE statement after you have manually configured the COM port for speed etc. The commands are, in order:

```
MODE COM1:96,n,8,1,p [enter]
MODE LPT1 = COM1 [enter]
```

Good old MS-DOS requires a colon after the COM1 designation in the first line, but not in the second, so watch the punctuation. You can write these parameters to a file using an editor or the COPY CONSOLE command in MS-DOS, and then call that file automatically when you start your computer. See details for the AUTOEXEC.BAT file, COPY CONSOLE command and the MODE command in your DOS manual.

Windows 3.x uses a global printer set-up routine which can be accessed by all applications, and printer setting is very straightforward in comparison with plain DOS.

Making a null-modem connector

If you're a dab-hand at soldering you can make a null-modem connector very easily. If you're not you can solder your fingers together easily. You can either modify an existing RS232 straight-through lead, or more properly use a couple of DB25 or DB9 connecters, some patch wire, and a couple of cable shells to tidy the whole thing up. All the components are available through Tandy, or mail-order through electronic supply companies such as Electromail and Maplin. Maplin's address can be found in Appendix 5.

YOU WILL NEED

■ A SOLDERING IRON.

■ ONE MALE DB25 OR DB9 CONNECTOR WITH BUCKET-TYPE SOLDER CONNECTIONS

■ ONE FEMALE DB25 OR DB9 CONNECTOR WITH BUCKET-TYPE SOLDER CONNECTIONS

■ TWO COMPLETE DB25 OR DB9 SHELL COVERS.

FIGURE **2.9**

25-way null modem cable

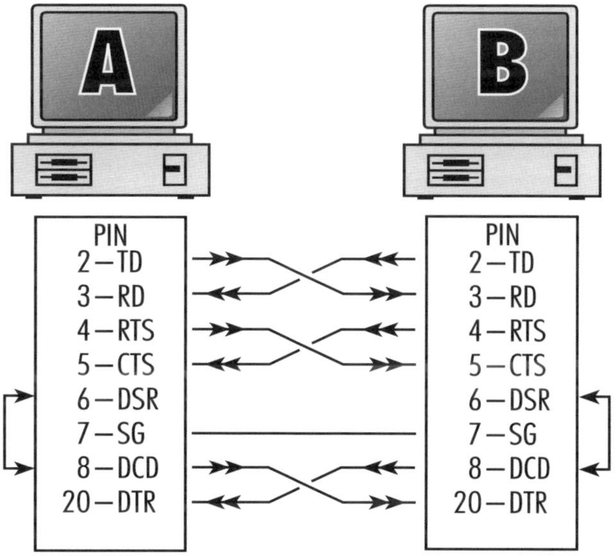

It's easiest to fully wire one connector first, and then start on the second. You may find that you need three hands to hold the solder, the hot soldering iron and the connector, and a good tip is to stick the connector face down on the bench with tape. The details are given for 9 pin and 25 pin connections in the following diagrams and will suit Amiga and PC type computers. If you use a Mac you will find that the serial port uses a special connector and that buying a ready made cable is the easiest solution.

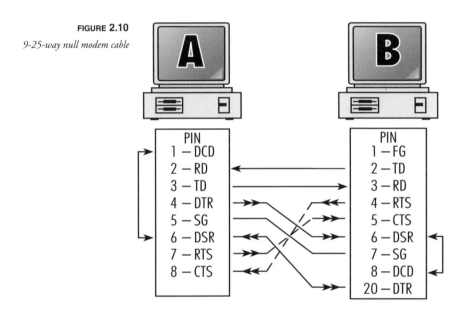

FIGURES 2.9 and 2.10 looks worse on paper than in real life and a null modem is quite easy to construct. Pin 20 on each side of the link is wired to pins 8 and 6 on the other side. Note that the adapter is symmetrical, it doesn't matter which end you connect to which computer. For the sake of completeness you should also connect pin 1 to pin 1 to make the Frame Ground connection, but this is not vital.

DTE – data terminal equipment

Means printers, computers, terminals. Almost anything with a keyboard will be wired as DTE. Some RS232 switch-boxes and terminal servers (concentrators) are wired this way. On a DTE: pin 2: is Transmit Data; pin 3: is Receive Data; DTE – DTE links are crossed over.

DCE – data communications equipment

All modems (called 'Data Sets' by comms engineers) and some professional radio equipment will be wired as DCE. On a DCE: pin 2: is Receive Data; pin 3: is Transmit Data; DTE – DCE links are straight-through.

PC users

Often need pins 4, 5, 6, 8, and 20 high (on) for basic comms to work and the easiest way to do this is to wire them together inside the cable connector shell.

Mac users

The Mac is one of those computers that seems almost perfect in its operation, until you take the lid off. The Mac has two serial ports, labelled Printer and Modem. The ports are not real RS232 ports, as they can also work at RS422 levels (a standard designed for longer range serial comms) and can go at faster speeds than many PC ports.

The Mac doesn't give a full implementation of either RS232 or RS422, but provides just enough of each to make everything work properly. In 1984 Apple decided that no-one would ever need the full range of RS232 handshake signals, and as a consequence the Mac ports on some Macs are limited to an analogy of RTS/CTS handshaking. There is no DSR or DTR sensing. This works well for printers, but some modems object to the lack of these two important lines.

The real answer is to buy a Mac modem cable and modem from a Mac dealer. Or you can make your own up if you are feeling adventurous. Either the printer or the modem port on the Mac can be used for modems, but the modem port is given various priorities over the printer port should you decide to multi-task, and it should therefore be used for fast modems. The lack of these lines becomes a problem for fast modem handshaking – you may have to turn DTR and DSR recognition/sensing off in your modem's configuration. Check the modem handbook for details.

Amiga serial ports

Amiga serial ports have all the usual RS232 lines plus a few more. The extra ones have nothing to do with serial comms.

ON AN AMIGA WATCH OUT FOR

- PIN 9: +12 VOLTS

- PIN 10: -12 VOLTS

- PIN 11: – LEFT CHANNEL AUDIO OUT

- PIN 18: – RIGHT CHANNEL AUDIO IN.

Additionally, Amiga ports differ between models – even the type of RS232 connector is not the same on all Amiga computers. The safe rule here is not to poke any old connector into the back of an Amiga and hope it will work. This will almost certainly lead to smoke and tears. Check the manuals first.

3 BASIC COMMUNICATIONS

"Initial difficulties are followed by supreme success"

3.1   Data – Whassat?

Now that we are all comms experts, or at least able to keep up our end of a conversation on hard-handshaking we should have a look at the stuff we are going to be squirting through our RS232 port. It's called data.

Data is information, or a code representing that information. When you wave to some-one in the supermarket queue you are transmitting coded visual data that might say "Hi, have you remembered to buy the kitty-litter?". A nod from the would-be purchaser of kitty-litter would mean "Yes" and the coded data transaction would be complete.

The term 'byte' is used to describe the smallest group of related data-parts recognisable by computer. Bytes are not inflicted by small carnivorous animals, but represent datawords and information. A byte is commonly made up of eight individual particles, and each particle is called a bit. The definition of byte changes with time and manufacturers handbooks, but correctly applies to six- or eight-bit words only. A 16-bit word is actually made of two eight-bit bytes and so on, but is sometimes mistakenly called a 16-bit byte.

'Bits' are the bits which are either on or off, 'bytes' are sequences of eight bits which represent a recognisable piece of data or information. The more bits in use by the computer the more powerful that system can be. A 16-bit computer is several magnitudes more powerful than an eight-bit computer, because it can handle a much larger range of data.

For those puzzled by this bland dismissal of five hundred billion dollars worth of computer research and development, the answer is to be found in multiplying two to the power of eight (256) and two to the power of 16 (65536). The results dictate the range and limits of all sorts of things, from the amount of memory that can be directly addressed, to the size of the operating system manual and the welcoming smile of the computer salesman.

We can safely disregard much of this bits and bytes stuff, because all we are really interested in is getting data down a pair of wires, and out again at the other end. A byte for our purposes, becomes a 'word' and a bit becomes a letter of that word. The language of comms is that of the bit, and the number of bits that can be transferred through a comms link is measured in 'bits per second' (bps). The more bits per second that can be transferred, the faster the link must be to handle the data traffic.

Bauds

Bits per second has also become synonymous with 'Baud' which is inaccurate. Baud is so called after J M E Baudot (1845-1903) a famous French telecomms pioneer and inventor. It was originally used to denote units transmitted per second (Baud rate) but is not much used today. Bits per second is a much more accurate indicator of how comms links perform and will be used throughout.

ASCII

In the early days of communicating computers the ASCII (American Standard Code for Information Interchange) alphabet came into widespread use. ASCII being a seven-bit system it could represent 128 (two to the power of seven) different characters in a binary system. Later on an eighth bit was added for error detection purposes but ASCII was still a 128 character, seven-bit alphabet, starting at 0, and finishing at 127. The coding system used numbers 0 through 31 for equipment control codes (sending ASCII code 07 rang the bell), punctuation characters started at ASCII 32, upper and lower case alphabet letters and numbers finished at 126. ASCII 127 sent the DELETE character. Later modifications were made by turning the parity error correcting bit into part of an eight bit word (byte) and this brought the ASCII alphabet up to 255 characters. The extra space was used for line drawing and graphics characters.

The Extended ASCII character set or 'eight-bit ASCII' came into general use with the introduction of the IBM PC, and it's the eight-bit ASCII code which is still the mainstay of textual information transfer between remote personal computers.

3.2   Modems

As we saw in Chapter 2, a physical electrical link can be used to unite computers, but what if the two computers are in different towns, or different countries? Early computer technology turned to the telephone system for an answer, and a direct analogy of human voice transmission and reception was developed. A box was invented which turned the ons and offs used by the computer into a series of noises. These noises were fed into the telephone voice circuits, decoded at the other end back into ons and offs, and fed into the remote computer's RS232 port. The transmitting box modulated the telephone signal, the receiving box de-modulated it. The MODulator/DEModulater (MODEM) was born.

Early modems used valve technology to do the hard work. This later gave way to transistor technology, and today's modems use high speed chips. Some of the earliest available modems for the personal user in the UK came from ex-military or PTT sources. A leviathan called the *Post Office Datel Model 2B* was available from surplus stores and consisted of a 19-inch rack stuffed with plug-in cards. These were labelled 'Modulator' and 'De-modulator' and 'Power Supply' etc, and the beast looked like something out of a Thunderbirds set. It weighed about the same as a two-drawer filing cabinet filled with paper, and auto-answer mode was made available by some judicious poking about with a hot soldering iron in the time-honoured fashion.

Modems shrank down to paperback book size with the advent of large scale integration on silicon chips, and are becoming smaller by the day.

Full and Half Duplex, FSK, and Bandwidth

The principles of modem data transfer are relatively simple. The basic principle, modulation, is similar to that employed in the 'Girl Guides Telephone', a couple of tin cans held apart by string and the joyful intentions of their owners. The 'GGT' (comms people love acronyms) works by allowing the operator to modulate the carrier (sound energy) with noises. The operator bellows into one can, the sound travels down the string in a wave of modulated energy, and vibrates the base of the receiving tin. The base of the receiving tin converts the wave energy into sound, which is heard (or not) by the listener.

In the example above one operator must listen while the other talks. This limitation is called 'half-duplex'. If we had a 'four-can GGT', with two pieces of string and twice the number of tin cans the operators could both hear and speak at the same time. In a modem the ability to transmit and receive simultaneously is called 'full-duplex' and modems can manage this conjuring trick down a single telephone circuit.

FSK

Modems 'modulate' by a process called Frequency Shift Keying or FSK. FSK is simply a way of turning ons and offs into stable recognisable tones. A modem will transmit one frequency for a '0' and another frequency for a '1' and each bit transmitted will be associated by a tone. The resulting warble is decoded by the demodulator. Early American modems used a frequency of 1070 Hertz for '0' and 1270 Hertz for '1' at the transmitting modem, and the receiving modem was designed to recognise these frequencies. A different set of frequencies was used in Europe, with the net result that it was virtually impossible to transmit or receive data between the two countries unless you had access to an American modem.

As modems have become faster, simple FSK processes have given way to multi-frequency devices and something called Quadrature Amplitude Modulation (QAM). You don't have to know about QAM or FSK techniques to use a modem, only that more complex processes are needed to squeeze data at a faster rate down a limited bandwidth telephone system.

Bandwidth and Bits Per Second

"The telephone system has deficiencies". This surprising statement applies mainly to computers, as humans tend to get on well with telephones. The telephone system was originally designed only for voice transfer and presents a real bottleneck to modem designers. Physical noise was and is a problem, contact switches cause electrical noise on telephone lines which tends to swamp the plaintive bleeps and whistles of modems. Modern digital exchanges often have to use the old copper cables installed years ago and loose connections and electrical noise still cause problems. The physical properties of the lines themselves pose a limitation.

As attempts were made to speed up data transfer rates the capacitive and inductive properties of phone lines placed a critical limit on transfer speed. In 1980 the specified frequency range for American telephone systems as a whole was 200 Hertz to 3700 Hertz, giving a bandwidth of around 3500 hertz. Early modems could transfer data at up to 300bps in full-duplex mode using this bandwidth. Attempts to overcome telephone bandwidth restrictions brought some odd devices and systems onto the market. One of the most notorious was the split-rate system, in which data is transmitted from the host at one rate and transmitted from the receiving computer at a slower rate. Split-rate duplexing means that the computer transmitting the largest amount of data gets the fast channel, and the receiving modem gets to use the slow channel to send back acknowledgements or the odd key press. In Europe a standard called V23 allowed for a 1200bps 'forward' channel from the host computer, and 75bps 'back channel' from the originating computer. One novel feature of V23 was that the transfer of large amounts of data from the computer using the 'back channel' took up huge amounts of call-time with subsequent billing implications. The PTTs were very fond of V23 for a while.

The modem market has since changed drastically. Data transfer (between modems) rates are currently at 14,400bps and set to rise dramatically in the near future. Having said this many commercial systems still use older slower standards, ensuring that modern modems retain some of the more archaic standards to maintain connection ability.

The CCITT

As you will have realised, the word 'standard' when applied to data-communications is somewhat laughable. Proprietary systems tend to lead the market, until someone comes along and makes a standard out of them. The process is then repeated as technology moves forwards faster than standardisation, and the market is thus led by the communications manufacturers. This is no bad thing, without it we might still be stuck with 300bps modems. In Europe the 'Comité Consultatif International Téléphonique et Télégraphic' (CCITT) exists to provide a means for standardisation of such things as data transfer methods and speeds, mobile and cellular radio links. (The CCITT is actually part of the United Nations). Only the USA tends not to follow CCITT recommendations but this is changing rapidly and most USA made modems now recognise all relevant CCITT implementations. It's usual when referring to a modem to describe it by its CCITT description, so a V23 modem is our old friend the 1200/75 split rate mode.

FIGURE 3.1

CCITT Modem speeds

ASYNCHRONOUS MODEM SPEEDS		
C.C.I.T.T	**Modem Speed** (Transmit / Receive)	**Duplex?**
V21	300 / 300	Full
V22	1200 / 1200	Full
V22 bis	2400 / 2400	Full
V23	75 / 1200	Full
V32	9600 / 9600	Full
V32 bis	14400 / 14400	Full

A modem that incorporates V21, V22, V22 bis and V23 is sometimes called a Quad modem. A modem that incorporates all five basic specifications is often called a Quin or Quad plus modem. Quin modems, and some quad modems generally offer some form of data compression and error checking system for faster, more reliable comms.

Modem handshaking

There are two sorts of handshaking available in virtually all modern data modems. Hard handshaking, as in the RS232 is available in all medium to high price modems. Some cheaper battery operated modems don't have this feature though and quite often use a three-wire link between DTE and DCE for further economy. They use soft handshaking to provide flow control.

Soft handshaking is the process where a data-handling device sends flow control signals by means of a software code embedded in the data stream. The code for 'send no more data' is ASCII code 17. The code for 'my small emergency is now over, please send more data' is ASCII code 19. The mnemonics for these codes are respectively: Device Control code 1 (DC1- generated as Control Q) and Device Control code 3 (DC3'- generated as Control S). DC1 has now become XON, and DC3 is now XOFF.

XON/XOFF handshaking works in much the same way as RTS/CTS handshaking, the data stream can be paused in either direction by simply transmitting XOFF and resumed with an XON. The codes are generally (but not always) stripped out by the modem, ie not passed through to the host device unless the modem is specifically set up to do so. The disadvantage of using soft handshaking is that embedding flow control carriers in a data stream increases the time taken to send that data, whereas hard handshaking acts directly on the internal hardware and is much quicker. In practice this speed differential isn't likely to be noticed much (except by benchmark freaks) at speeds around 2400bps or lower, but can seriously affect data rates much above this. As modem speeds climb higher we will see hard handshaking regaining popularity, hence the need to highlight handshaking methods here.

There is also an element of the soft handshaking process used in some error-control methods, where data is re-transmitted if the other end of the link detects an error. In this case the process is more properly called 'acknowledge/not acknowledge' (ACK/NACK).

Handshaking on the dial-up link

So far we have only discussed isolated cases of handshaking in an ideal world. In the real world handshaking and throughput problems plague every owner at some time, especially if bits per second becomes more important to the user than the actual data being transmitted – (the benchmark freak again). In a real system we have at least four devices hooked up via COM ports and in a real system all sorts of problems creep in.

FIGURE 3.2

Handshaking over the virtual link

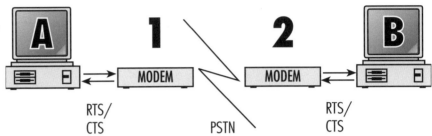

In FIGURE 3.2 we see a common link-up topology. Computer A (DTE) is wired to modem 1 (DCE). Modem 1 transmits and receives over the Public Switched Telephone Network (PSTN) to and from modem 2. Computer B is connected to modem 2.

THE HANDSHAKING LINKS WE HAVE HERE ARE

■ COMPUTER A TO MODEM 1 – DTE TO DCE LINK, 'LOCAL' HARD HANDSHAKING. NO PROBLEMS HERE, THE RTS/CTS LINES BETWEEN THE MODEM AND THE COMPUTER DO THEIR STUFF AND FLOW CONTROL EFFECTIVELY.

■ MODEM 2 TO COMPUTER B – DTE TO DCE LINK, 'LOCAL' HARD HANDSHAKING. NO PROBLEMS HERE EITHER, THE RTS/CTS LINES BETWEEN THE MODEM AND THE COMPUTER DO THEIR STUFF AND FLOW CONTROL ALSO.

■ MODEM 1 TO MODEM 2– DCE TO DCE. WHAT HAPPENS HERE?

In practice the three links work independently: the DTE to DCE links control data flow between each modem and the computer, if one computer wants the other to stop transmitting then it toggles the hard handshake line and the modem translates this to stop transmission from the remote. The remote modem receives and translates this signal (a special frame type called RR/RNR) back into a hard handshake between it and its own DTE.

Slower systems will use XON/XOFF handshaking all the way through. Computer A will send data to computer B, B will fill up and send an XOFF through the modem to computer A. The XOFF signal goes through both modems to computer A which stops transmitting. For this system to work both modems have to be set to pass the

XON/XOFF codes through to the RS232 ports, without stripping them out.

This is called transparent soft handshaking, one of the world's great pieces of abstruse comms jargon. Try it on your friends, or as a chat-up line at modem press launches: "Hi baby, my name's Clint Thrust. Wanna talk about transparent soft handshaking?"

The Baud Rate Jungle – data compression and error

No, no, no, no. It's bits per second, or bps, not 'baud rate'. Here's why. In our diagram above, the two computers and the two modems must all transmit and receive data at the same speed. This is an asynchronous (without timing) system. An extra letter or bit is added to the front and back of each word (byte) as it is sent, to denote the start and stop of the byte. These are called 'stop bits'. Ten bits per eight-bit word are transmitted by the modem.

In order for the receiving modem to recognise these characters it must be set to the same speed as the transmitting modem, or garbage will occur as the data is sliced back up into words, starting at the wrong point. Up until the late 1980s this was a rule that applied right the way through the computer – modem – modem computer link. All the speeds had to be set correctly, and the number of stop bits had to be the same. 'Parity', a simple error checksum system, also added an extra bit to the word, and this too had to be set correctly all the way down the link if it was used.

A comms system would use parameters such as: 300 baud, 8-bit data, no parity, 1 stop bit, abbreviated to 300-8-N-1. Archaic dial-up systems run by PTTs stuck to the older format of: 300 baud, 7-bit data, 1 stop bit, even (or odd) parity, abbreviated to 300-7-E-1 or 300-7-O-1. However, we now have speed buffering and data compression. Data compression is a system that compresses data to a half or a quarter of its length for efficient transmission over the virtual link, and de-compresses it at the other end. The net saving appears in the amount of bandwidth taken up, and so faster speeds can be used over the virtual link for a given amount of data.

Speed buffering is a technique used to accept data at a high rate from the DTE and hold it memory until it can be dealt with by the modem. This is usually achieved by placing data into an area of random access memory (RAM) inside the modem. Many computers and terminals have a hard time of generating the split bps rate needed for V23 operation and so generate data at 1200bps for transmission at the slower speed of 75bps. Speed buffering in the modem puts the data into modem memory and spools it out at 75bps.

Data compression means that the DTE to DTE rates are much higher than the rate going over the PSTN link and the amount of data transferred between computers is several magnitudes higher than the actual 'baud rate' – the 'number of pieces of data' transmitted by the modem. One problem brought about by the newer generation of fast modems is that an error correcting modem with internal data compression can bat data through the PSTN faster than many computer RS232 ports can handle it. Some current modems offer a DTE-DTE throughput of up to 57,600bps. which is about on the limit for current RS232 technology.

Error correction

Error correction is needed in all modems to reinstate missing bits or bytes of data. Alas, many early modems missed out on error correction, and conversations on dial-up services went along the lines of:

"Hi Fred, H^ws the weat!%^&%^&%er today? Damn this b$%$%$% noise!"

In today's communications Utopia, error correction is fitted to most fast modems and to many slower ones. Error correction also goes hand in hand with data compression and a fast error corrected link is a joy to use. It is a complex subject, sufficient to say that there are as many types of error correction devices on the market as there are errors to correct, and the CCITT eventually came to the rescue with a number of recommendations. The US manufacturer Microcom took a commercial lead in error correction with a range of software enhancements. These were the proprietary MNP series. Levels 2 to 4 were popular amongst comms freaks and a few corporate users in the USA, but a quantum leap in global user acceptability came when the CCITT V42 standard arrived, which was based around a well established protocol called LAP/D. (Link Access Procedure – Data). LAP/D was subsequently modified and became LAP/M – Link Access Procedure – Modem.

The V42 specification included MNP 4 which allowed V42 modems to talk happily to users without an error-correcting modem, through the error-correcting software in their computers. (If your V42 modem tells you that it is connected using an 'alternative protocol' it means it's using MNP 4). Then MNP 5 came along, equipped with data compression and error correction. Effective data throughput could be increased for the price of the new software and Microcom claimed an effective throughput of 17,400bps over a 9600bps link under ideal circumstances.

CCITT V42 also allows for something called 'fallback'. This is a procedure where the DCE-DCE speed of the modems is reduced if a large numbers of errors are occurring over the link. As the numbers of errors decrease, the line speed is again increased. In the USA Hayes took advantage of V42 to produce a Quin modem with its own proprietary speed/error control system. Hayes 'ping-pong' protocol on the 'V Series Smartmodem 9600 + Quad' used a pseudo full-duplex system with one fast channel and one slow channel. The channel transmitting the data got the fast channel, and a fast turn-around system was used to make the half-duplex operation look like full-duplex to the DTE.

An average throughput of around 12,000bps or higher is obtainable with one of these modems, the only drawback is that there has to be a similarly equipped modem at the other end of the link.

V42 bis, V32 and the future

The CCITT, in its ineffable wisdom, disregarded MNP 5 and went for the throat with V42 bis, ('bis' means 'again' or second version) a protocol which added a data compression algorithm called LZ. (Lempel-Zev) to the existing error correction schemes. V42 bis gives a compression ratio of up to 4:1, and a maximum DTE-DTE throughput of around 38,400bps on a 9600bps link.

A further CCITT error correcting/speed standard called V32 was added to the fray, confusing all and sundry. V32 modems use an error-correcting mode called trellis-coding, where the modem makes a (very good) guess as to what the data should be when compared to a pre-defined trellis pattern stored in its firmware.

The next modem bombshell will be V.FAST, a modem speed standard which offers up to 28,800bps full-duplex. Recent agreements have been reached between a consortium of US manufacturers, including US Robotics, Motorola Codex, General Datacomm and Octocomm Systems, and CCITT ratification of their recommendations looks like being set for 1993. V.FAST modems should then be on the market by the end of that year in the US, and by early 1994 in the UK.

4
COMMUNICATIONS HARDWARE

"There are perils and obstacles in the way of success"

4.1   Who needs a modem?

Owning a personal computer is like owning a car. You can use a car for lots of things, but the chances are it's going to spend two-thirds of its life sitting on its tyres in the drive. Similarly many personal computers sit on desks or in homes day after day, with nothing else to do other than run spreadsheets, type letters or handle databases.

The solution to Bored Computer Syndrome is a telephone modem. By adding one to your computer your Amiga, Mac or PC suddenly comes alive with new software downloaded for the cost of a phone call, or with fresh ideas from other people. Without a modem your computer is deaf to the world at large.

Plug in a modem and you'll soon realise that there is a huge world out there waiting to be explored. There are over 10,000 bulletin board systems in Europe, a thousand of them in Britain, and a worldwide network of news services (Usenet), research and global electronic mail services (Internet). There are more recreational services than you could ever hope to connect to in a single lifetime.

If you travel away from home, a portable computer with modem is a great companion. Don't forget that telecommunications don't stop at Dover – it's possible to use your modem in virtually every EC country. Many EC countries, including Britain, also have vast networks of public videotext services available such as Minitel in France which takes 107 million hours of calls each year. You're never alone with a modem…

Corporate users

If you are stuck for that Windows driver, or are looking for a definitive answer to that EMM386.SYS problem, you can get the answer quickly, and regardless of the time in your part of the world. Computer support is a snap if your support department has access to dial-up services such as CIX and CompuServe. Updates of programs, printer drivers, and utilities always appear on dial-up services faster than they drop through your letter box. A modem can be the gateway to almost instant PC support. And with a modem and a subscription to a third party service such as CIX or CompuServe your computer and modem can send faxes, electronic mail and even paper mail, to anywhere in the world, often for less than it would cost to dial direct.

Recreational services

With a modem both you and your computer can make new friends on services like CIX, the definitive UK Bulletin Board System. You can download any of the zillions of free public domain (PD) files which are there for the asking and you can send mail and data to your friends and enemies alike at the push of a button or the click of a mouse. In fact, a modem is the second most useful accessory you will ever buy.

Costs

Many people are put off buying and using modems. They think that they will run up huge bills, or that modems are impossibly difficult to use. Neither of these myths is true. Using a modem to access your electronic mail every day can cost less than £10 per month. Modems are cheaper than ever before, and there is a lot of great shareware (low-cost) and public domain (free) software around to drive them. A basic 2400bps modem can be bought for less than £100. You can even communicate with Australia over the Internet for the price of a call to CIX.

4.2   What do you need for comms?

To get up and running with modems you need telecommunications software for your PC, a modem, and an RS232 cable. There are pitfalls for the unwary in trying to buy these items, let alone ingetting them all to work together. No wonder comms is called a 'black art'. But it's all much easier than it looks and, because everyone else who is a regular modem user has been up the same learning curve, you can rely on lots of help being available. It's a friendly world out there.

But before you rush out with your credit card there are a few things to consider. Should you buy an approved modem, or an unapproved modem? Should you really be looking at installing ISDN (Integrated Services Digital Network)? Do you need fax capability? Is a portable modem as good as a stand-alone modem?

This section covers the hardware needed to start communicating. We look at modems, facsimile and ISDN equipment. These are the devices which connect computers to networks over wide areas and are sometimes call wide area network (WAN) adapters. Devices for local area networking (LAN) such as Ethernet or Token Ring adapters are not covered as they are a separate and equally large subject and deserve a book to themselves.

Buying a modem

Buying a modem is a similar process to buying a car. Rules for both transactions are much the same.

SCHOFIELD'S LAW STATES

- IF YOU GO FOR THE FASTEST, MOST SOPHISTICATED MODEM AVAILABLE NOW IT WILL BE SUPERSEDED BY SOMETHING ELSE, EVEN FASTER AND MORE SOPHISTICATED IN TWO YEARS OR LESS.

- GENERALLY SPEAKING, MODEMS, LIKE CARS, ARE NOT BENEFITED BY AN UPGRADE POLICY FROM MODEM MANUFACTURERS.

- IT DOESN'T MATTER HOW MUCH YOU SPEND, YOUR FRIEND DOWN THE ROAD WILL HAVE BOUGHT A BETTER MODEM AT HALF THE PRICE YOU PAID, WITH TWICE THE NUMBER OF FEATURES.

Which modem?

The sort of modem that you buy will depend on your budget, and your needs. If you're a corporate buyer then price (within reason) should be no object as a fast modem will pay for itself with saved call charges. But remember that if you transfer a lot of data on a regular basis then you should be looking primarily at ISDN. There are many things to consider if you want a modem for recreational or personal use. Speed, price and support considerations should all play a part in your decision, as should compatibility with the services you wish to access. You must also consider whether or not to buy an approved modem. Approved in this case means 'approved for use in the UK'. The body responsible for approval is the British Approvals Board for Telecommunications (BABT).

Approved and non-approved modems

In the UK you can now buy a modem from American, Taiwanese, French, German or British manufacturers. If your purchase conforms to CCITT standards then, in theory, you should be able to plug it in and connect to other similar modems. But the market abounds with cheap 'cloned' modems, and it's not unknown for some of the lesser known brands to fail to connect at higher speeds, or to drop the line on long file transfers. Bear in mind that unless you have direct access to the manufacturer's technical support department in the UK, you are not going to be able to deal easily with problems caused by that cheap no-name modem you bought via mail-order.

In the UK the Trade Descriptions Act says that "Goods should be fit for purpose" and in this case a modem which doesn't work properly should be returned to the dealer for replacement or refund. The reality is that if you have a grouse with a distant mail-order supplier it will cost you time and money, probably in excess of the price paid for a cheap modem, to sort it out.

If a county court case does arise and the supplier operates from a distant part of the country, you may well have to attend the court nearest the supplier, to sort the thing out at some expense.

If you do buy an unapproved modem it's also important to realise that you may have difficulty in making a claim under the 'fitness for purpose' clause of the Trade Descriptions Act. If your modem has not been approved for use on UK services you may find yourself without a leg to stand on if you go to court over the inability of said modem to work properly. Also, if you do buy an unapproved modem and have subsequent problems with the telephone line to which it is attached you are not going to get much sympathy from the PTT (Post Telephone and Telegraph) supplier.

Modems and consumer legislation

The actual policing of the legislative process which governs all of this is currently in a mess, and a large one at that. The relevant part of the Telecommunications Act says that you may be liable for prosecution for using an unapproved device and, according to BABT, there have in fact been a number of prosecutions. However, according to OFTEL there have been "no prosecutions of this kind as yet" which leaves the entire viability of the testing and approvals process open to criticism. Even British Telecom seems to be in the dark as to what the approvals process is for. When asked why we have such an unworkable approvals policy, one very senior BT spokesman said: "BABT exists to stop hackers blowing BT engineers out of manholes". This is not a particularly accurate or useful point of view.

Just before this book went to press a definitive 'non-answer' was received from the Trading Standards department of the author's local authority. The gist of the reply to a question which asked for clarification of the point about unapproved modems being 'fit for purpose' was that, as far as Trading Standards Officers (TSOs) are concerned the issue has not been tested in a court and is therefore open to conjecture. The TSO who wrote the reply added that he had the greatest difficulty in getting any relevant information out of OFTEL, and the entire issue was open to conjecture and misinterpretation. His personal opinion was that an unapproved modem could still be returned to the supplier for a refund under the 'fitness for purpose' test, as the modem should be capable of working correctly, regardless of any law which might prohibit actual connection.

The entire process of telecomms approval is about to come under review in 1994 as pan-European approval standards are now needed. There is some thought that this new approvals procedure will make it illegal for unapproved modems to be sold, let alone connected to a network. This proposal confirms the author's belief that only approved telephone equipment should be used on the networks as there is so much FUD (fear, uncertainty, doubt) around at the moment that it is the only policy that makes any sense.

You should not hold your breath waiting for the Government to get around to sorting this out, as history shows that you will have a long wait. The only way to play safe is to buy approved equipment, especially as future legislation may make it illegal to sell unapproved modems. You could be left with an expensive white elephant if this does happen and you want to upgrade.

To sum up, buying an approved modem is a Good Thing, if only because OFTEL has not yet decided whether or not it will prosecute you for doing otherwise. You should stay firmly on the side of the angels.

And whilst you are at it you should avoid the strange English habit of paying rock bottom prices for everything and then grumbling about poor quality. Buy your approved modem from a reputable dealer or supplier who will hold your paw if things go wrong. A good maxim when buying a modem is 'buy cheap – buy twice'. A second is 'caveat emptor' (buyer beware). A third point to remember is the phrase 'Action may be taken against offenders'…

BABT approval

The British Approvals Board for Telecommunications is an independent body which was set up after the 'liberalisation' of the telecomms equipment market in 1981. It is funded only from the fees levied on equipment suppliers and the typical cost for approving a modem is currently around £1,200. There are extra charges levied for quality audits and for testing, but the add-on cost to the end user is likely to be negligible, despite protestations by some manufacturers. Approved devices with speeds of 1200bps or less are given a Green Dot sticker stating that the product is approved. Higher speed devices do not have to carry the Green Dot sticker, but still have to be approved. All untested and unapproved equipment sold in Britain must bear a red triangle to warn users.

Most modem users realise that only approved equipment may be connected to UK services, but few realise that this applies not only to services provided by British Telecom but to those provided by any UK PTT such as Mercury or the Hull Telephone System. This ban also includes the cellular and CT2 networks. For the recreational user BABT approval seems like just another bureaucratic obstacle but in real terms BABT approval adds little to the end-user cost and an approved modem is certified safe for connection to the PSTN. It should not cause interference or suffer overly from noise – or blow BT engineers out of manholes.

BABT approval focuses only on safety and compatibility issues (not 'fitness for purpose') and BABT is not the authoritarian organisation that some people would have you believe. Think of BABT approval as being a similar sort of vital safety process as the one which car manufacturers have to go through with before a new model launch.

One final advantage resulting from BABT approval is that an approved modem will probably come from a reputable source and that service and upgrades are more likely to be available.

Buying a modem from abroad

There is a large disparity in the price of computers, software, modems, cars, petrol and almost anything else you can think of between the UK and the USA. It's become common for goods sold in the UK to cost around twice what they cost in the USA, for reasons which are beyond most of us. When pressed on the subject many of the vendors claim that Europe 'is a more expensive place' than the USA and that their prices must reflect this. Also any US company that has dealers abroad has to fund the dealership through increased sales margins on product. The money to pay for the BMWs and the stripey shirts has to come from somewhere.

Whatever the reason for the pricing anomaly it is common to be able to buy a modem mail-order from the States for around half the UK price. But notwithstanding such niceties as BABT approval you may find that buying a single modem from abroad to save money is not the bargain it appears to be.

Let's consider the fictitious T-Bone Sextuple Standard Fax Modem. It has all CCITT modes up to V32 bis, a couple of Bell modes thrown in, and a superfast but slightly non-standard fax capability. It also has a digital alarm clock built in. The modem costs $200 in the States, £200 plus VAT in Britain. Should you buy a 'T-Bone' from the States with your credit card?

FIGURE 4.1

USA versus UK modem prices (representative prices from advertisers in an American magazine)

DETAILS	USA		UK
	$	£ @ $1.55 = £1	£
Modem	200	129	200
Shipping	25	16	–
VAT	–	22.50	35
Import Duty	–	6.50	–
UK Phone Lead	–	10	Included
		£184	£235

Had you remembered that you generally have to pay VAT and import duty on goods bought abroad? Anyway, you have saved £51 on the deal and you do a small inelegant jig in front of the postman when your parcel arrives ten days later.

But wait. In real terms you have bought a non-approved modem that isn't supported by any UK company. If it happens not to work when you take it out of the box you are up a certain well-known tributary with no viable means of propulsion. You will also lose any saving you may have made by the time you have phoned or faxed the States and paid for shipping back to the supplier for repairs. Oh, you are not covered by the Sale of Goods Act either. It doesn't have any jurisdiction over 'foreign' suppliers. And you will have to claim back the VAT and import duty you have paid – not from the supplier but from the UK Customs and Excise people. It's a procedure which can only be generously described as 'cumbersome'. Finally your new modem is supplied with a 110-volt mains adapter which won't like our 240-volt supplies one little bit. And it has a phone lead terminated in an American RJ11 plug which won't fit your BT socket…

Does buying from the States make sense? It can do. Books, CD-ROMs and software are generally much cheaper if bought this way, but they tend not to go wrong very often. There's sometimes a different story with hardware – you may be quids in while it's working, quids out when it's not.

Hayes compatibility

This is one of the most abused phrases in the communications industry. 'Hayes compatibility' refers to the codes sent to the modem from the DTE to control it. All Hayes commands start with 'AT' (for attention) followed by the command. A Hayes modem uses 'ATD' to dial a number. The phrase 'Hayes compatible' therefore refers to a modem which uses the Hayes command set but is not necessarily fully compatible with Hayes modems.

Many non-Hayes modems use a sub-set of the Hayes commands, modified for their own use. These commands may start with 'AT' the Hayes Attention command, but that's about as far as it goes. The only fully Hayes compatible modems appear to be those manufactured by Hayes Microcomputer Products Inc. There is a full listing of (genuine) Hayes commands and S register settings in Appendix 1 for your guidance.

If you buy a modem from another manufacturer you will probably find that many of the commands have a similar function to those listed, or that many are missing altogether from the sub-set used in your modem. Many non-Hayes 'Hayes compatible' modems differ in the way in which they use S-registers (modem control parameters). If you are having trouble with your modem when operating under automatic software control – checking for S-register compatibility might help solve the problem. In the USA a standard now exists for 'Hayes compatibility' which goes some way to removing much of the hype associated with the phrase.

To conclude – the phrase 'Hayes Compatible' should generally be taken with a large sack full of salt, and then ignored, unless you are a Trading Standards Officer or your name is Dennis C Hayes.

The TIES debacle

Intelligent modems generally have two modes of operation: 'Command' mode allows the modem to accept commands such as 'dial that number' or 'answer that phone' from the DTE. 'Receive/Transmit' mode is the mode where the modem has control over the DTE and is sending data back and forth over the virtual link. In Receive/Transmit mode any keypress from the computer is transmitted as data through the modem, in the normal scheme of things. It follows from this that if you want your modem to stop transmitting data and return to obeying your every wish there has to be some sort of mechanism in place which allows you to do this.

The software mechanism is called the 'escape sequence'. The hardware mechanism is called 'pulling the plug out'. The first solution is usually more elegant and desirable than the second.

The escape sequence is a series of codes and time intervals which the modem recognises in the data stream coming from the computer as being a command to say 'enter Command mode'. Most modems will still keep the line open (off-hook) when made to enter Command mode in this way until told to hang up.

If as a budding modem designer you decide that a useful escape sequence would be to send 'GET OFF THE LINE' to the modem to make it enter Command mode – you would find that this method would work quite well, at first sight. It's not every day that you encounter the phrase in upper case in data-streams and you might get away with it for a while. But eventually you would start to get complaints from people who were experiencing modem hang-ups when transmitting a particular text file via one of your modems. You've guessed it. Their file would contain your escape sequence of

```
'GET OFF THE LINE'
```

This problem was recognised in the early 1980s by modem guru Dale Heatherington. His solution was to surround the escape sequence with 'guard times' to alert the modem that a real escape sequence would be the next piece of data from the DTE. It looks like this:

```
[guardtime] [GET OFF THE LINE] [guardtime]
```

Of course Dale didn't use such a lengthy escape sequence – he used three plus signs '+++' surrounded by the timing sequences. The result was that it became virtually impossible to transmit the entire escape sequence accidentally, although it could be easily programmed into terminal emulation programs.

The Hayes company patented the 'Improved Escape Mechanism with Guard Time Mechanism' as US Patent 4,549,302 and the result is often referred to as Hayes 302 or Heatherington 302 by modem manufacturers.

Hayes 302 has worked on tens of thousands of installations worldwide without a hitch for over a decade. In 1991 a new escape sequence appeared in modems other than those manufactured by Hayes. While it used the '+++' characters of Hayes 302 for compatibility purposes, it did not surround the characters with guard times. The net result was that any piece of data containing three recognisable plus signs hung up the modem or put it into Command mode. The phenomenon was named TIES for Time Independent Escape Sequence. (If you think that no one in their right mind would put three plus signs in a file, bear in mind that this chapter, created as an electronic file, has done it twice already.) TIES was and is a potential problem area for modem buyers, especially as the term 'Hayes compatible' is often used on modems with TIES embedded into them.

Modem manufacturers do not advertise that their product is blessed with TIES, for some reason. The only real way of checking whether a modem is tied up by TIES is to send three plus signs in ASCII format as part of an ASCII file transfer through the modem. If the modem returns to the Command mode or hangs up you may have a TIES modem. If you bought your modem as being 'Hayes compatible' you have a great case for refund under the Sale of Goods Act, notwithstanding any complications of the Trade Descriptions Act and 'approval'.

TIES is currently embedded in modem chip sets from a particular manufacturer and it is finding its way into many lower priced modems. The best approach before buying a modem is to phone the technical department of the company you are interested in. If it has never heard of TIES, or cannot say if its modem is compliant with US patent 4,549,302 (Hayes/Heatherington 302) then you may care to allow that fact to influence your purchasing decision. If you do need more information on the subject there is a paper *The Issue of the Reliable Modem Escape Sequence* available from Hayes UK.

Asking your friendly cut-throat computer dealer if he knows anything about TIES chip sets or obscure US patents may result in a certain amount of physical damage to yourself, especially in a shop full of people on a busy Saturday morning.

4.3 Types of modems

There are four distinct physical forms of modems. Whichever type you buy will be dictated by your interest, your technical ability and your existing equipment.

Stand-alone modems

These have their own box and power supply and live on a shelf or by the side of the computer. They don't need much in the way of physically installation: a lead plugs into the main power socket, a second plugs into the phone socket and a third plugs into the RS232 socket (or PCMCIA slot). Many stand-alone modems have a duplicate phone socket on the rear plate for plugging in a telephone. This socket will usually disconnect the phone when the modem is in use.

Stand-alone modems are relatively small, consume little power, have useful lights or a display on the front which tell you what is happening over the link and need little technical knowledge to physically install. They will also work with almost any computer equipped with an RS232 port, and a single stand-alone modem will usually work with the IBM PC or compatible, Apple, Amiga or Atari computer, or a simple RS232 terminal.

If you have a portable computer you will find that a mains powered box with a large power supply will weigh heavily. Portable computer owners usually opt for one of the other three physical forms.

Installation of stand-alone modems differs from one manufacturer to another. A few will work straight out of the box, but many others will need switch and internal settings changed to fine tune some aspects of operation.

Card modems

A card modem is a printed circuit board carrying modem circuitry which plugs into an internal slot in the computer. Card modems are often slightly cheaper than the stand-alone equivalent as they don't need a case or a separate power supply. Advantages are low price and portability; disadvantages are a lack of informative lights or information displays on most card modems.

Many cheap card modems offer 'Quin' operation and fax capabilities, and dedicated card modems are available to fit inside many portable computers.

Card modems need a little technical knowledge to install, especially if you have network or other cards already installed. You may also find that installing an internal modem yourself can invalidate the warranty terms on some computers. The price of card modems is now so low that it is tempting to buy one regardless of any other considerations but the phrase 'buy cheap, buy twice' should be remembered!

Portable modems

Modern technology has now brought the size of a modem down to that of a packet of cigarettes, with room for the battery inside the case. Pocket modems are good for travellers or for Original Equipment Manufacturers' (OEM) use. They suffer the disadvantage of using battery power which can fade at crucial moments, but the advantages of light weight and portability often outweigh this.

Some pocket modems are self powered from the RS232 line, but these can give problems with hard handshaking in some cases. Battery powered modems also tend to work with a wider range of equipment. Quin and fax capabilities are available. Cheap, imported and unapproved pocket modems might seem like a bargain at first sight, but many cheap, imported pocket modems lack things like error correction, data compression, speed buffering and even handshaking. It pays to be careful when buying such an animal as it may not turn out to be quite the bargain it seemed at first sight.

Decent portable modems are desirable things and UK prices are still relatively high, reflecting this.

Acoustic coupling modems

Some of the earliest modems were acoustically coupled to the PSTN by attaching a rubber cup to the mouthpiece and earpiece of the telephone handset. They suffered from the problems of noise breakthrough but had the advantage of working wherever there was a conventional telephone.

Acoustically coupled modems are now coming back into fashion as the various countries of the world have all seen fit to equip their telephone networks with differing sockets. Acoustically coupled modems are quite often integrated with pocket modems and are useful for globetrotters. All modes are now available, but the problem of noise breakthrough hasn't completely gone away. Most error-correcting systems deal satisfactorily with this problem, up to a point, at the expense of a slight decrease in throughput.

Acoustically coupled modems can only be as good as the telephone handset to which they are coupled, and using an old telephone with a carbon microphone installed in it is asking for trouble, if only on the transmit side of things!

Integrated computers/modems

The computer with an in-built modem is really a hybrid of the portable computer and battery operated modem and suffers the disadvantages of both. Many proprietary internal modems cannot usually be upgraded cheaply and can become superseded within a year or two, although they will still communicate at the rates for which they were intended. The manufacturers of such devices have now mainly taken to the plug-in card method of installation, but if your portable computer uses a proprietary modem slot (many do) then you may find that future modem upgrades become a question of upgrading the entire computer. A pocket rocket (portable) modem may be a better bet.

One consequence of the constant terrorist attacks on aircraft is that airport security is now thorough to the point of fanaticism. Many German airports are weighing portable computers and checking the weight off against the manufacturer's specification. If your portable computer has an internal modem this will increase its weight and the consequent interest of airport security guards. Taking the modem out before you travel is one solution. Carrying a pocket rocket modem is another.

4.4   Common modem features

Many modern modems share similar internal features. Autodial, the ability to dial numbers from a store held either within the modem or on computer disk is now almost mandatory, as is the ability to answer the phone and make a connection to a calling modem (auto-answer). Other features such as error correction are not present on all modems and may not always be needed.

BEFORE BUYING A MODEM IT'S IMPORTANT TO CONSIDER

- WHAT YOU WILL BE CONNECTING TO
  If the only service you wish to use uses a proprietary standard such as 'HST' or Hayes 9600 'ping-pong', it may be preferable to buy a modem with these features, but only in addition to CCITT standards, not in place of them.

- WHAT YOU WILL BE USING TO TALK TO THE MODEM
  If you are using an error-correcting software package in your computer (such as Odyssey) you may not need to spend extra money on an error-correcting modem. In practice this tends to apply to modems up to quad standards only.

- THE AMOUNT OF DATA TRANSFERRED

  If you transfer lots of data on a regular basis it will be worthwhile buying the fastest modem available to minimise call charges. If you just want to lurk around the bulletin boards or send an occasional file back to the office then a quad modem will be adequate, until the comms bug bites fully. Many current quad modems now have V42 bis compression and can provide a computer-computer throughput of 9600bps over what is essentially a 2400bps link. This is a Desirable Feature. But don't forget to consider ISDN if you use a modem for more than a couple of hours day and there's similar equipment at the other end of the link.

- WHERE ARE YOU TALKING TO?

  If you only wish to communicate with UK services then you will need less features than if you wish to direct dial the United Arab Emirates. Many international lines go via satellite links and error correction is mandatory for 100 percent successful direct direct-dialled links to some remote parts of the world. If you try to set up an international point-to-point link with a standard non-error-correcting quad modem at both ends you may be disappointed.

- UPGRADABILITY

  If you intend to become a long term comms user you may wish to consider buying an upgradeable modem. Many manufacturers don't offer upgradeability, which is not to the consumers' benefit. Like cars, modems become obsolete very rapidly; unlike cars, modems don't wear out. Currently Hayes UK has a general upgrade policy for most of its modems and this is to be welcomed.

- WARRANTY

  Many modem manufacturers now offer a two year warranty. If you're buying a modem make sure you ask the dealer about warranty terms. Electronic equipment is very reliable these days and tends to fail either within days of purchase, or the day after the warranty has expired. Always send back warranty registration cards too. Your statutory rights won't be affected if you don't but you may lose your rights to any free or low cost upgrades that come along.

4.5 Some useful modem features

- AUTO-DIAL (AD)

  The ability of a modem to dial a number, or a series of numbers from a store of pre-programmed numbers. Many modems have an internal store which will hold at least four numbers which is useful if you are using a dumb terminal or teletype. If you are using a personal computer to drive a modem it is more useful to hold telephone numbers in the communications package. Many packages will hold hundreds of phone numbers.

■ AUTO-ANSWER (AA)

The ability of a modem to answer an incoming call and connect to it. Vital for auto-mated communications and present in almost all modern modems. An auto-dial, auto-answer modem is commonly advertised as an AA/AD device.

■ ADAPTIVE DATA COMPRESSION (ADC)

Proprietary system used on many modems made by Hayes. It's ignored on many 'Hayes compatible' modems. ADC adjusts compression to the type and content of the data being transmitted and can be used with V42/LAPM.

Asynchronous 'without timing': modems for dial-up PSTN access are asynchronous and use start and stop bits to segregate datawords. Synchronous-only modems are specialist beasties and are used for mainframe or leased line purposes.

■ AUTOMATIC SPEED-FALLBACK

The ability of a modem to recognise the speed of modem at the opposite end of the PSTN or virtual link and match communication speeds. Also mistakenly called 'baud rate shifting'.

■ SPEED-BUFFERING

The ability of a modem to send or receive data to or from its own computer at a throughput different from that being used on the phone link. A V23 1200/75 modem will often use speed buffering to equalise its own computer speed to 1200bps, whilst sending data out at 75bps. Flow control between the computer and modem prevents overflow conditions. Most modern modems speed-buffer although some imported 'pocket rocket' modems lack this feature, and consequently cannot use V23. If V23 mode is important to you then make sure your potential purchase can speed-buffer, with the correct handshaking (XON/XOFF or RTS/CTS) for your needs.

■ S-REGISTERS

An area set aside for user configuration in the modem's nonvolatile memories. S-Registers control the way the modem operates. For example: setting S-Register 0 to 2 with ATS0=2 [enter] will allow the modem to answer an incoming call after two rings.

■ ERROR CORRECTION

Many modems have this feature built in as MNP 4 or LAP/M or V42 bis. Modems without internal error correction can have data error corrected at the computer end if the communication package in use supports this. Odyssey supports MNP 5 error correction. Older error correction standards included 'ARQ', used on some 1200bps half-duplex systems.

■ DATA COMPRESSION

The ability of a modem to compress data into smaller packets for transmission over the virtual link. This speeds up the overall transfer rate. The CCITT standard is V42 bis which gives a 4:1 ratio in optimum conditions. Others are MNP 5 and MNP 7, and ' BTLZ'. MNP 5 offers a 2:1 compression ratio in addition to error correction. In practice this gives up to 4000bps throughput on a 2400bps link. Non-compressed files, such as ASCII text, will transfer at over 3100cps average on a V32 bis modem. A compressed file will travel at around 1200-1600cps over the same link. If you are using MNP 5 on a link and transferring pre-compressed files you may get an increase in overall speed by turning the feature off. Some contemporary comms programs like Odyssey which use MNP 5 now have an automatic switch built in to them that minimises the effect of MNP 5 on compressed files. On the other hand V42 bis doesn't seem to cause so many problems during transfers of compressed files and may usually be left on. Trial and error may be needed to fine tune your own system to maximise throughput.

Almost all dial-up services use some form of data-compression on files stored on their disks. If you transfer a compressed file via a second method which tries to compress it even further you may actually increase the time taken to effect the transfer. For those of you with an eye on the future, the data compression algorithms within V42 will only be effective up to around 14,400bps (V32 bis). Any new standard will need a work-around or a new set of routines to overcome this.

■ BELL MODEMS

These use the American Bell standards such as Bell 103, a 300/300bps standard. In days of old a Bell modem was needed to talk to modems in the USA, but most of the world now uses CCITT modems. Who said bureaucracy had no uses?

■ QUAD AND QUIN MODEMS

A quad modem uses the four basic CCITT modulation standards: V21, V22, V22 bis, and V23. A quin modem is a quintuple-standard modem which uses the four basic CCITT standards plus V32.

■ SEX MODEM

A sextuple-standard modem which uses the four basic standards, plus V32, and V32 bis. The term 'Sex modem' does not feature in manufacturers' catalogues, for some reason.

■ FEATURE NEGOTIATION

Most error correcting modems have Feature Negotiation. It is used by an originating modem (the one making the call) to ascertain if the answering modem has similar error-correction or error-compression features to itself. If it hasn't, the answering modem will try a different error-checking protocol or throughput rate until carriers are locked. Most modems equipped with this feature allow it to be disabled as some early quad or V21/23 modems get themselves in a sweaty knot when being hissed at by a negotiating modem. The CCITT recommendation V32 bis standardises feature negotiation methods for modems. If you find that you cannot connect to a service with feature negotiation enabled at your modem then you should disable it as a matter of course and try again.

■ DIAL-BACK

A security feature in which a called modem will auto-answer the phone, and call a preprogrammed internal number to verify user identity.

■ DATA ENCRYPTION

A feature where the modem encrypts data from the computer for transmission across the phone link. A similar modem decodes the data at the other end of the link. Encryption standards are almost certain to be proprietary and two similar modems must be used.

■ REMOTE SET-UP

Allows remote modem parameters to be set over the virtual link as opposed to over the local computer-modem link. Remote set-up can be useful for corporates, but tends to be a rare feature on budget modems.

■ X.25 PAD

X.25 networks operate on the packet switching principle and a modem with X.25 PAD (packet assembly/disassembly) capabilities can connect directly to such a system. Most packet switching services in the UK are operated by PTTs and accessed by asynch dial-up, although there are corporate systems on which a modem with an X.25 pad can be used. This feature is present in all Hayes 'V series' products.

■ POOLED MODEMS

Modem pooling is an unfortunate phrase. It doesn't mean that your modems have melted and dripped on the floor. It means "having a number of modems in a rack hooked up to a clever device which lets one computer set them all up, even if they are connected to different computers". Most mainstream manufacturers sell modem racking equipment together with trick hardware to allow any or all the modems to be set up via a single terminal. Such racks are often fan-cooled and the modems consist of cards which slide in and out of the rack. Pooled modems are mainly used in commercial applications and on large-ish bulletin board systems.

■ NET MODEM

A newcomer to the UK modem market. Net modems appear as a node on a Local Area Network and allow any certified user to access them. They are not yet common in the UK but have been around for some years in the US. Net modems generally have an Ethernet port on the rear instead of an RS232 socket.

■ FAX MODEM

This is usually a quad modem or better standard modem equipped with the CCITT standards for fax transmission. Fax modems need to be used with special software.

4.6 Other types of comms equipment

The telephone modem is isn't the only critter that can send data down phone lines. The fax machine out-sells modems by about fifty to one and is perhaps the most used piece of consumer telephony equipment, aside from the telephone. Video-phones are just around the corner, but will not become commonplace until we all have fast digital lines brought into our homes.

ISDN has also quietly arrived and is doing well in the corporate sector. Once that enters the home there will be an astronomical increase in the use of fast data-comms by domestic users.

Facsimilie machines (Fax)

Fax machines are not a new idea; early scanning fax machines made use of a rotating drum which was helically scanned by an optical sensor moving along a linear path, like the old cylinder phonographs.

A modern fax is basically three devices in one: an image scanner, a thermal printer, and an auto-dial modem. They come in a variety of models: basic fax machines have a receive and transmit function; more expensive models feature the ability to transmit and receive grayscale (half-tones – useful for photographs); others have an answer-phone built in. The more you pay the more user features you get, unlike a modem where paying more money generally brings only higher speeds.

All contemporary fax machines are Group III compatible, which means that they transmit and receive at up to 14,400bps although some machines feature Group II compatibility to ensure that they can communicate with earlier machines. Group I machines, established in the late 1960s are now obsolete, as are the later Group II devices. ISDN might bring us closer to the Group IV fax machine which uses a 64Kbps link to transmit a sheet of A4 paper in around two seconds.

Faxes boast many of the features of modems such as auto-answer and auto-negotiation. Auto-dial memories are a useful feature and many faxes can act as a simple photocopier. (Beware! Fax paper is coated with a thermal-sensitive layer which responds to heat, sunlight and mugs of coffee by turning black. If you wish to preserve your incoming faxes for posterity they should be photocopied on a normal toner-based photocopier.)

Plain paper fax machines replace the usual thermal printer of the fax machine with a laser or ink-jet printer and so avoid the problem. The cost per received fax is sometimes higher with this sort of machine, although the output of a plain paper fax machine is noticeably superior to that of a thermally printed fax.

Fax card modems fit into an internal card slot of a personal computer. They need to be used with special fax software and are often combined with 2400bps modems. Fax card modems offer a cheap way to acquire a fax machine but it is not possible to directly fax existing paper documents with a card fax, unless such documents are scanned and digitised into computer-readable form before hand. However, fax cards are good for receiving fax transmissions – the output from a fax card reproduced onto a laser or ink-jet printer is usually of high quality.

The market for fax machines has taken off in the last two years and prices are falling all the time. Correspondingly, manufacturers are building yet more features into fax machines and some explanation of these is needed.

Fax compatibility

Should be a minimum of Group III. Some older machines are Group II only and should be avoided unless they are on offer at a good price, as not all modern machines have Group II compatibility. Many fax card modems offer a range of proprietary fast methods, useful if you have an identical fax card at the other end of the link. Unfortunately, most people don't and a card fax should be chosen with Group III compatibility.

SOME USEFUL FAX FEATURES

- ANSWERPHONE
Often built in to fax machines at virtually zero cost to the end-user.

- DIALING MEMORES
Useful for storing destination phone numbers for access via a single key-press.

- PAPER CUTTER
Slices incoming faxes into pages. Not an essential function and omitted on some budget machines.

- AUTO-PAGING
Calls a prearranged number to tell you that a fax has been received. The fax can then be retrieved from the machine with a coded keypad.

- FINE MODE
Sets the machine to the maximum resolution (measured in dots per inch – dpi) Faxes sent in fine mode take longer to transmit as more data is sent.

- AUTO REDIAL
Re-dials the last number if it is engaged.

- FAX MEMORY
An area of Random Access Memory (RAM) inside the fax machines which can store incoming faxes if the machine is out of paper, or store outgoing faxes for queuing for timed transmission, or for multiple destination faxing of a single document. Fax memory can be used with the stored numbers on some fax machine to automatically dial several destinations in and transmit a stored fax.

■ MULTI-FILE TRANSMISSION
Allows discrete documents stored in memory to be transmitted to different destinations automatically.

■ SECURITY MAILBOX
A feature which holds received documents in memory until a password is entered by the named recipient.

■ FAX SWITCH
A fax machine normally needs a dedicated phone line so that it can receive documents at any time. A fax switch is a device which switches an incoming voice call through to a telephone receiver, or switches a fax message through to the fax machine so that only one line is needed. Fax switches can be external or internal and can pay for themselves after the first year on line rental charge savings alone. A fax switch can also be used to switch between a modem, a fax machine and a telephone, but models with this capability are often quite expensive. Some phone users are put off from continuing a call if they hear a fax switch at the other end of the line.

■ POLLING
Allows one fax machine to request transmission from another. Polling is often used by mailing companies to distribute information. Most machines that have a memory capacity offer polling, and a password feature is often available to prevent data held within the fax machine to be polled by unauthorised fax machines.

■ COMPUTER PORT
If fitted to a fax machine this is likely to be a parallel or serial port. Not much use for anything on a stand-alone fax machine although computer hobbyists seem to enjoy destroying them by inadvertently applying the wrong voltages.

4.7 ISDN

ISDN (Integrated Services Data Network) adapters fall into the internal card or stand-alone categories – the important difference being that stand-alone ISDN adapters must connect through our old friend the RS232 port and this presents a serious limit to the amount of data that can go through it. Current ISDN adapters connected in this way can usually achieve around 38Kbps – just over a quarter of the full throughput that can be achieved over a multiplexed ISDN link. Card adapters should be able to manage the full throughput but may require a computer with a fast processor and data bus to manage this.

The Hayes company again rapidly set new standards for controlling ISDN adapters and the Hayes Enhanced ISDN AT command set works in much the same way as it does on modems. You can even use your existing comms software to drive an ISDN adapter, although you are likely to be limited in some way.

Dedicated ISDN software often allows the two 64Kbps B channels to be patched together to form a 128Kbps link. On the mechanical side – external ISDN adapters usually have a couple of RS232/V24 ports, a telephone handset and a socket for fax or answerphone and are generally no more difficult to operate than a standard modem. Previous statements about the overall desirability of BABT approval stand.

External ISDN adapters are now available from UK PTTs and they generally have more features than the internal products designed for a particular computer, although this will change as the market becomes led by consumer demand. PTTs may also start to rent out ISDN adapters, and this might be useful until prices for equipment starts to fall.

4.8   Portable communications

Once you have been exposed to dial-up comms you will decide that your life is either made richer by them, or that the entire thing is a black art. If your opinion is of the latter then this book has failed and you should give it immediately to a worthy cause. On the other hand you may find that 'comms' becomes as much a part of your life as eating and that you cannot go anywhere without taking a portable computer and a pocket rocket modem along with you.

Fortunately, the computer manufacturers now make this possibility attainable, with cheap pocket computers (palmtops) and notebook computers being available. Many palmtop computers – those little plastic things which masquerade as 'Personal Dis-Organisers' are quite up to the task of driving a modem, assuming that they have a serial port, telecomms software, and plenty of internal storage available.

Of the current batch of palmtops on the market, the ones that stand out as being comms-friendly are the Atari Portfolio, and the Psion Series III. Hewlett Packard also makes a dinky machine which can be removed from anywhere on your person in seconds by any trainee pickpocket. It's price alas, is above mere rubies.

If you decide that you do need a portable comms machine then make sure it has a serial port and that comms software is available and your dealer has it in stock. The market life of many palmtop computers is less than one year, and you might be disappointed if you decide that you want a serial port for that palmtop you bought 13 months ago. If you move up to the notebook market then almost any machine is suitable, as almost all of them have a serial port nowadays.

One problem with notebook computers is their extreme weight and bulk. It may only be the size of a piece of A4 paper, but your notebook computer, with battery charger, manual, spare batteries and executive dingo-hide carry case is likely to weigh more than your wife would care to deem 'portable'. If it weighs more than a bag of sugar, then it ain't portable – it's 'transportable'. Ask her.

Tandy and Amstrad now market small computers which are ultra lightweight and can be carried in one hand without the risk of groin injury and subsequent marital discord. The Tandy machine is interesting as it is a derivative of the Tandy 100, one of the first portable computers to gain mass acceptance by the world's journalists. (The T100 was also much loved by mid-1980s telephone hackers.) The Cambridge Z88 is also lightweight and useful for comms, and has the great advantage of a silent rubber keyboard and half a megabyte or so of store on a fully expanded machine The Z88 is still in production after some years, but probably will not have much more of an extended life span

The lightweight and useful Amstrad NC 100 has basic comms built in but may not drive all modems properly.

The author uses an Atari Portfolio to keep in touch. Like many palmtops, it is not possible to word-process on the tiny keyboard, but the thing talks amiably with dial-up services, and seems to know all about data transfer and suchlike. The machine is also handbag friendly – a phrase which is little understood by macho computer salesmen. The purchase was greatly influenced by an article in CompuServe magazine which carried a photograph of a man on a mountain top energetically waving a Portfolio to prove how lightweight it was. Either that or he hadn't read this book and was signalling for help in sorting out his parity settings.

One consequence of using a small machine for comms is that many of them have a small screen. If these are used on any of the many dial-up services which believe everyone is equipped with an 80 column by 25 line screen, then information will scroll off the top of the screen of your portable. One solution is to use V21 or V22 speeds with these machines, as the slower data transfer rate means that you stand a chance of being able to read at least half of your mail. Faster modems are useful if you can log the data to disk or memory as it comes in.

4.9 Summary

MODEMS

■ A NEW BABT APPROVED QUAD MODEM NOW COSTS AROUND £100 PLUS VAT; APPROVED V32 BIS MODEMS COST AROUND £400 PLUS VAT. FAX PLUS QUAD MODEMS CAN BE HAD FOR AROUND £140 PLUS VAT AND PRICES ARE DROPPING ALL THE TIME.

■ LOOK FOR MODEM DEALS WHICH OFFER FREE TERMINAL SOFTWARE OR CREDITS ON A DIAL-UP SERVICE. A ONE YEAR ON-SITE SERVICE WARRANTY OR EXTENDED FIVE YEAR GUARANTEE IS WORTH BETWEEN 10 AND 15 PERCENT OF THE PURCHASE PRICE AND SHOULD BE VIEWED AS A DESIRABLE BONUS.

■ UNAPPROVED MODEMS MAY BE SLIGHTLY CHEAPER THAN SOME APPROVED DEVICES BUT SUPPORT MAY BE A PROBLEM.

■ MOST DIAL-UP SERVICES NOW HAVE AT 2400BPS CONNECTIONS AVAILABLE AND THIS SHOULD BE CONSIDERED A MINIMUM SPECIFICATION.

■ V42 ERROR CORRECTION IS OFTEN SUPPLIED INSTALLED IN NEW MODEMS, BUT SEPARATE ERROR-CORRECTING SOFTWARE SUCH AS ODYSSEY WILL GIVE ERROR-FREE COMMS OF UP TO 4000BPS ON A 2400BPS CONNECTION AND THIS MEANS YOU CAN USE OLDER (CHEAPER) MODEMS WITHOUT ERROR CORRECTION ON SERVICES THAT SUPPORT MNP 5 OR V42 AT THE REMOTE END OF THE LINK.

■ SECONDHAND MODEMS USUALLY FIND THEIR WAY ONTO THE MARKET BECAUSE THE ORIGINAL OWNER HAS UPGRADED TO A FASTER DEVICE. BUYING THIS WAY CAN BE USEFUL AS ENTHUSIASTS TEND TO UPGRADE REGULARLY AND PRICES ARE LOW. BEAR IN MIND THAT A MODEM WITHOUT A MANUAL WILL BE AS USEFUL AS A CHOCOLATE TEAPOT IF THE MODEM TURNS OUT NOT TO BE STANDARDISED, AND THAT THERE IS NO PROTECTION FOR BUYERS OF SECONDHAND EQUIPMENT UNDER THE TRADE DESCRIPTIONS ACT.

■ THE MOST USEFUL AND CHEAPEST SECONDHAND MODEMS ARE THE QUAD DEVICES, AS THESE OFFER RESPECTABLE SPEEDS AND CAN BE USED WITH LOW COST, ERROR-CORRECTING SOFTWARE. A SLOWER DUAL-SPEED MODEM SUCH AS A 21/23 DEVICE WILL SERVE FOR A WHILE AS AN INTRODUCTION, BUT THE NOVELTY OF SLOW DATA TRANSFER WEARS OFF IN DIRECT RELATIONSHIP TO THE SIZE OF THE RESULTING PHONE BILL. IT'S PROBABLY BETTER TO PUT THE MONEY TOWARDS A 2400 OR QUAD MODEM.

■ STAY CLEAR OF OLD BELL-ONLY MODEMS, MOST SERVICES NOW USE CCITT STANDARDS.

FAX MACHINES

■ A DECENT (APPROVED) FAX MACHINE, WITH DOCUMENT FEEDER, GRAYSCALE AND FINE SETTINGS SHOULD

COST AROUND £350 PLUS VAT. YOU WILL PAY MORE FOR EXTRA FEATURES SUCH AS MEMORY OR POLLING, OR GET THESE FEATURES AT THE EXPENSE OF OTHERS. IT'S A GOOD IDEA TO ASK A FEW EXISTING USERS OF FAX MACHINES FOR AN OPINION AS TO THE PERFORMANCE OF THEIR MACHINE BEFORE BUYING.

■ FAX MACHINES ARE COMPLICATED BEASTIES AND ARE NOT AMENABLE TO SERVICE PROCEDURES CARRIED OUT WITH KITCHEN SCISSORS AND FATHER'S OLD CLAW-HAMMER. THEREFORE AN ON-SITE MAINTENANCE AGREEMENT IS WORTH SEARCHING FOR EVEN IF YOU ARE A DOMESTIC USER, AS ARE EXTENDED THREE OR FIVE YEAR WARRANTIES.

■ GOOD VALUE SECONDHAND FAX MACHINES ARE AS RARE AS KNOWLEDGEABLE HIGH STREET COMPUTER SALESMEN. THE STAND-ALONE FAX MACHINE IS A DESIRABLE OBJECT AND CONSEQUENTLY THERE ARE FEW REAL BARGAINS. IF YOU'RE OFFERED SOMETHING THAT LOOKS TOO GOOD TO BE TRUE THEN IT ALMOST CERTAINLY IS.

■ BEWARE OF GROUP II ONLY MACHINES – THEY ARE NOW OBSOLETE AND YOU SHOULD LOOK FOR A GROUP III DEVICE. ALSO IF YOU ARE OFFERED A FAX MACHINE WITHOUT A MANUAL THEN IT IS LIKELY TO BE STOLEN/GROUP II/NOT FULLY WORKING/NOT SALEABLE TO ANY OTHER MUG. MAKE SURE YOU GET A MANUAL IF YOU DO BUY SECONDHAND. A FAX MACHINE WITHOUT A MANUAL IS ALMOST UNUSABLE, AS MOST OF THE INBUILT FEATURES OF FAX MACHINES ARE ACCESSED VIA A SET OF COMPLICATED MULTIPLE KEYPRESSES.

■ IF YOU ARE DESPERATE FOR FAX CAPABILITY THEN YOU MAY FIND THAT A NEW FAX MODEM CARD IS CHEAPER THAN A SECONDHAND STAND-ALONE FAX MACHINE, AND WILL SERVE WELL AT THE SACRIFICE OF SOME EASE OF USE AND CONVENIENCE. YOU WILL BUY A GROUP III COMPATIBLE ONE, OF COURSE.

5
MICROSOFT WINDOWS AND WINDOWS COMMS
"With sincerity there will follow brilliant success"

5.1 Windows

Windows is not the 'killer application' of 1992 we all fondly believe it to be. Windows was first announced in 1983, two years after the first PC machines started shipping in quantity. In true Microsoft style the product eventually hit the shelves in November 1985, when Windows version 1.01 became available. The product ran on a twin 360K floppy based PC, and needed 384K of RAM. Windows 1.01 used tiling, as opposed to overlapping windows, to present user information as this reduced the processing overhead.

Windows 2.0 followed in 1987, five years after the first version had been announced. Windows 2.0 had a different look and feel about it, as by that time Microsoft was shipping OS/2 Presentation Manager and some of the development work found its way into Windows. Among the new features of Windows 2.0 were overlapping windows, and a brave new memory management scheme launched by a coalition of Lotus, Intel and Microsoft. The scheme outlined a memory bank switching arrangement which would allow PC users to escape from the 640K memory barrier imposed during the development of the PC in 1981. The specification was called LIM 3.2, after initials of the main protagonists.

A year later Microsoft split its Windows range into two products. Windows 2.0 became Windows 286, aimed mainly at the older 80286 based PCs. The LIM specification was improved slightly to LIM 4.0, and the XMS memory management scheme came into being. This allowed Windows 286 users access to the first 64K of extended memory. The second product was Windows 386. This version offered multi-tasking support for the new generation of 80386 chips launched by Intel.

Windows 3.0 was announced on May 22, 1990 amidst much hype, and was one of the most widely publicised roll-outs of computer software ever.

Windows and Data-comms

Windows 3.0 makes an utter dog's breakfast of fast serial comms. The program gets itself in a knot over serial port interrupts and addresses, especially with serial ports 3 and 4. In fact it can't drive ports three and four properly in Real and Standard modes until ports one and two have been used. To compound the problem Windows 3.0 expects serial ports three and four to be at addresses which are not usually used on the vast majority of PCs.

The history of the humble serial port on the PC is a chequered one, to such an extent that it is a wonder that the blessed thing works at all.

The UART mysteries

The IBM PC serial port was originally designed to send and receive data at a paltry 2400bps. Asking it to cope with ever higher speeds is ludicrous. There are a couple of workarounds to get serial ports to run at higher speed, but we are rapidly reaching the upper limits of technical feasibility when we try to push PC serial ports at much above 38,400bps.

PC serial ports are driven by a single chip called a Universal Asynchronous Receiver/Transmitter (UART). UARTs are unremarkable things in their own right and serve to take data from the parallel data circuits inside the computer and convert it to a serial format for the outside world. Data coming in from the serial port is then re-converted back to parallel data for use by the PC. The UART performs this bi-directional conversion and also adds a bit of housekeeping, such as sorting out the external requirements of parity and data formats.

MS-DOS, the operating system for the PC, uses a technique called 'polling' to get the data from the serial port via the UART; that is, it only goes and gets a character when asked to. This in turn means that an individual instruction has to be sent to grab each character coming into the port. On a link running in one direction at 9600bps this is around every millisecond, if data is not to be lost.

UART polling might have worked in olden times when the IBM PC was not expected to sell more than 10,000 machines world-wide, or when serial comms were considered to be almost faster than light at anything above 1200bps. Above 9600bps polling becomes unusable, generally speaking. One solution is to use the inbuilt ability of the UART to cause an interrupt. If the UART raises a flag to say "I have something for you", the processor is interrupted from carrying on with its present task and has to go off and see why the UART is holding up a flag. The UART interrupt is usually raised (depending upon the programmer's whim) when there is data to be transmitted, or data has been received, and data in this case means one character.

Of course this is a bland understatement of the innermost inter-relationship between the convoluted brains of programmers, and the bit registers of the UART, but we need to know only that interrupt (flag-waving) driven comms are potentially much faster than polling. In fact one can only wonder why MS-DOS and the IBM PC used polling in the first place.

The original PCs used a UART chip called an 8250, a device with no buffers or memory. The 8250 would usually work after a fashion in interrupt mode up to around 9600bps but could start to lose data at speeds above that. Chip manufacturers National Semiconductor (NS), ever eager to help out, released the 8250B which got over some of the bugs in the 8250, and did this so thoroughly that few of the original comms programs written for the 8250 would work. Luckily for NS, IBM released the AT (Advanced Technology) PC which used NS's new 16450 UART. In theory this animal could run at over 100Kbps, but the AT was such a stodgy performer that it still could not keep up at half this speed, despite being interrupt driven and the 16450 having an internal one byte buffer to hold the data. That's how things stayed for a while, the problem was simply ignored, mainly as no-one was asking for fast serial comms in 1986. This was an era when 1200 baud modems were considered to be pretty neat.

Fee Fo FIFO

Think that's the end of the problem? No siree. After the AT, IBM invented the PS/2 system, which brought its own set of UART problems. A chip called the 16550 was to blame this time. This chip speeded up the transfer process by providing a 16 byte first-in first-out (FIFO) buffer. The buffered chip could hold the data long enough for the PC to get around to asking for it, and speeds of up to 115Kbps were bandied around by the men in suits.

The 16550 was an abject failure. It was fitted to IBM's Model 50, 60 and 80 computers, and had the habit of losing the data held in the FIFO buffer, a feature which is less than useful in a comms set-up. NS rapidly brought out the 1655OA to compensate. This did actually work but the clone manufacturers had by that time started copying the 16550 (copies are marked 'UM82C550') and thousands of PC clones were fitted with a UART chip rather less suited to fast comms than it should have been. The UM82C550 doesn't actually have the FIFO bug of the 16550 – it just doesn't set bit 6 when it's using its buffer, so programmers (and therefore programs) cannot tell if it is FIFO-ing or not. At least the 16550A works, at the moment.

COM port clashes

We were talking about Windows, remember? Why does Windows not readily recognise COM3 and COM4 on PCs? If you have ever looked at the BIOS settings in your PC, or at the diagnostic screen that comes up when you switch the thing on, you may have seen that your computer has four serial ports COM1 through COM4. This is not quite the advantage it seems, because an AT type PC only allocates two interrupt lines (IRQ3 and 4) to serial port use. Each port has to have its own interrupt line for flag waving and, if this line is busy, then other flag waving taking place on the same line will not be noticed by the processor. Therefore COM3 and COM4 have to use the same interrupt lines as COM1 and COM2 and the net result is that they don't work if the other ports are in use. On AT based machines you can sometimes get away with allocating IRQ5 to COM3, but an XT computer doesn't have this line available.

FIGURE **5.1**

Windows COM port clash in terminal

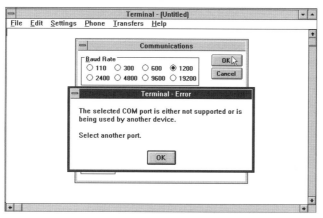

FIGURE **5.2**

Windows 3.1 COM port settings

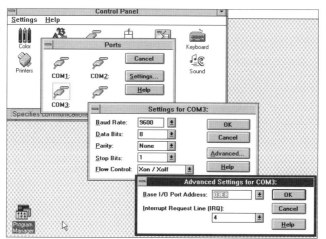

There are software tweaks which get around this problem, mainly by using polling techniques on the upper COM ports, but the reality is that PC comms are a set of ill-matched compromises and will remain that way until backwards compatibility with systems designed in 1981 is dropped.

IBM didn't even learn its lesson when it introduced the PS/2 computer. All ports above COM1 are allocated to IRQ4, probably for the sake of backwards compatibility. It's this set of engineering compromises which make Microsoft stay away from using COM3 and COM4 in Windows wherever possible. Can you blame them?

5.2 Windows and UARTs

Windows 3.0 users have problems of their own, caused by the integration of a powerful application which lives on top of a not so powerful operating system and architecture. You are unlikely to get decent fast comms performance under Windows by using standard DOS comms programs. As Windows is multi-tasking, it freezes all the interrupts in use while it switches between other programs. The net result is that UART data can be lost while this is going on.

Now if Windows 3.0 knew about FIFO UARTs this problem could be avoided, but it doesn't, and it isn't. To get around the COM port address problem you can set the correct port addresses in the SYSTEM.INI file if you are trying to use ports 3 and 4. The lines you need to amend are:

`[386Enh]`

`COM3base=3E8h` (for comm port 3 on most PCs)

`COM4Base=2E8h` (for comm port 4 on most PCs)

You can use Notepad to edit the file and a utility such as Checkit to identify the actual port addresses in use. If that fails and you own a small boat you will find that the Windows 3.0 program disks and manuals can be usefully employed as an anchor. Otherwise you should use them to upgrade to Windows 3.1 as soon as possible.

Windows 3.1

Windows 3.1 is much better at comms than Windows 3.0 although the system timing of some PCs objects to being manipulated by the product. This sometimes results in slow throughput and unexplained hang-ups. But you can get along quite well under Windows 3.1 running on a 33MHz 386 or a 486 based machine, as these (usually) have the necessary speed to manage the UARTs of the PC at a reasonable rate. But many users still have problems, and these will increase as we try to get Windows to talk to ever faster devices through a comm port and system architecture first designed for 2400bps.

The best solution for the distraught but determined Windows comms user is to fit a Hayes Enhanced Serial Port. This will take the processing load away from the beleaguered PC and give a comms throughput up to around 57,600bps. Couple it with a V32 bis modem and a fast Windows comms program and your problems will be lessened.

A small performance benefit can sometimes be obtained by upgrading the UART on the serial port, but if you are having serial port problems they are likely to be also caused by system timing – especially on anything other than a 486 or fast 386-based PC. (On 486 and above machines there is often enough processing power to prevent data loss.) In this case a straight UART upgrade will have little effect, especially if your comms program knows nothing about 16550s. Above 38,400bps and things start to look bleak. Windows 3.1 combined with PC architecture and a serial port is still bogged down by the hardware used to support it.

If you do insist on using COM3, and COM4: with Windows 3.1 you can set the address and IRQ settings in the Control panel/Ports/Advanced dialogue box. But this is not for the faint-hearted, if you have a network card which uses the Interrupt Request (IRQ) line you choose you could end up disabling the network card and the serial port. In Windows no one can hear you scream...

5.3 Bus comms

The 'bus' is the series of internal slots (sockets) found on the motherboards of PCs. In common parlance they are usually called expansion slots, as you can plug printed circuit boards into them and 'expand' (or limit) the capabilities of your machine. The bus on the majority of PC compatible machines runs at 8MHz. Some go higher, but often 8MHz is provided as a default or option, on the faster machines. Most of that 8MHz bandwidth is available to comms users, but with the proviso that the bus is paralleled across other cards in the machine which may require processing time to service.

Bus mounted cards such as the Hayes ESP can provide comms more reliably and at a much higher rate than can a serial port, and devices such as fast ISDN cards with a throughput of 128Kbps are now becoming common. Our fascination with the use of serial ports will lessen with time as ISDN becomes common place – but until then Windows users will still have to fight with recalcitrant comm ports and comparatively slow speeds.

Does Windows 3.1 drive expansion bus cards properly? You betcha it does. It's already possible to pass real-time video data into Windows 3.1 from ISDN and to display the resulting picture on screen. This while formatting a floppy disk and writing poisonous letters to bank managers at the same time. The truth of the matter is that it's the architecture of the PC which is unsuitable for running fast serial port based comms under Windows, and the sooner we all throw our modems away and move to local bus based ISDN the better.

5.4   Enhanced serial ports for Windows

The Hayes company realised the shortcomings of the standard PC UART and developed the Hayes Enhanced Serial Port (ESP), a card which plugs into the internal bus of the PC. This uses 16550A chips coupled to on-board processors to speed up data throughput, a feat which is managed by sidestepping the PC interrupt bottleneck and using Direct Memory Addressing (DMA) techniques. The Hayes ESP for Windows also has a 1024 byte buffer to hold data while Windows is away doing its rounds of the wheezing PC operating system.

One of these devices can turn your clunking old PC into a blitzkrieg comms machine when coupled to a V32 bis modem. Speeds up to 112Kbps and over are now possible. Other machines, such as the Mac and Atari, use different chip and processor types and don't seem to suffer the internal UART and interrupt problems of the benighted PC.

Non-PC computers often have the buffering feature of the UART duplicated or enhanced in software, and a new software driver may be installed to speed up operations in some cases. Serial drivers on the Macintosh can be replaced from a floppy disk and the Amiga computers can use a shareware software utility called Baud-Bandit which improves serial data transfer characteristics by a desirable amount. The software and advice on loading it, together with wholesale condemnation of the PC and its architecture can be downloaded from many recreational bulletin boards for free.

Mac users can sit smugly in front of their machines and V32 bis modems without worrying about UARTS and comms ports. Mac serial ports are specified to 230.4Kbps, and higher with external clocking.

5.5   Comms and Windows graphics

Windows Terminal

If you use the Terminal program in Windows you will notice that most of the input from your modem comes in as a new line at the bottom of the screen, causing the screen to move up a line each time. This scrolling effect is of no real consequence in DOS based packages, but Windows treats screen characters differently and needs a finite amount of time to move screens of information up by one line. That time increases in direct proportion to the amount of information on the screen.

The problem gets worse if you use a higher screen resolution as there are correspondingly more lines to move around. This graphics bottleneck can drastically affect the throughput of incoming text.

One answer is to fit a graphics accelerator card to boost the display speed of your computer, another is to take the money you would have spent on fast serial ports and graphics accelerators cards and spend it on a Mac, Amiga or Atari computer, none of which suffers from these problems.

Most of the above problems tend to show up on slower PCs such as models based on Intel 286 and 386SX processors. Faster 486 based machines may have sufficient processing power to overcome some of the problems.

Searching for the lurking...

If despite having read all of this you still want to make your PC comms go faster, you are faced with just one final problem. How do you find out whether you have a fast UART in your PC?

There are three methods. The first involves a screwdriver, an anti-static wrist-strap, and removal of your serial card to inspect its chips for the magic number 16550A. The second method involves picking up the phone and asking your supplier. The third method involves running a diagnostic utility that will tell you what is lurking inside that old tin box in the corner that you are pleased to call a computer.

MSD.EXE

There are any number of diagnostics for the PC such as Norton Utilities, PC Tools and Checkit, but not all of these are up to date and know about buffered UARTs or bit register 6 compatibility The best place to search for information and free diagnostic tools for the PC is the IBM support conferences on CompuServe dial-up service. Type Go IBMCOM and list files here.CIX is also sometimes useful in this respect, but you need accounts to use either.

If you have neither, and sufficient sense not to poke around in your PC unless you have some technical knowledge, then you can call Pan Technology – a specialist computer hardware and software design company. Pan offers a useful and unique service – if you send a formatted virus-free PC disk and return postage, Pan will send you a couple of public domain utilities which will enable you to track down your UART type and the number of ports on your PC. Pan Technology will also send you a price list containing details of updated serial ports, UARTs and other interesting pluggy-in, comms-related things for your PC. The address is in Appendix 5.

Windows 3.1 users should find a file called MSD.EXE in the Windows directory. Clicking on it brings up Microsoft Diagnostics. The Comms section there will list out your comm ports and their addresses, together with the UART type detected among other things.

FIGURE 5.3

Microsoft diagnostic screen showing serial port configuration

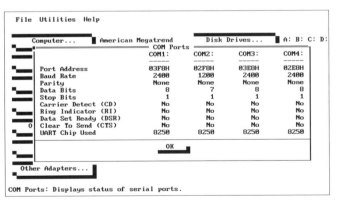

FIGURE 5.4

*What Port serial port diagnostic,
available on many BBSs.*

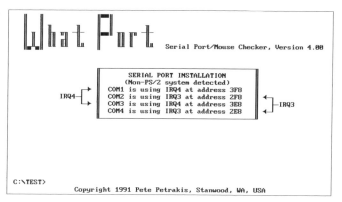

Expert advice regarding UARTs should be heeded – there are now several manufacturers of compatible buffered UART chips and, as we have seen, not all UARTs are created equal. Mr Peter Ellefsen of Pan Technology will regale you with expert advice, and horror stories about PC comms, if you choose to use his service.

Remember – if you do take the serial port out of your computer then you may find that all the chips are soldered into place and that replacing the UART involves burnt fingers and soldering irons. As mentioned before, soldering irons and computer technology are best kept apart, and your only practical recourse in this case is to fit a replacement or second serial card. This would also apply if your serial ports are integrated with the motherboard electronics, as is often true with many purpose built 'branded' PCs.

Generally speaking a 16550A is of little use unless your comms software specifically supports it, so you should check whether this is so before getting over-excited about the possibility of fitting one to your PC. 16550A support will always be mentioned in the manual for your software, if it is present in the package. And remember that you may have to fiddle with the comm port address settings if you add a second card. On an XT that's going to be difficult.

6
TELECOMMS SOFTWARE

"The superior man carefully appraises the start of a venture"

6.1   Comms programs

A comms program acts as the interface between your brain and your modem, using your computer as a translation device. There are over a thousand different comms packages, many are much the same as each other. Writing about them is like writing about word processing software. It's easy to enrage partisan users of such and such a product, or offend others by not mentioning that a certain package is available.

Many telecomms software products offer identical features, but presented in a different way to the user. If you have an Amiga, Atari, or a PC you will find that comms programs generally tend to look much the some as each other. If you are running Windows on a PC or a terminal emulator on a Mac you will have a different interface, but will see many of the same features as in other comms programs.

No software?

If you have a computer with an RS232 port and a modem, or simply want to play around with comms but don't have any software, there are several ways of obtaining it.

- IF YOU HAVE FRIENDS OR SOCIAL OR BUSINESS CONTACTS WITH A SIMILAR MACHINE TO YOURS, ASK THEM FOR INFORMATION OR HELP. MOST WILL BE PLEASED TO GIVE IT FREELY.

- CHECK IN THE RELEVANT INTEREST MAGAZINE FOR YOUR COMPUTER FOR PUBLIC DOMAIN OR SHAREWARE RE-SELLERS.

- ASK YOUR COMPUTER USER GROUP.

- CHECK WITH BULLETIN BOARD SYSOPS OR VALUE ADDED NETWORK SUPPLIERS' SALES OFFICES. MANY OFFER TERMINAL EMULATION SOFTWARE, OR CAN RECOMMEND A SOURCE.

- USE THE SPECIAL OFFERS AT THE BACK OF THIS BOOK

Getting hold of a comms program

You may previously have found it difficult to track down telecomms software for your computer, especially if it is not a PC or a Mac or is more than five years old. This is a situation worthy of inclusion in the next Catch 22 movie. The bulletin boards of the world are stacked high with free comms software for every machine capable of telecommunication. All you have to do to get it is to download it, using your telecomms program.

The best place to start looking for a terminal emulation package is with the supplier of the modem. Many suppliers now bundle (give away with the product) software with modems and, while this may only be of the 'get-you-started variety, such software will at least let you log on to a bulletin board or host system. There you can generally find alternative programs which may better suit your purpose.

Many freely available comms packages are distributed on the shareware principle, and are often (not always) significantly superior to similar programs from commercial sources. Shareware works on the basis that you can run the program for a while to test it and if you decide you like it you then pay for it. Unfortunately there seem to be two sorts of shareware. There is shareware distributed in Britain which generates comparatively little revenue for authors, and shareware distributed in the USA, which generates much higher revenues per copy in use. No more moralising, but please, if you use a shareware product – register it. You'll keep shareware alive and everyone will benefit from the results.

FIGURE **6.1**

Oddyssey, the shareware comms program

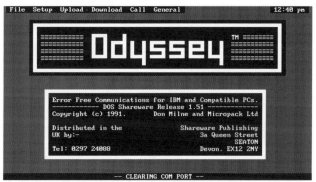

Public domain software is generally free; the terms of the licence might say that you may distribute or use the software, but without modification.

A commercial product is one that you pay commercial rates for and may not generally copy without permission for fear of dawn swoops by the Federation Against Software Theft (FAST).

6.2   Which package?

There are hundreds of different telecomms programs available world-wide and it is not possible (or desirable) to single out individual packages as paragons. At the end of the day telecomms software is there to act as an interface between your and your computer/modem combination, and a remote computer somewhere else in the world. Some do it better than others.

Comms software usually talks through an available I/O (input/output) port of the computer. This port will usually be the RS232 serial port, although there are comms packages which provide specialised communications through parallel ports. A comms package can be a relatively simple thing, or it can include dozens of features, many of which will not be used. The desirability of any package will usually depend on the ability to transfer data as quickly as possible with a given modem, and with as few errors as possible. Other considerations, such as the ease of use of the user interface, usually take second place, although contemporary packages are much better about presenting information in human readable form than some early attempts.

Most recreational and corporate users of modems don't use them for much else other than dialling up text-based information services on a PSTN point-to point basis. If you want to run sessions over an X.25 pad or use the enhanced features of a proprietary comms port or some non-standard modems you'll need additional software.

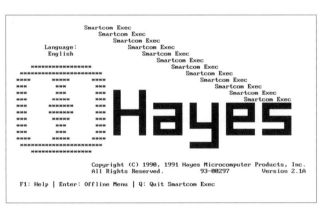

FIGURE **6.3**

Rencom Plus – has multilingual support

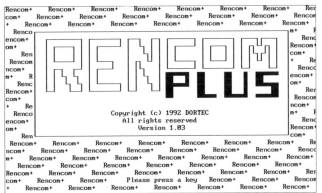

Many comms packages now support almost every conceivable feature but you may run into problem areas if you need a non-English language interface such as German or Spanish, or wish to access European services such as Minitel or Teletel. You will also need fax software if you wish to use any fax capabilities that your modem might have. Fax software is often combined with basic telecomms software, so the one package can be used for both purposes. See the special discount coupon at the back of this book for Rencom Plus.

Roll your own!

If you have access to a high level programming language and a few months of development time you can quite probably write your own comms program as the basics are very simple. Data has to come in through the serial port, be recognised by the computer, and displayed on the screen or printed or saved to disk. To transmit data a comms program has to read data in from a file or the keyboard and squirt it out of the serial port.

A small comms program written in BASIC might look like this:

```
5     Rem Sue-Com!
10    Rem The Earth Shaking Comms Program
20    Rem Copyright Sue Schofield, World Domination Inc
30    Open "Com1, 300,N,1,E" for output as #1
40    Do While inkey$="":LOOP
50    If INKEY$ = "!" then goto 80
60    Print #1, Inkey$
70    Goto 40
```

```
80    close #1
90    END
100   Rem Send cheques for 50 pounds to World Domination Inc
```

That's about the size of it. The receive routine is much the same, except that `'out-put'` becomes `'input'` and `'print #1'` becomes `'input #1'`. Gnarled old BASIC hackers will find their toes curling up at the use of GOTOs in the example program.

Now if you type this program into your computer you will find that while it has a net worth of something less than £50, it might just work, depending on what sort of BASIC you have. Alas it would take you some time to build a good comms program in BASIC, and programs written in a high level language tend to run relatively slowly, so you would not hope to write a very large commercial application using this method. But some of the most successful bulletin board systems have been written in BASIC, and you could certainly have fun writing a small comms program in this way.

If you do decide to persevere, and there is no reason why you shouldn't, you will find that there are many add-ins for home-brew comms programs available on the recreational BBSs, including ZMODEM and other file transfer protocols. Some comms programs have their own built-in high level programming languages, and this could be a useful starting point. A compiled version could be used for 'roll-your-own' comms programs to speed things up, and Microsoft's QuickBasic 1.4 or Visual Basic for DOS would be a good starting point for PC owners with a programming need.

6.3   General comms packages

If you wish to communicate with larger computers you may need a particular type of terminal emulation (such as VT102 or Wyse) and most popular communications packages support most of the common terminal emulations. For general dial-up use many remote systems use teletype (TTY) emulation, which corresponds to plain ASCII. (Always try TTY emulation as a starting point in setting up a comms link.) Some systems for the IBM PC use American National Standards Institute (ANSI) codes for controlling such things as screen colours and character positioning and the availability of these features on your machine can often be detected by the remote. ANSI screens are customarily in colour, and this brings a new dimension to boring old black and white comms.

FIGURE **6.4**

Hayes' Smartcom EZ for the Mac –
free with Hayes Optima modems

FIGURE **6.5**

Zterm – shareware comms
program for the Mac

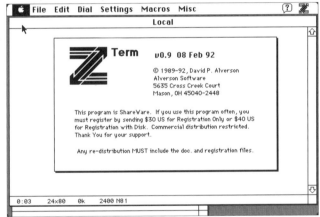

The user interface is different on many comms packages and is a point of interest
amongst aficionados. Probably the easiest interface to use is one with pull-down
menus and mouse support, but opinions differ.

Dedicated host-user software

Some commercial terminal emulation programs are fine-tuned to interface with the remote
host system and use the processing power of your computer to draw windows, display
graphics and generally improve the lot of the user. The result is huge improvement in
terms of usability when compared to the 'glass-teletype' presentation of most other systems,

at the small expense of having to transfer extra data between the computers to provide graphical and other instructions.

Remote access software

This provides a modem link through which many of the functions of the remote computer can be accessed across the virtual link. Such packages are often used for help-desks or software maintenance. Most remote access packages provide 'dial-back' a feauture which calls a predetermined number back to maximise security.

Remote access software is useful for system developers, or for anyone with a computer in one place that needs to be accessed from the other. It's often possible to run programs on the remote machine with the display appearing on the originator's screen. Most commercial remote-access software is written for business computers such as the PC and Mac, but public domain versions appear for other machines from time to time.

File-transfer software

File-transfer software provides a way for transfer of data files from one computer to another. The software uses proprietary protocols and dedicated cables to achieve fast transfer between two computers, usually via the parallel ports. Some file-transfer packages also provide serial terminal emulation for use on dial-up links. File-transfer software is useful for transferring data from a portable computer to a desktop model, and is often bundled with portables, or programmed into Read Only Memory (ROM) chips.

You can emulate this function with two serial ports, a null-modem cable and a comms program, although the mass transfer and management of files is likely to take a little longer.

ZMODEM, a file transfer protocol is good for transferring large numbers of files, as the wildcard characters (*.*) can be used to send entire directories and there are likely to be few errors on a properly set up direct link.

Off-line readers

An Off-line Reader (OLR) is a telecomms program that grabs data from the host system and allows browsing of the data off-line to save call charges. OLR software is dedicated to a particular host system, and a different OLR is usually needed for each service you use. OLRs reduce the time spent connected to the host system, and drastically reduce host connect charges and PSTN call charges. They are available for most Value Added Networks (VANs) and both shareware and commercial packages are available.

FIGURE 6.6

Semaphone, the Mac OLR for CIX

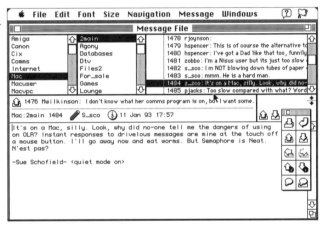

OLRs for CompuServe users include Autosig and TAPCIS for the PC, CompuServe Navigator for the Mac, ST/Forum and QuickCis for the Atari, and Whap! for the Amiga. Many of the programs are shareware or public domain and can be downloaded for the price of connect charges.

Integrated telecomms software

Many commercial integrated programs offer 'office-automation' features, a phrase which in reality means that the package contains a database system, a word-processor and a spreadsheet. Some of these packages also contain cut-down telecomms software. These packages generally allow incoming data to be copied directly into reports or spreadsheets and are sometimes useful for their sheer simplicity. Most of them seem to have 'Works' somewhere in the title.

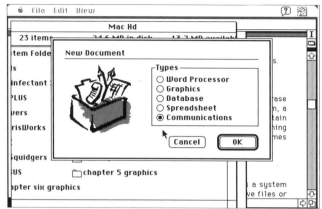

Bulletin Board System (BBS) software

BBS software is a wide and diverse topic. A bulletin board is a system where people can leave and collect messages, send and receive files or just chat to other users. Many BBSs offer all sorts of value-added services such as on-line game playing, doorways to active programs or wide area network (WAN) links to other systems.

There are tens of thousands of them world-wide, and you can start up your own BBS for the price of a phone-line and a dedicated computer. Much BBS software is shareware or public domain and can be had for the asking. Running your own BBS is a great way of passing the time if you're housebound, and is also a useful way of providing a friendly 'front-end' to some elderly corporate electronic mail systems.

Conference systems software

Conference systems are similar to BBSs but tend to be larger, and have a larger number of discussion areas each related to a different topic. Many conferencing systems have dedicated off-line readers (OLRs) available for them.

Modem games programs

So called modem games are designed for two players, joined together either with a null-modem cable or dial-up link. Two friendly players joined in this way can shoot, slay, expunge, and decimate each other or the entire population of the planet, with only minor damage incurred to the phone bill.

6.4 Comms program features

The general features of basic telecomms programs are described below. Bear in mind that not all packages have all features, and price is no indication of quality or functionality of a comms program. If you have a Hayes compatible modem and have given yourself a nasty shock by reading through the Definitive Hayes command set in Appendix 1, you should bear in mind that only enthusiasts need to remember every last command. Your comms program should do all the hard work for you.

■ DIALING DIRECTORY

Stores a list of names and associated telephone numbers. Most dialling directories allow the selection of the speed and parity settings associated with the number, as well as describing the name of the macro or script file that will be activated when carrier is detected (DCD going high).

■ AN ASCII EDITOR

is useful within a comms program for composing messages, or viewing ASCII files. Many comms programs have their own in-built editors, or allow the user to call up an external editor program.

■ UPLOADING

If you are sending files to a remote system you are 'uploading' them. The upload option will normally bring up a menu of File Transfer Protocols so that one can be selected.

■ DOWNLOADING

Receiving files from a remote system is called 'downloading'. Again, selecting this option will normally display a menu of file transfer protocols.

■ MACRO CAPABILITY

A macro is a series of keystrokes stored as a file. A macro can be generated which sends the keystrokes to send your password and thus log you in to a service. See: Script Files

■ SCRIPT FILES

A script file is a series of commands stored in a file which can be called and activated as a mini program. Script files are commonly attached to numbers in a dialling directory to provide auto-log-on facilities for the service associated with the number. They may also be used to program the communication facilities within the software package and even write dedicated telecomms programs. There are no de facto standards for script languages, but some comms programs share language fragments. Some script languages are complete programming environments in their own right, and can prove useful if you want to write or modify a comms program.

- LEARN MODE

A startlingly useful feature. Learn mode watches your session and writes a script file or a macro to automate the process. Learn mode is mainly used to construct auto-log-on procedures, the resulting file can be then associated with a number in the dialling directory to send log-in information to the host system.

A learned script resulting from a session might look something like:

```
{ Learned Script file > SUE-COM 01/04/93 }
SEND ATD 12345
WAITFOR "Welcome to the Bank Of England"
SEND "ESC ESC"
WAITFOR "Your name?"
SEND "SUE SCHOFIELD"
WAITFOR "Your Password?"
SEND "TECHNOSCRIBBLUS MAXIMUS"
WAITFOR "Login verified" 10 secs
PRINTER LPT1 ON
DISK CAPTURE "C:\LOADSAD.OSH" ON
SEND "COOEE!"
WAITFOR "How much money would you like, Sue?"
SEND "LOTS"
WAITFOR "Start your Download now"
SEND "Are you joking?"
HANGUP
DISK CAPTURE OFF
PRINTER LPT1 OFF
```

This is a basic example, many log-on sequences are much longer, especially if Value Added Networks such as Packet Switch Stream are being accessed. Automatic learn mode is the easiest way to build script files for such purposes, although machine generated scripts might need some fine tuning by hand for best results.

If you work in a corporate environment you should look for a comms package that automatically compiles its script files. Uncompiled script files left as text on a disk might contain service and account passwords and are easily readable by others.

- DISK LOG/CAPTURE LOG

This feature collects incoming and outgoing data during a session and saves it to disk for recall at some later point. Disk logging is normally a manually selected operation although a script file can usefully be used to initiate disk logging at the start of a session.

- QUEUE DIALLING

Allows dialling directories to be tagged for auto-dialling. Queue dialling reads through a list of tagged numbers and dials each one in turn. If the number does not connect on the first try it will be re-tried for a pre-defined number of times. Sometimes called 'Round Robin dialling'.

- SCROLL BACK

Scroll-back data is part of a session which is automatically logged to a RAM or disk buffer and can be referred back to whilst the session is still under way. One otherwise well-thought-of comms program calls its Scroll-back feature a 'Peruse Buffer'.

- TERMINAL EMULATION

Different computer systems use different methods of reading data from keyboards and displaying data on screen. An ASCII terminal (sometimes called TTY) is the most common method for personal dial-up comms, but if you are connecting your computer to a large mainframe computer you may find that it uses a different terminal standard. Most comms programs support at least four terminal emulations. If in doubt start your on-line session with TTY or ASCII. Most recreational bulletin boards support ANSI.SYS or ANSI.BBS emulation.

- SHELL

Shell suspends the terminal emulator and drops the user back to the operating system. Shell is useful for shuffling or deleting files while on-line. Unless you have a true multi-tasking computer, Shell will usually suspend operation of the terminal emulator. With a multi-tasking machine some comms programs will allow Shell to operate as a separate process so you can do useful things while your comms package runs up the phone bill in the background.

- CHAT MODE

Chat mode is something for nothing. It is useful if you have established a link and wish to 'talk' to the person at the other end. In normal terminal mode you would not ordinarily be able to see your end of the conversation. The program takes incoming data and displays it in the top half of the screen. Your output is displayed in the bottom of the screen. Some chat modes wait for you to press enter before your line of chat is sent, and thus offer basic line editing features. Chat mode is a great way of talking slowly to people at ten words per minute or less, at some expense.

- PARAMETER SET-UP

Usually a set of menu options which allow the setting up of default parameters which are called when the program is run. If you had a quad modem you might set your start-up parameters to 2400bps, 8-bit data, no parity, 1 stop bit. If your computer has more than one RS232 port (many do) you would also tell the program which port would normally have the modem attached. The default parameter set-up is often overridden from the dialling directory where individual parameters can be set for each number to be dialled. Some comms programs only allow parameters to be set up from the dialling or phone directory.

- CR/LF CONTROL

Carriage return and linefeed control. A carriage return character (ASCII 13) returns the cursor to the start of the line. A linefeed character (ASCII 10) moves the cursor down one line. Both are need to start a new line of text. Most on-line services provide a CR/LF combination to effect this automatically. However, if you are loading word-processing or text files from one computer to another you may find that all the lines have run together producing garbage. In this case you need to tell your comms pro-gram to add a linefeed to each carriage return as it comes in. If you use a particular service and find that the incoming data is double spaced, your software is adding an extra linefeed and you should set the program to remove it.

- HALF- AND FULL-DUPLEX – CHARACTER ECHO

Full-duplex is the transmission of data both ways down each end of a data link. Half-duplex is the transmission of data in one direction only at a time. In a full-duplex sys-tem it is common for the receiving terminal to echo data from the originating termi-nal back down the link. The data is then displayed on the originating terminal. Your keyboard entry is displayed on the screen only after it has been echoed back from the other end of the link as an elementary form of error checking.

On a half-duplex system this cannot take place and your terminal has to be set to pro-vide 'local echo' so you can see what you are typing. If you use local echo on a full-duplex link you will see your keyboard entry appear twice on your screen.

```
LLiikkee TThhiiss..
```

In this case turn local echo off.

(Mistakes with local echo and CR/LF translation are the two most common problems for people new to comms.)

■ HOST MODE

Host mode places your modem and computer in a state of readiness, awaiting a phone call from a remote user; in effect, your PC becomes a mini Bulletin Board system and will allow a caller to take (limited) control of your machine. The modem is put into auto-answer mode and waits for the DCD or the ring indicator (RI) to go high, or for some other indicator to say "someone is calling, answer the phone". The auto-answer facility of your modem is controlled by register S0; you can alter the number of rings after which a modem answers by issuing (to your modem) the command AS0=n (where n is the number of rings). If a host mode is not working, try some adjustments to this setting.

Once a phone call is received and answered, the host mode option on your comms software swings into action. Depending on the comms software used, the remote caller will be asked a few questions; usually their name and password. Once connected to your machine, callers have access to your hard drive so security *must* be a consideration, if only to prevent accidental damage to your data. Again, depending on the particular package in use, host mode will have a range of security features which you configure to suit your preferences. It is essential that you are able to restrict access to certain areas of your hard drive and allocate more than one level of password security. For example, you might need to have 'priviledged access' and 'normal access' to your machine; with priviledged access limited to yourself and normal access to others.

Once the logon formalities are dispensed with, and the remote caller has given a valid name and password, they are presented with a range of options. The remote caller might, typically, be presented with:

`F)iles, U)pload D)ownload C)hat G)oodbye`

The caller can now issue commands to achieve the purpose of their call. The host (ie. your) machine will display the options and commands selected by the caller. This makes it easy to see what is happening and whether to take preventative action, such as cancelling the call. The `U)pload` option allows the remote caller to transfer files from their machine to yours; conversely, the `D)ownload` option allows transfer of files from your machine.

As part of the setup for your host mode, you should specify where on your hard drive the remote caller is allowed to upload to or download from – for PCs, the root directory is not a good idea. Imagine long distance tampering with your AUTOEXEC.BAT and CONFIG.SYS files.

Consider the specific example of someone working as a freelance translator. For a PC user, separating translated work into a directory called C:\TRANSLAT would make sense. During host mode setup this would be the directory to nominate for downloads by a remote caller (the translation agency).

In relation to PCs, the caller might be given the opportunity to halt the comms program and obtain access to the opperating system; 'shell out to DOS', as it is often called. This could provide opportunity for accidental or deliberate damage since the caller is able to run programs from the DOS prompt of your machine, your PC's memory permitting.

Host mode is usually driven by a script file. If you want to attempt some programming (using the script language), customising your host mode is one possible option. Look for a file called HOST.SCR or something similar, this file contains the code which drives your host mode.

If during the course of your business you need to travel to a client's premises, having a portable machine with a modem and your own office machine left in host mode is one way to solve any unforseen information needs, such as price lists.

■ TRANSLATE TABLE
This is a feature of some comms programs which allows incoming characters to be scanned and replaced by others. It's useful for building your own terminal driver for a particular system, or for simple encoding of text files for transmission to a similarly configured terminal.

■ PRINTER LOGGING
Useful for capturing incoming data directly to a printer. (If the printer is off-line or runs out of paper it could hang your session.)

■ FILE VIEW
Handy feature that lets you view a file stored on your machine. Useful for checking newly downloaded files before you log off, or for making sure that you are about to send the correct file via an upload. Some dial-up services offer file view, remember it's their computer and software that is doing the work in this case and you are paying the call and connect charges.

■ FILENAME TRANSLATE

Found on some commercial programs such as Hayes Smartcom Exec. Filename translate gets around the limitations of the eight character prefix, three character suffix filenames of PCs running MS-DOS. If you want to download a file called 'SNAZZYPIccys-OF.NAKED-MODEMS' from a Mac and you're using a PC you will find that your PC comms program stops with an illegal filename error or some such when it tries to write the program details to disk. Filename Translate truncates the filename to match the parsimonious expectations of MS-DOS. The example file would be automatically renamed to 'SNAZZYP.ICC' in this case and saved to disk.

This list of features covers only the basics found in most telecomms programs but should be enough to give a feel for what to expect before we start to go on-line for the first time. You will notice that the phrase 'file transfer protocols' was used in the Upload and Download sections and we are going to have a look at those next. Don't worry if this section seems technically daunting. You will soon recognise which FTP to use in given circumstances and most people get by using only two. For the sake of completeness and compatibility with older systems most common FTPs are listed here.

6.5   File transfer

File transfer protocols consist of chunks of software (modules) which live within telecomms programs. Often these software modules have been bought from a third party and incorporated into the software by the comms program author, or they may have been written from a specification. This modularity makes it possible for FTPs to be added to some comms programs, and in these cases the FTP modules are often called external FTPs or external protocols.

Many FTPs work in similar ways. They break a file up into segments, each called a packet, and then surround that packet with information regarding the packet itself. This information often includes the size of the packet and a checksum, calculated from the number and status of the bits inside the packet. This packet is sent to the receiving computer, where it is decoded. If all is well and the checksums match, then the receiver sends an OK to the transmitter to say that "All is well, so far, please send the next packet". This process is called ACK/NACK – acknowledgement/no acknowledgement. If the transmitting program happens to get a NACK then the packet is resent until an ACK is received. The process is then repeated for the next packet.

It can be seen from this description that the larger the block size sent the fewer ACKs per file are needed to wave it through. This speeds up the transfer process and larger block sizes are associated with faster FTPs. Some FTPs use a dynamically allocated block size – that is the size of the packet (or block) of data is made larger or smaller depending on the number of ACK/NACKs received. The more NACKs, the more errors, and block sizes are therefore reduced. If more ACKs than NACKs are received then the block size is increased. Kermit is a good example of this, especially in its Long Packet Kermit or Super Kermit implementations.

Binary or ASCII

Binary files differ from ASCII files – a computer program is generally a binary file, and some of the output files of word-processors and databases are binary. If you want to download a game or utility from a host system you will be downloading a binary file and should use a non-ASCII transfer protocol.

Streaming protocols

So called streaming protocols are used to speed up the file transfer process. They manage this by not bothering to send any ACK/NACKs unless there is an actual error in the packet. Data 'streams' through the link until an error is found. Streaming protocols such as ZMODEM should only be used over links which have inherent error checking such as those provided by two modems fitted with MNP 4/5 or V42/V42 bis. This strategy leaves the hard work of error checking to the micro-processors in the modem, and takes a large processing overhead away from the computers on the link. The result is fast throughput.

ZMODEM was also the first FTP to implement resumed file transfer. If the connection is lost between two computers in the middle of ZMODEM file transfer, the transfer can be re-commenced from where it was dropped when the modems are reconnected. ZMODEM is the current favourite for UK comms users, although new protocols such as BLAST, HYPERPROTOCOL and others lie in the wings.

UNIX gurus have their own file transfer protocol, imaginatively called 'FTP'. UNIX lovers sometimes object to non-UNIX FTPs being called FTPs, but they should be ignored. UNIX gurus are a funny lot.

Common FTPs

■ ASCII

ASCII transfer is the simplest of all protocols, and is hardly a protocol at all. ASCII transfer has no error checking other than that in place at each end of the virtual link and errors can occur on non-error-corrected systems. ASCII is only used for the transfer of 'plain text', a phrase which can also mean plain text with ASCII control characters such as Form Feed, Linefeed etc. buried in it. ASCII transfer generally uses XON/XOFF (DC1/DC3) handshaking over the virtual link and most dial-up systems send ASCII text as a matter of course. Pressing [CTRL] [S] on the receiving terminal will generally stop data flow from the host; pressing [CTRL] [Q] will restart it.

ASCII transfer is great for transferring word-processing files from one incompatible machine to another, a process used in the construction of this book where text was written in a variety of locations and on a variety of machines, and transferred into the main WP system via ASCII transfer.

■ XMODEM

XMODEM is the grand-daddy of many error checking systems and was developed in the late 1970s by Ward Christensen. It is one of the first public domain 8-bit protocols. The original version of XMODEM used a 128 byte block and a cyclic redundancy code (CRC) or checksum method of error control. CRC is tried first and then XMODEM shifts to the checksum method if the first three CRC requests are not acknowledged.

Some systems do not always properly implement XMODEM and this may be recognised by two or three CRC error messages at the start of the transfer process.

■ YMODEM AND YMODEM BATCH

YMODEM was developed by Chuck Forsberg as an error-correcting transfer protocol for use with binary program files. YMODEM originally could only send a single file at a time; YMODEM BATCH allows the user to tag a series of files for transmission, and the protocol then transmits each one sequentially over the link.

■ YMODEM-G

This protocol is important because it expects error-detection and recovery to be performed by the communicating hardware. YMODEM-G 'streams' data in 1kilobyte packets without interruption until it is instructed to stop from the other end of the link. The protocol is specifically for use with high speed error correcting modems where it will achieve a fast throughput of data. A YMODEM-G BATCH version is also common.

- MODEM7

  This is an elderly protocol used mainly on CP/M systems. It is not supported by many dial-up systems these days which is a shame as many older CP/M computers make great comms terminals for basic email work. MODEM7 sends a header before each block of data and supports both CRC and checksum methods of error detection.

- TELINK

  TELINK is a variant of XMODEM. It adds file size and creation date information to the file header. TELINK is used on many FIDONET bulletin boards.

- WXMODEM

  Another XMODEM variant. It uses a full-duplex 'sliding window' format that allows up to four blocks to be sent without requiring an acknowledgement. This speeds up the transfer process by reducing the time taken by turn-around processes.

- SLIDING WINDOW KERMIT

  Usually abbreviated to Kermit and named after the frog in the Muppet Show. The Sliding Window variant sends data over one half of a full-duplex link and watches for error correction signals on the other channel. If conditions are optimum the packet size is increased. Some older or commercial computer systems cannot accept an 8-bit data transfer and Kermit gets over this by using a feature called 8-bit prefixing. Kermit usually works when all else fails, especially on long-distance direct dial links or packet switched services. It's especially useful for personal computer to mainframe file transfers. Kermit can need a little special setting-up to fine tune performance but 'out of the box' settings usually work well. The latest variant Super Kermit uses larger blocks and multiple sliding windows and is much more efficient. Useful for file transfers from mainframe and UNIX computers .

- SEALINK

  Yet another XMODEM variant. SEALINK is a sliding window protocol that is tolerant of delays caused by satellite links or packet switched networks. It is not widely used today due the increased use of inherent error correction on these networks.

- CIS B AND CIS B+

  For CompuServe Information Services. Dedicated file transfer protocols used only on this service and developed from XMODEM. These protocols support resumed transfers, a feature which will pick up where it left off if communications are dropped for any reason.

- IMODEM

  Not much in evidence on dial-up systems, but another non-error-correcting high speed streaming protocol.

- FAST

  Yet another invention by Hayes Inc. FAST is a blitzkrieg protocol placed in the public domain by Hayes. Alas, no one uses it.

- ZMODEM

  The dial-up user's friend. ZMODEM is a streaming protocol and should only be used with error correcting hardware. It provides for resumed transfer, lengthy time-outs and data compression. If you enable ZMODEM auto-detect, your system will scan the incoming data stream for a ZMODEM header and start the transfer process when it sees one. All you have to do is request the remote system to send you the file with ZMODEM, your terminal software will do the rest.

Which to use?

The two most favoured transfer methods in use at the moment are ASCII for plain old text files, and ZMODEM with error-correcting modems. If you don't have any error correction on your system, try an XMODEM variant or Kermit. If you are transferring files across directly between two personal computers without using modems then assume that the line is clean and try ZMODEM. Any errors that you get will be probably be due to either handshaking problems or slow serial ports.

It's worth experimenting with FTPs – if you have a friend in the office with a modem you can try dialling each other up across the PABX (Private Automatic Branch Exchange) and sending files across to each other. The experience gained in this way will stand you in good stead when you first use an external dial-up system.

6.5 Points to remember

- IF YOU ARE USING AN ERROR-CORRECTING MODEM DON'T USE AN ERROR-CORRECTING FTP SUCH AS XMODEM OR ITS VARIANTS. ERROR CORRECTING SOMETHING THAT HAS ALREADY BEEN ERROR CORRECTED IS NOT CONDUCIVE TO A FAST THROUGHPUT. USE YMODEM OR ZMODEM OR A SIMILAR STREAMING FTP FOR MAXIMUM SPEED.

■ IF YOU DON'T HAVE AN ERROR-CORRECTING MODEM, SUCH AS ONE OF THE OLDER QUAD STANDARD
MODEMS, YOU SHOULD USE AN ERROR-CORRECTING FTP SUCH AS XMODEM, YMODEM OR KERMIT. IN THIS
CASE YOU MIGHT FIND THAT YOUR FILE TRANSFERS ARE PERFECT, BUT MESSAGES OR TEXT FROM THE HOST
SERVICE ARE GARBLED DUE TO LINE NOISE. IN THIS CASE YOU SHOULD USE A COMMS-PROGRAM WITH
INBUILT ERROR CORRECTION AND SWITCH TO YMODEM OR ZMODEM FOR FILE TRANSFERS.

■ GENERALLY SPEAKING, USE OF AN ERROR-CORRECTING MODEM WITH A STREAMING FTP WILL GIVE THE
SHORTEST TRANSFER TIMES.

6.6   File compression programs

Most bulletin boards and dial-up systems compress the files stored on their disks to
save space and to speed up downloads to users. There are dozens of file compression
utilities around. Most of them can squash a word-processing file down to less than 50
percent of its original size. You will find that you will need to amass at least a couple
of these programs to decompress the files you receive.

A good example of a file packer/unpacker is the LHA.EXE program by Haruyasu
Yoshizaki ('Yoshi') which can also create self-extracting archives. You will find file
archivers/unpackers/squashers on virtually all bulletin boards and their use is often
self-explanatory. If you have a PC or an Amiga you will find that LHA or PKZIP is
often used. Mac users will usually need a copy of Stuffit or the CPT decompressor.

Downloading compressed files

Compressed files can be downloaded using any of the FTPs mentioned in the previous section. If you have a modem with MNP 5 or are using MNP 5 in your software
package, you might try turning this feature off when downloading compressed files.
This is because MNP 5 can actually increase the size of a compressed file as it tries to
compress it even further. Some comms programs such as Odyssey will manage this
feature automatically.

V42/V42 bis users don't have to worry about compressed files as V42 will automatically turn off its own compression algorithms when it comes across a compressed file.

7

GOING ON-LINE

"With experience there will be good fortune"

7.1   Head first

Going on-line for the first time is like jumping into a river after you have learned the theory of swimming from a book, only more frightening. But after your first attempt everything, including why you bought this book in the first place, should start to make sense. If it doesn't there's a great market for second-hand books about modems.

TO GET ON-LINE YOU WILL NEED

■ A COMPUTER OR TERMINAL.

■ A TELEPHONE DATA MODEM OR ISDN ADAPTOR AND SUITABLE CABLES

■ TELECOMMS SOFTWARE IF YOU ARE USING A COMPUTER

■ AN ADJACENT WORKING TELEPHONE SOCKET (WITH DIALTONE)

■ THE NUMBER OF SOMEWHERE TO CALL.

Some services use different data structures and transmission methods to others. Services run by PTTs and commercial organisations often use 7 bit data, even parity and one stop bit. These services usually have a maximum speed of 2400 bps (V22 bis) or less although this is changing as faster modems become available.

Recreational services almost always use 8 bit data, no parity, 1 stop bit. If you get garbage at your first attempts to login you might check that you have the right set-up for the service you are using. Try one setting and then the other before you assume the remote service is at fault.

Modems equipped with V42 or MNP error correction need some special considera-tion. Because they can send data to the modem at up to four times the transmission speed. In this case you'll get the best throughput if you set your computer to modem speed at four times the transmission speed. So if you have a V22 bis (2400 bps) modem equipped with V42 you would use 9600 bps, if it (or the software you are using) is equipped with MNP 4 or 5 you set 4800 bps. Things get slightly more com-plex with V32 bis (14,400) modems. While they are theoretically equipped to munch data at 57,600 bps you will hardly ever see this in practice. In fact 38,400 is the fastest speed that is suitable for these modems on most computers (Macs, Amigas and PC's equipped with fast UARTs) and this is verified by the awful truth that there are virtually no commercial or recreational services that drive their modems at speeds over 38,400. There's no real advantage in setting 57,600 bps at your end.

The following example assumes that the modem you are using knows all about the Hayes Command set, and that it recognises ATD as the dialling prefix. A full description of the Hayes command set is given in Appendix 1.

Here's a brief list of the Hayes commands you will need to control your modem:

```
ATD number [enter]
```
 – example ATD 0815691774
```
ATZ [enter]
```
 – reset modem to stored defaults
```
ATA [enter]
```
 – answer call
```
+++ATH
```
 – Hang up

Don't forget that only a desperate person or a techno-freak would normally choose to control a modem in this way. Virtually all comms packages should properly control the modem for you without you having to resort to phrases such as `ATS36=4Q0&W0`.

Most comms programs use a predefined key to hang the modem up. It's quite often `ALT H` on PC's and a mouse click on a Mac, but check your documentation before you go on-line for the first time. If you can't find the hang-up command you can tell a Hayes modem to hang up by typing three plus signs (+++) followed by ATH, but this is hard work. Remember that only a techno-freak or die-hard enthusiast chooses to control a modem in this way. Normal human beings should expect the computer do all of the hard work. Isn't that why you bought it?

You must also realise that comms programs use different ways of handling call set-ups for dialling services. Many of the DOS and AMIGA shareware programs use a dialling directory, which holds phone number, parity, line speeds and phone number information. Others such as Smartcom for Windows and many Mac programs take the 'document' approach – where each service you will call is allocated a separate file containing the call set-up parameters. You should spend time exploring your comms program to find out just what each menu choice does. All comms programs for dial up use are very similar in the terms of the facilities they offer, it's just the method of presentation that takes time to learn. And take no notice of lengthy over-technical explanations from well-meaning friends, relatives, and magazine editors – you don't need an lot of technical knowledge to sort problems out. As long as you get an 'OK' when you use a terminal emulator to send AT to your modem, you are two thirds of the way there.

Going on-line...

STEP 1

Unplug all the equipment from the mains. If you leave it plugged in you are unlikely to be electrocuted but computers and modems can be damaged by making connections when they are connected to the mains, switched on or not. (It's to do with earthing and static). Also read the modem manual thoroughly before you apply power to it or connect to anything, and be sure that you know its maximum DTE-DCE speed, and whether or not it uses speed buffering. If you have the choice at this stage your modem should be set up to recognise DTE transitions, and auto-answer mode should be set to 'off.'

■ IF YOU ARE USING A DUMB TERMINAL
Set it to the usual speed of your modem. If your modem says 9600 or 2400 on the front then set it to that speed. If it says 21/23 or similar on the front set your terminal to 300 bps, and if it says quad on the front of the modem try 2400 as a starting point. Set Stop Bits to 1, and data bits (or word length) to 8. Set Parity to 'None'.

Dumb terminals usually carry some intelligence and software settings are sometimes made from a menu called by a key marked 'menu' or 'set-up'. Older terminals are usually set up with a bank of small switches on the rear. In both cases you may need access to the handbook for that particular terminal.

If you are using a computer and comms software you should configure your software parameters in the same way. Ascertain which serial port you are using and its name and enter that into the configuration too. Then save the configuration to disk.

FIGURE 7.1

Setting your comms software parameters in Windows terminal

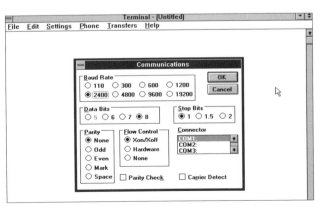

It's much better to configure software before you plug the modem in at the first instance as some modems lock up if they don't receive data at the right speed.

STEP 2

Connect the straight through serial cable between the computer and modem. Connect the modem to the phone line and power everything up starting with the modem. With a terminal there is nothing else to do, with a computer you should now run the terminal emulation software.

7.2 Success :-)

If there is a light on the modem marked DTR or TR (for data Terminal Ready) this should come on when the terminal or computer is working. In the case of a computer this usually means when the comms software has detected the serial port and ini-tialised it. The DTR light is usually driven from Pin 20 of the RS232 interface.

If you have done everything correctly, your DTR light is on and there is no smoke, you can try talking to your modem to wake it up. Type AT on the keyboard and press the [enter] key. The modem should respond with 'OK', or '0' or some other recognisable word or number.

■ YOU SHOULD NOW BE ABLE TO SET UP A CALL. THIS ONE CONNECTS YOU TO CIX:

EXAMPLE: ATD 0813901244

■ IF YOU ARE CALLING FROM AN OFFICE EQUIPPED WITH A PABX YOU MAY NEED TO PUT A '9' IN FRONT OF THE NUMBER TO GET AN OUTSIDE LINE. IF YOUR PABX IS PARTICULARLY ANACHRONISTIC YOU MAY HAVE TO TELL YOUR MODEM TO PAUSE FOR A SECOND OR TWO UNTIL THE PABX SUPPLIES DIAL TONE. IN THAT CASE USE THE ',' (COMMA) TO DENOTE A 2 SECOND PAUSE AFTER THE NINE.

EXAMPLE: ATD 9,0813901244

■ IF YOU HAVE AN OLD CROSSBAR EXCHANGE (PURRING 'OLD- FASHIONED' DIAL-TONE) YOU MAY NEED TO USE PULSE DIALLING. PUT A 'P' AFTER THE ATD COMMAND.

EXAMPLE: ATDP 0813901244

■ IF YOUR MODEM TRIES TO USE PULSE DIALLING ON A DIGITAL EXCHANGE (YOU CAN HEAR TONES WHEN YOU

DIAL A NUMBER) PUT A 'T' AFTER THE DIAL PREFIX TO INSTRUCT THE MODEM TO USE TONE DIALLING.

EXAMPLE: ATDT 0813901244

You may hear the modem dialling the number followed by various bleeping noises. If you have a V32 or higher modem you will hear hissing and chiming noises as the modems negotiate. If you hear nothing at all but your modem connects then your modem's speaker is turned off.

You should see something like the following if all goes well:

FIGURE 7.2

CIX opening screen

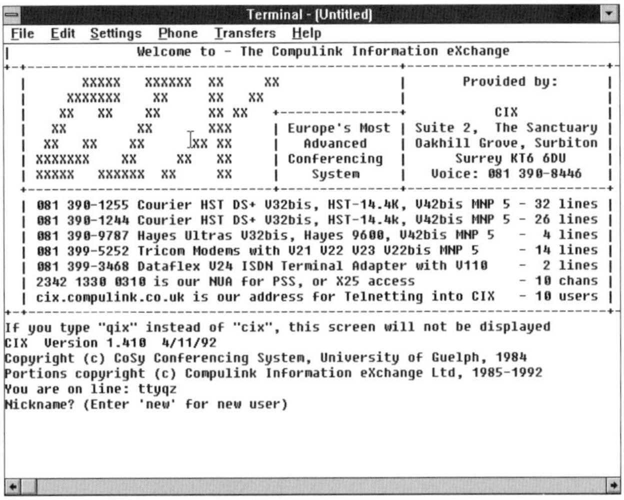

```
                          Terminal - [Untitled]
 File  Edit  Settings  Phone  Transfers  Help
|              Welcome to - The Compulink Information eXchange
+-------------------------------------------------------------------+
|     XXXXX    XXXXXX   XX      XX       |          Provided by:      |
|    XXXXXXX     XX     XX   XX          |                            |
|    XX   XX     XX     XX XX   XX  +-----------------+     CIX       |
|    XX          XX       XXX       | Europe's Most   | Suite 2,  The Sanctuary |
|    XX   XX     XX     XX  XX      |    Advanced     | Oakhill Grove, Surbiton |
|    XXXXXXX     XX     XX      XX  |  Conferencing   |    Surrey KT6 6DU       |
|    XXXXX    XXXXXX   XX       XX  |     System      |  Voice: 081 390-8446    |
+-------------------------------------------------------------------+
| 081 390-1255 Courier HST DS+ V32bis, HST-14.4K, V42bis MNP 5 - 32 lines |
| 081 390-1244 Courier HST DS+ V32bis, HST-14.4K, V42bis MNP 5 - 26 lines |
| 081 390-9787 Hayes Ultras V32bis, Hayes 9600, V42bis MNP 5   -  4 lines |
| 081 399-5252 Tricom Modems with V21 V22 V23 V22bis MNP 5     - 14 lines |
| 081 399-3468 Dataflex V24 ISDN Terminal Adapter with V110    -  2 lines |
| 2342 1330 0310 is our NUA For PSS, or X25 access             - 10 chans |
| cix.compulink.co.uk is our address for Telnetting into CIX   - 10 users |
+-------------------------------------------------------------------+
If you type "qix" instead of "cix", this screen will not be displayed
CIX  Version 1.410  4/11/92
Copyright (c) CoSy Conferencing System, University of Guelph, 1984
Portions copyright (c) Compulink Information eXchange Ltd, 1985-1992
You are on line: ttyqz
Nickname? (Enter 'new' for new user)
```

Type CIX at the login: prompt to get to the opening screen.

Comms etiquette

TIPS FOR YOUR FIRST LOGON TO ANY SERVICE ARE

■ DON'T JUST DROP THE LINE TO HANG UP YOUR MODEM. GO THROUGH THE 'GOOD-BYE' OR LOG-OFF SEQUENCE WHENEVER POSSIBLE. THIS PREVENTS YOU BEING CHARGED FOR TIME YOU HAVEN'T USED ON COMMERCIAL SYSTEMS, AND STOPS THE SYSTEM OPERATORS (SYSOPS) OF RECREATIONAL SYSTEMS HAVING TO GET OUT OF BED AT THREE IN THE MORNING TO RESET MODEMS.

■ MOST RECREATIONAL SYSTEMS REQUEST THAT YOU LEAVE YOUR NAME, ADDRESS, AND PHONE NUMBER AT YOUR FIRST LOGIN. THIS IS NORMAL, YOU WON'T RECEIVE JUNK MAIL – IT'S TO CUT OUT NUISANCE CALLERS.

■ ALWAYS USE LOWER CASE FOR COMMS – UPPER CASE MEANS YOU ARE SHOUTING!

■ TRY USING AN EMOTICON TO EMPHASISE A POINT IN CORRESPONDENCE – IT MAKES PEOPLE SMILE :-), RATHER THAN FROWN :-(, WHEN VIEWED WITH THE HEAD PLACED ON THE LEFT SHOULDER.

■ DON'T USE THE SAME PASSWORD ON DIFFERENT SYSTEMS IN CASE IT'S DISCOVERED.

■ CHANGE YOUR PASSWORD MONTHLY ON COMMERCIAL SYSTEMS

■ BE NICE TO PEOPLE! :-)

7.3   Failure :-(

Abject failure is common for first time comms users, mainly because one small part of the setting up process has been overlooked. Check everything again, including comm port addresses, connections and settings. Then read on.

Modem trouble shooting

If you cannot talk to your modem the most likely explanation is that some part of your setting up procedure is wrong, or the modem has had its voice disabled or you are using the wrong cable or 9 pin to 25 pin RS232 adapter. You may also have an older V.25 Bis Command Set modem or a modem that uses its own command language.

Before you do anything else try sending the following tests, and follow each one by:
AT [enter]

TEST 1
[CTRL] [Q]
AT [enter]

Hold down the Control key and press Q. This is in case your modem has been told to shut up with an XOFF. CTRL Q sends XON.

TEST 2

Send ATF, the Hayes 'reset all factory defaults stored in non-volatile memory' command.

```
ATF [enter]
AT [enter]
```

This should reset a Hayes compatible modem to the defaults stored in its memory.

TEST 3

Send the command to turn on reporting.

```
ATQ0 [enter]
AT [enter]
```

This means "Please enable the sending of your innermost thoughts (Result Codes) to the terminal". If Q is set to 1 then the modem will just sit there dumbly while you contemplate defenestrating it.

TEST 4

Talk English, or at least American.

```
ATV1 [enter]
AT [enter]
```

This means "Display your innermost thought as words, not numbers". Its complement 'ATV0', means "Display your innermost thoughts as numbers". At this stage you might see an 'OK' response.

7.4 Modem diagnostics

If none of the above works then you may have a hardware problem and/or a software problem. Try the following:

If the modem lights flash

■ IF YOUR MODEM WINKS AT YOU AS YOU TYPE BUT YOU RECEIVE GARBAGE THEN YOUR SETTINGS DON'T MATCH THOSE OF THE MODEM OR YOUR CABLE IS WRONGLY WIRED. CHECK SPEED AND PARITY SETTINGS

FIRST. SOME OLDER 21/23 MODEMS USED TO COME FROM THE FACTORY WITH PARITY SET TO EVEN AND 7 BIT DATA – CHANGING YOUR SETTINGS TO MATCH THIS MIGHT GET RID OF THE GARBAGE.

■ THE SD (SEND DATA) LIGHT SHOULD FLASH AS YOU TYPE AT THE KEYBOARD. IF THE RD (RECEIVE DATA) LIGHT FLASHES THEN YOU A USING A CROSS-OVER (PRINTER) CABLE. CHANGE IT FOR A STRAIGHT THROUGH (MODEM) CABLE.

■ IF YOU HAVE A NON-HAYES MODEM THEN YOU WILL NEED TO CHECK THE MANUAL IN CASE THE MODEM NEEDS A PREDEFINED RECOGNITION SEQUENCE. OR TRY SENDING A SERIES OF CARRIAGE RETURNS, OR "*" PLUS CARRIAGE RETURNS.

■ MAKE SURE YOUR SOFTWARE IS IN 'TERMINAL MODE' AND NOT IN SETUP OR MENU MODE.

■ CHECK YOUR MODEM MANUAL TO MAKE SURE THAT YOUR MODEM IS NOT IN 'DUMB' MODE (SET WITH SWITCHES ON SOME MODEMS).

If the modem lights don't flash

■ IF YOU HAVE MORE THAN ONE SERIAL PORT MAKE SURE THAT THE MODEM IS PLUGGED INTO THE PORT DESIGNATED BY YOUR SOFTWARE. (TURN OFF EVERYTHING BEFORE YOU DO ANY UNPLUGGING)

■ YOU MAY BE SET TO A DTE-DCE SPEED TOO HIGH FOR YOUR MODEM TO RECOGNISE. TRY 300 BPS OR 1200 BPS AS A STARTING POINT AND WORK UPWARDS.

■ YOU MAY BE USING THE WRONG CABLE OR A CABLE WITH A FAULTY CONNECTOR.

■ YOU MAY HAVE A CONFLICT WITH THE 'INTERRUPT' SETTINGS OF ANOTHER DEVICE SUCH AS A CD-ROM CARD, SCSI OR NETWORK CARD IN YOUR SYSTEM. (CARD MODEMS ARE PRONE TO THIS SORT OF CONFLICT) THE ONLY REAL WAY TO CHECK THIS OUT IS TO DO A TRIAL BY REMOVAL TEST:

TURN OFF THE MACHINE AND REMOVE ALL ADDITIONAL PLUG IN CARDS, OTHER THAN DISPLAY, MEMORY AND DRIVE CONTROLLER CARDS. TRY THE MODEM AGAIN. IF IT WORKS THEN YOU HAVE AN INTERRUPT CONFLICT WITH ONE OF THE OTHER CARDS – YOU CAN FIND OUT WHICH BY TRIAL AND ERROR. INTERRUPTS ARE NORMALLY SET WITH JUMPERS ON THE CARD AND YOU WILL NEED THE RELEVANT INFORMATION FOR EACH CARD TO IRON OUT THE PROBLEM.

If your modem still doesn't respond after all of this then you, or your dealer are in for some prolonged detective work. It's probably best to try all of the software settings again to make sure that it is the equipment that's at fault and not you before harassing your dealer.

Go and have a cup of tea, and mull over the fact that most modem errors are caused by humans, not modems. If you consider that this description fits you, then you should be able to fix the problem. Drinking cups of tea and sitting in semi-darkened rooms sometimes helps, as does talking to other people...

7.5   Garbage

Garbage is an important part of modem communications. Without garbage modems would be boring. You need to see garbage on your screen from time to time to re-affirm the fact that you are human, and therefore make mistakes. If you never ever see garbage on your screen then there is something drastically wrong with you, or you are a computer programer, which amounts to the same thing.

How to deal with garbage

Garbage is caused either by allowing human beings lose on highly complex things like modems and computers, or by letting PTTs lose on highly complex things like telephone systems. The end results are the same to all intents and purposes; your computer and modem sits there spurting stupid symbols at you.

For most part the British PTTs do their job well, and garbage free lines are the norm in the UK, regardless of anything that an aggrieved modem user might tell you. From this you should be able to deduce that garbage on comms is more often than not the fault of the operator, usually because some setting has been overlooked.

Parity Errors

Parity errors are sometimes easy to spot as you can often read some of the on-screen data when they are present. FIGURE 7.3 shows a parity error caused by the transmitting computer being set to EVEN parity and the receiving computer set to NO PARITY. The text says 'This is a parity error' If you have semi-readable garbage on your screen try setting your parity to something else, such as EVEN or ODD parity . Most recreational services use NO PARITY, most commercial services use EVEN parity.

One of the problems with parity checking is that it's not always used in a coherent way. Parity checking only exists on 7 bit systems, an extra bit is added which indicates whether the total number of data bits in the packet is odd or even. The receiver then checks this against the 7 bit data packet and flags an error if the parity bit doesn't agree with the contents. On an 8 bit system such as used in personal computers there is no parity checking – the ten bit packet (start bit, – 8 data bits – stop bit) doesn't allow for it. So you often have to guess whether an older system will use odd or even parity, and if it does you won't be able to send or receive 8 bit files to or from it, unless you use Kermit, which can cope with older 7 bit systems. Parity checking is a real anachronism, not one personal computer in the world uses it. And 7 bit systems cannot use extended ASCII which means that word processor and other programs which save their data above ASCII 127 cannot have their files sent via a 7 bit system. Most older commercial services use 7 bit data with even parity, but often you won't know until you've spent hours fiddling with the settings in your comms program.

FIGURE 7.3
Parity error

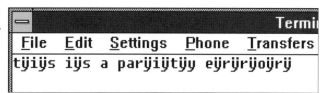

Speed Errors

With speed errors is often impossible to read anything on your screen coming in from the modem. What appears to be a speed error can also be complicated by the fact that your parity settings may also be wrong. A combination of speed and parity errors can take some time to sort out. The only real way to do it is by trial and error. Some comms engineers use a box of tricks called an RS232 line analyser to sort out speed and parity settings, but these cost more than a decent V22 bis modem. Trial and error is really the only way to check these problems out, unless you are very wealthy. Then you would pay someone else to do it for you. FIGURE 7.4 shows speed errors caused by the transmitting station being set to a faster speed than the receiver.

FIGURE 7.4
Speed differences between computers

High Bit or 8 Bit errors

Systems which use 7 bit data transmission mainly belong to commercial organisations such as national telephone systems and value added network (VAN) providers. They use seven bit data because it is only the newfangled personal computers that need 8 bits, and the 12 years that has elapsed since the birth of the IBM PC is but the twinkling of an eye in the lifespan of a national telephone system.

7 bit data goes all the way up to ASCII 128 which is more than enough to represent the English alphabet, much of which we stole from the Arabs in the first place. Commercial systems do not generally pander to the needs of personal computer systems whose 8 bit systems can continue up to ASCII 255. On a personal computer the extra characters are used mainly for graphics characters, and comprise the 'extended character set'.

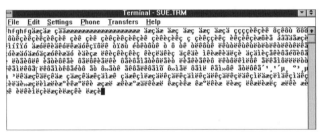

Consequently if your personal computer is set to 8 bits, and the transmitting system is set to 7 bits you will be interpreting (slicing) the wrong data particle (bit) out of the incoming byte. This can be recognised by seeing lots of extended characters such as those with umlauts appearing on your screen. Having lots of graphics characters (such as line drawing symbols) appearing on a personal computer screen is often a symptom of wrong bit size selection. Try setting your parameters to 7 bit data instead.

Handshake errors

Sometimes called 'overrun errors', handshake errors manifest themselves where one end of a link is using a different sort of flow control to the other, or more usually, is using none at all. Handshake errors appear on the screen as broken up text or graphics – you can read most of what appears – but chunks of text appear to be missing, or get overwritten by more incoming text. Some comms programs such as Smartcom

Exec can detect data loss caused by flow control problems and post a warning to tell you this is happening. Most comms programs don't have this ability.

The first step in dealing with garbage caused by flow control problems is to make sure that you have some form of handshaking in place at your end of the link. Try setting both your modem and your computer or terminal to XON/XOFF handshaking as a starting point. If that gets rid of the garbage then the fault is obviously at your end. If it doesn't then you have a problem.

On a typical dial-up link there are three sets of handshaking going on, between the two sets of computers and modems (DTE-DCE flow control) and between the modems themselves. It's almost always going to be your end of the link that isn't set up properly, so check everything out again. Remember that if you have hard-handshaking set between your computer and modem then the serial port, your software, your modem, and your modem to computer serial cable must all be capable of supporting RTS/CTS handshaking. If any part of this link doesn't support it then you only have XON/XOFF to fall back on.

Most PCs manage hard-handshaking well, as do Amigas and Ataris. But many portable computers that run on disposable batteries don't have proper hard handshaking implemented because it uses a lot of battery power, and these machines are more prone to hard-handshake problems than mains powered machines, or computers that are equipped with rechargeable power cells. Portable battery operated modems are particularly prone to handshake problems, many imported pocket modems have no handshaking at all and need XON/XOFF to be implemented at the computer to provide 'transparent soft handshaking' (see chapter 2) over the whole link.

Users of Apple Macs need to pay particular attention to the serial cable in use between their modem and computer, up until the introduction of the V32 modem there was no real need for hard handshaking on modems, and many older Macintosh modem cables are not fully wired for it. (You can check if this is so either by using an RS232 patch box, or more easily by unscrewing the cable connector cover and checking that pins 4/5 at the modem end of the cable are connected to the cable. For real peace of mind Mac users need an RS232 diagnostics tool of some sort to fully check out their serial cables if handshake errors persist.

It takes a practised eye to spot different sorts of garbage, but it can be done. Unfortunately different makes of computers produce different sorts of garbage, – it's much easier to categorise all forms of screen garbage as human error and start from scratch if garbage occurs. It only takes a little practice to become familiar with the communications parameters in your comms package, and once they are set up for each service you use there will be little need to change them.

If you are confused by any of this then remember that much will become apparent with familiarity. The best way to get going is to have a go, and then refer back to this section if you hit problems. Modern modems and comms programs are very much advanced from the stuff we had to deal with back in the early eighties, and you should be able to take a modem out of its box, plug it in and use it.

FTPs

Which file transfer should you use for which service and type of file? The answer is fairly straight forward. If you are hooked up using 8 bit data setting then you can use any one you want. If you are hooked up to a 7 bit service and you want to transfer binary data or word processing files you will have to use Kermit. 7 bit system cannot see the extended ASCII alphabet which lives inside an 8 bit framework).

If you have a comms package that supports ZMODEM and an error-corrected modem then try ZMODEM as it's one of the fastest FTP's around and can transfer files in batches by using the wildcard descriptor (Send *.* means send all files). If not, then try XMODEM with non-error corrected modems. XMODEM isn't terribly fast but works well on older equipment that doesn't support V42 or MNP4.

If you are having real problems try Kermit, which can talk to almost anything, eventually. You will also need to use Kermit to make a PC, Mac or Amiga talk to a UNIX based host computer, unless it supports the Internet FTP command.

For transferring ASCII files between personal computers of any type use the ASCII transfer routine that comes with your comms package but remember to look for an option which enables Extended ASCII or 8 bit ASCII. Otherwise your comms program might strip out all of the characters above ASCII 127. Or you can compress the files with a utility such as PKZIP, Stuffit or LHA and send them with ZMODEM. Forget using some of the more exotic ftps such as SEALINK – most of the time you will find that ZMODEM or XMODEM does everything you need. And if it doesn't, have a go with Kermit. It seems to succeed when all else fails.

8

INTER-SPECIES FILE TRANSFER

"There is no leader, no union. Great Misfortune"

8.1 Between the lines

It is a dark and stormy night. Your dear lady wife has just completed her 500,000 word romantic novel set in 17th Century Cornwall and asks you to drop the floppy disk off at the publishers on your way to the office in the morning. But the publisher wants the work on a PC disk, and your wife has used an Amiga to write the book. Alas! Alack! What to do?

There are many ways to effect file transfer between different species of computer. Most of them involve some technical knowledge, but if you have gotten this far without throwing the book out of the window then you posses all of the information you need. The first thing to decide is which format the data is in, and precisely what is needed by the Publisher.

In this case he wants plain ASCII text so your task is simplified. Your wife's word processor has a Print to Disk option which saves the work as plain ASCII, with carriage returns only at the end of paragraphs. You simply hook up the Amiga to the serial port of your laptop PC via a null modem lead, and use a comms program at each end of the link to upload the text from the Amiga to the PC. This example is the most usual requirement for intermachine file transfer, and is also the easiest to master. ASCII files can generally be transported between machines with little difficulty. But in many cases life becomes much more complex.

Binary file transfers

Imagine that the publisher had wanted not only the text for the book, but screen shots to illustrate the bit where the virginal daughter of the Squire meets the gamekeeper under a suitably shady tree. Your wife has lovingly created this vivid image in a paint package and the resulting PCX image file is sitting on her hard disk.

Non-ASCII files, that is non-text files are called binary files, and need to be transmitted and received using binary transfer. Again, in this example you can use the same comms package at each end of the link, but you will use a File Transfer Protocol to move the data. The easiest one to use on direct (non-modem) links is ZMODEM, because ZMODEM headers are recognised by the receiving computer, which then initiates the file transfer procedure. You only have to fight with the keyboard on the transmitting computer. If you have a multi-tasking computer such as an Amiga or Mac the transfer can continue in the background whilst your wife gets on with her latest blockbuster.

Many older comms packages don't have ZMODEM – but they will almost certainly have XMODEM or KERMIT, and either of these may be used to transfer the file. ZMODEM only has a little inherent error checking but it's unlikely that errors will occur on a direct connection. If they do occur than it's almost certain that the speed over the link is too high, or that there is no mutual handshaking (over-run control) in place.

A good starting speed for direct transfers is 9600 bps, and it's a useful idea to set handshaking to XON/XOFF if you are not sure about the way your lead or null modem adaptor is configured. Why? Because your null modem lead may have the handshaking lines RTS/CTS wired out, so hard handshaking will not work in this case. XON/XOFF slows things down slightly, but we are not so worried on a direct connection as we are not paying phone charges.

This method of direct connect file transfer will work for most computers that have a serial port, and for most simple binary files. The only requirements are that you have a null modem lead between the serial ports, that you have a comms program on each computer, and that you know a little about what's going on. The process is easily managed with a little practice.

8.2   No Port in a storm

There are occasions when you need to capture data from a computer without a serial port. Some early dedicated word processors and memory typewriters often had serial printer ports, but no comms software. Capturing data in the form of ASCII text from these machines can sometimes be done by getting your receiving computer to pretend that it is a printer, and connecting it to the serial printer port of the word processor via a null modem connector. This can work surprisingly well if you can manage to sort out the handshaking requirements of the word processor or typewriter you are capturing the data from. This may be more difficult than it sounds as many dedicated machines of this type pay no heed to handshaking conventions. But remember that if there is a serial RS232 interface of any sort on any machine it's almost always possible to capture data from it, with only nominal exasperation.

Schofield's Second Law states that RS232 data capture is exasperating in inverse pro-portion to the amount of data being transferred, so persevere.

An RS232 patchbox is often useful in these cases. It's a small box that allows cross-connection of RS232 signals. Prolonged use of them makes your hair fall out.

Parallel port capture

Some dedicated WP systems don't have a serial port. They have a parallel port, in which data is sent (usually to a printer) down eight wires at once. This makes the prospect of data capture a little more difficult. But it can be done. A device called a parallel to serial convertor can be inserted between the parallel port on the WP and the serial port on your computer to effect the conversion. These convertors are not all born equal, because there has to be some way of effecting flow control between both ends of the link, and many cheap convertors never seem to get this process quite right. But if you are desperate to grab the data from on older WP system, which uses a parallel printer port then this may be one solution worth trying. Parallel to serial convertors are sold by electronics and Office Suppliers retailers, and are sometimes called Protocol Convertors.

There are also boxes on the market which store the data from the parallel port for printing either at a later date, or on a serial printer. They are generally marketed as print buffers or print spoolers, and some of the more advanced ones will take data in from a parallel source and release it through a serial port where it can be grabbed in the normal way. Again, this is perhaps a specialist area, but may be worth considering if you can find no other way of getting your vital data from that old WP system you are about to replace.

8.3   Binary file conversion problems

In many ways it is not the actual mechanism of transferring files between various computers that is problematical, it is the conversion between one computer format to another which gives the most problems. It's even possible to hit snags converting files to run on the same machine but under different application programs – word processing files being the most notorious examples.

Most word processing programs will only directly accept files written in the native format of the application, although many have file translation facilities built-in to allow work created other applications to be read. But what is Word Perfect 4.2 format to one program may be something different to another, and format conversions can go wrong in a spectacular if unamusing fashion. There are any number of Word Processing File translation programs available which will convert from one native format to another, Word for Word for the PC being a good example. But there are other factors which can prevent transfers from working properly, and most of these problems occur on computers which use a Graphical User Interface (GUI).

GUI Phooey

Windows for the PC is a GUI, as is System 7 (the current Mac interface), Amiga Workbench and Atari TOS. All of these systems can make file transfers between each other difficult for a whole variety of reasons.

Windows

Native Windows applications exist on your hard disk as executables – that is files which can be executed by the operating system. If you send one of these files over a serial link to another PC it should run perfectly well. But Windows has to be able to run older DOS based programs which it does by allocating a Program Information File (PIF) to the application. The PIF contains details such as memory and video requirements, and is generally needed along with the application to make sure that it runs properly under Windows. If you forget to transfer the PIF you could have problems in getting the application to run properly.

*FIGURE **8.1***

Windows Pif File – needs to be
transferred with DOS programs

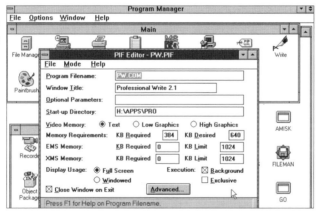

DOS based programs do not have a Windows Icon attached to them by default, but this still has to be transferred as a separate process in order for Windows to correctly allocate memory and other parameters for the program. Native Windows applications have the Icon buried in the executable, and do not need a PIF to tell Windows how to handle them. The best way make sure that all of this information goes into the same packet as the file is to add the relevant parts into a compressed archive file and then move that to the destination. PC programs such as Xtree Gold make this process easy, as do file compression programs like PKZIP, and LHA.

It's possible to download Windows or DOS programs from a bulletin board or another computer onto a non-DOS computer, and then copy them to a disk which can be read by your PC. They will then run. But this is not the case with the Mac transfers which use a PC or other computer as a transfer host will be problematical.

FIGURE 8.2

PKZIP, a file compressor for the PC

```
PKZIP (R)   FAST!  Create/Update Utility   Version 1.1.  03-15-90
Copr. 1989-1990 PKWARE Inc. All Rights Reserved.  PKZIP/h for help
PKZIP Reg. U.S. Pat. and Tm. Off.

Usage: PKZIP [-b[path]] [options] zipfile [@list] [files...]
Options summary - consult the PKWARE documentation for additional information
  -x<filespec!@list> = eXclude filespec(s)           -z = add zipfile comment
  -d = delete files                  -f = freshen files     -i = add changed files
  -l = display license info          -u = update files      -m[u,f] = move files
  -a = add files                     -b = create temp zipfile on alternate drive
  -c = add/edit file comments        -C = add comments to new files only
  -k = keep same ZIP date            -o = set ZIP date to latest file
  -q = enable ANSI comments
  -r = recurse subdirs                       -$[drive] = save volume label
  -t[mmddyy] = Compress files on or after specified date (default=today)
  -e[x,i,s] = use maXimal compression/Implode only/Shrink only
  -<p!P> = store pathnames ! p=recursed into ! P=specified & recursed into
  -<w!W><H,S> = ! w=include ! W=don't include ! Hidden/System files
  -<j!J><H,S,R> = ! j=mask ! J=don't mask ! Hidden/System/Readonly attributes
  -v[b,c,d,e,n,p,s,r,t] = view ZIP [Brief listing/show Comments/sort by -
        Date/Ext/Name/Percentage/Size/sort Reverse/Technical (long) listing]
zipfile = ZIP file name.  Default extension is .ZIP
file    = Names of files to compress. Wildcards *,? ok. Default is ALL files.
@list   = listfile containing names of files to add or view etc.
          y key to continue
```

8.4   Mac file transfers

The Macintosh series of computers will download files from most any source and show them as an on-screen Icon. Mac files on bulletin boards are often stored in Self Extracting Archive (SEA) format, which lets them unpack themselves onto your hard disk when you click on the Icon. Other files in *.SIT format need a de-archiver such as STUFFIT to decompress them.

FIGURE 8.3

'Stufit' file archiver for the Mac

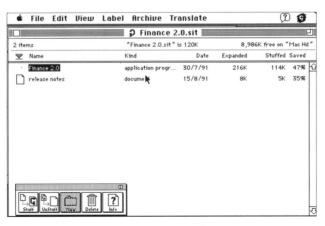

An Apple utility for the Mac called 'Apple File Exchange' (AFE) allows the Mac to read and write to PC format disks – in theory you can download binary files onto your PC and then transfer them into the Mac on PC disk, via AFE. But this process does not work directly. Your application ends up on the Mac desktop as a document file and cannot be run. However most text and some word processor files can be transferred with AFE and will work properly.

Macbinary

The Mac is a remarkable machine in many ways, not least in the way that it handles internal data and programs. The Mac stores its native files in a two-part format consisting of a 'resource fork' and a 'data fork'. One or both of these forks (areas of storage) may be present in a Mac file. The Data Fork is a non-exclusive program area, that is it can be used by programers for any purpose, such as a container for a program loader or other utility. The Resource Fork contains data in a way analogous to a database file, there are a number of resources such as icons or executables, menus and pictures. Each resource has a type designator to define its use, and an 'Indentifier', which identifies it amongst the resources in use.

It's possible for programers to store a display routine in the data fork, to call a picture from the resource fork and display it, for instance. This structure is unique amongst personal computer systems but if you download Mac files onto a PC they are stored as a single file. PC's know nothing about Data and Resource forks and Macbinary files transferred from them can no longer be recognised by the Mac when you make the transfer. AFE considers them to be document files as it cannot see the full structure, and makes them non-executable.

There are two solutions. The easiest is to connect your modem to your Mac and use it like nature intended. The second way is a tad more complex…

Macbinary translators

If you have downloaded binary Mac files onto your PC or Amiga then you need to re-format them into the binary format that the Mac uses. There are three utilities that can do this. Whichever one you use depends upon the nature of the storage method used to hold the file on a non-Mac computer. The programs are BinHex4, BinHex5 and AFE MacBinary Translator.

BinHex4, translates binary files into text and allocates them an extension of HQX. A screen saver program converted in this way might be called SAVER.HQX. HQX files are actually ASCII files that contain an alias of the binary data, but being ASCII they can be moved around easily between machines. (They can also be transmitted quickly over MNP4 or V42 modems). HQX files can be moved into your Mac with AFE, and then BinHex4, is used on the Mac to convert them back to binary. The BinHex utilities are very useful for Internet file transfers. The Internet cannot directly handle binary files, so they must be converted to ASCII text first. Similar utilities called UUENCODE and UUDECODE exist in the PC world.

BinHex5 is a utility that converts both parts of a Mac file into a format called MacBinary. And MacBinary is also recognised by an additional translator for the AFE called 'AFE MacBinary>Mac'. This is the easiest method to use, you simply place the translator into the AFE folder, and select MacBinary when you make the transfer. AFE MacBinary >Mac works fairly seamlessly in translating files, and the apparent complexity of this explanation shouldn't put you off from using it.

FIGURE 8.4

Apple File Exchange for the Mac reads and writes MS-DOS disks

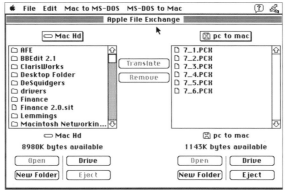

There are in fact two types of MacBinary, the original and MacBinary 2. The latter was released in 1987 to counteract problems with file type recognition and is compatible with the original. Most Mac comms programs recognise the format of a file when it comes in (or goes out) and can turn MacBinary processing on or off at will. Earlier programs often needed manual intervention.

Most of the Mac files on CIX, CompuServe and other systems are stored in MacBinary format. BinHex 4 & 5, and the AFE MacBinary Translators are available from most BBS's as Shareware. The catch is that Apple do not supply AFE MacBinary as part of the AFE program suite. AFE MacBinary is Shareware and can be downloaded from many BBS's, but this is of no use if your only modem is connected to a PC full time. You will not be able to load Mac files from your PC disk unless you have one of the correct translators. And you cannot load the correct translator (itself in MacBinary format) unless you have the correct translator.

PC to Mac help

There are a suite of utilities which copy a disk image of a Mac disk containing the translators onto a PC disk, which can then be used to make a Mac disk with your PC. They are available on CIX in the MACvPC conference and are fully described there.

Remember that most comms packages written for the Mac know about MacBinary and perform the conversion automatically. It follows from this that using AFE or BinHex5 can be avoided if your files are transmitted to the Mac either directly from the PC into a Mac comms package.

If all of this fails, and you cannot get a direct connection to work with a null modem lead you can try the final solution of EMAIL-ing the files to yourself via your bulletin board, and down-loading them on the Mac. Long-winded perhaps, but it works.

8.5   The Amiga

1992 was a good year for Commodore. They released a slew of new Amiga's – two of which, the A600 and the A1200, make great comms machines. These machines are priced at the low end of the personal computer market, which makes them even more attractive.

The generic Amiga can communicate well with other machines, as it comes with a fast serial port as standard, and there are a number of utilities that allow these machines to read and write PC disks. CrossDos, MessyDos, and MultiDos are just three. All are Shareware and can be found on most large BBS's. These DOS convertors work well and are useful for Amiga owners who use PC's (Note that the A600 and A1200 use 720k disks). Of course you cannot run a PC file on an Amiga unless you have a PC emulator for the Amiga, of which there are many, but there are none of the file conversion problems that occur with the Mac/PC combination for instance.

Amiga word processing files are normally converted to ASCII for transfer to a PC, but binary files can be transferred straight to MS-DOS disks with few problems, if a convertor is installed.

Amiga applications and font files will usually have a *.INFO file attached to them and this must be transferred with the application if it is to run properly at its destination. Amiga files on BBS's are generally compressed with LHA, a file compression routine which performs much the same function as STUFIT for the MAC, or PKZIP for the PC. LHA can also preserve the directory structure of packaged files, a single file containing a full BBS system can be automatically unpacked into the correct directories by LHA.

There are no real nasties to watch out for when transferring files from an Amiga, which is in keeping with the generally benevolent nature of these fine computers, and most of the DOS disk readers and file decompression routines are available on many BBS's.

8.6   Dedicated file transfer programs

The PC Industry has recognised the need for file transfer programs, and in many ways has created the need for them by selling 'lightweight' portable computers. Often these machines lack a disk drive to save weight – the real reason being that the batteries and chargers which one has to lug around with many of these machines are so heavy that adding a disk drive would be the straw that breaks the Sales Managers back.

Many modern PC's have a parallel port which is bidirectional, that is the port can receive data as well as transmit it. This is news to MS-DOS; it was never designed for such underhand trickery, therefore programs which use this facility have to manipulate or bypass the PC's operating system in order to get the data into or out of it.

A remarkable PC program called Laplink can install itself onto the host PC via the parallel port, and transfer data into it from the portable, a feat which it manages with much aplomb once you have told the PC how to set up its parallel port. But Laplink, and its imitators will not work on all PC's as not all of them are fitted with bidirectional parallel ports. There is a version of Laplink for the Mac, too.

The easiest way to find out if your PC has a bidirectional port is to phone the supplier. The hardest way is to pay money for a file transfer program and then find out that it doesn't work.

The bidirectional parallel port represents a security hazard for PC Managers – if some Slimy Furtler (latest street jargon – they used to be called Hackers) can get into your locked PC by the cloacal means of the parallel port then where does that leave your well meaning security procedures? Some PC manufacturers (notably Olivetti) have recognised this problem and have put a selectable facility into the BIOS (Built In Operating System) of the computer to lock off the parallel port in either direction. Others haven't – and it is a sad fact that not many PC Managers yet recognise this as a security threat.

8.7 Nightmare on Linefeed St.

Carriage returns and line-feeds are the most important characters in the computer alphabet because without them you wouldn't be able to read or write more than one line of text. These two control characters instruct the text formatting parts of the computer or printer to carry out premeditated acts of violence upon the helpless text.

A carriage return (CR – ASCII 13) instructs the cursor, or print head, or laser beam to return to the start of the line. A line-feed (LF – ASCII 10) moves the virtual paper up a line in your computer, (or in reality moves the cursor to the next line down), and form feed characters (ASCII 12) move the paper up a page, or tell the computer to insert page breaks .

The CR and LF characters are needed to start a new line of text. They do not (generally) appear on the screen in word processors or editors, unless the program in question has a facility to show them. On paper the effects are all but invisible, but when you save electronic text to a file all sorts of strange happen with the CR/LF pair, depending mainly on what sort of computer you are using. The Mac, and the Amiga generally get things right as far as the CR/LF pair is concerned – 'right' in this case meaning that text stored as an electronic file should have a carriage return/line feed only at the end of each paragraph. On the PC the convention for text files is to have a CR and a LF at the end of each line. This is possibly a throwback to the days when IBM designed typewriters for a living. (The Mk1 Selectric was every authors dream). On other machines it is often the case that when a Carriage Return is encountered the machine adds the necessary Line Feed.

If text files formatted with CR/LF's at the end of each line are imported into a Desk Top Publishing (DTP) or page layout package the carriage returns at the end of each line prevent the text from flowing to the right margin. It is not easily possible to right-justify this sort of text and these carriage returns (known also as hard returns) have to be stripped out manually for publishing purposes. PC text files are therefore not the most useful things for inter-machine file transfer, unless the end-of-line carriage returns are stripped out.

Several software developers have seen the light and now have the correct translators built into their word processing programs. The hard return/line feed problem was encountered in putting this book together as text files produced in the PC package 'Pro-Write' contained both hard returns and line feeds. They had to be stripped out by loading the text files into Ami-Pro (an advanced DTP/WP package for the PC) before loading the files into the Mac for final editing and indexing.

FIGURE 8.5

CR/LFs in the Nisus word processor in their rightful place.

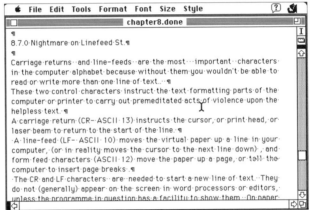

It's possible to write your own CR/LF stripper in Basic without too much bother if you don't have any other way of doing it, but many PC comms programs know about the CR/LF problem and remove the offending codes during the ASCII file transfer procedure.

Mac comms programs, and the Mac AFE utility are wise to the ways of the PC and many of them will strip or add line feeds depending on the direction of the transfer.

TAB Formatting

Tabs are another problem for ASCII transfer. The Mac does not use the ASCII code 9 (Horizontal Tab) and therefore imported tabbed documents appear as jumbled garbage. Tabs should be replaced by multiple spaces in this case. Form feeds are also mostly ignored – which in effect means that the nice four-page article you prepared for your publisher containing tabs and a form feed at the end of each page is going to appear as a complete mess when it reaches his machine. The safe rule is to use no tabs, form feeds or any other formatting in text destined for use on another machine architecture.

Other problems occur with font spacing translations between machines, and Mac users can sometimes get around the insatiable desire on PC word processors for proportionally spaced fonts by using the Monaco 9 font for typing up work before conversion. Monaco 9 is a mono-spaced font (each letter is the same width) and there is then a fair chance that the overall look of the document will be mainly preserved after conversion.

Read.Me Last

It's become popular for computer floppy disks to have text files added to them which provide last minute instructions for users. These files are ASCII text files and are often labelled READ.ME or some such. Many of them are also formatted for printing. This is achieved by using 66 lines per page as a default and putting a form feed on the end of every 66th line. Of course this is not much good if your printer has a sixty four line page length default (like the HP Deskjet) but it's a start.

These files are usually generated from the 'Print To Disk' option found in word processors. This option saves the page and line length options, but adds form feeds in the correct place. The result is an ASCII file which can be printed without the need for the host program in which it was written to be present. Page numbers and headers and footers are also preserved.

Print-to-Disk files are difficult to load into a second WP as text files, as the headers and footers mess things up and if you send a file which is formatted in this way to your publisher he or she will hate you forever.

FIGURE 8.6

The printable ASCII character set

0 ¦	16 ¦	32	48 0	64 @	80 P	96 `	112 p	128 ¦	144 ¦	160	176 °	192 À	208 Ð	224 à	240 ð
1 ¦	17 ¦	33 !	49 1	65 A	81 Q	97 a	113 q	129 ¦	145 ´	161 ¡	177 ±	193 Á	209 Ñ	225 á	241 ñ
2 ¦	18 ¦	34 "	50 2	66 B	82 R	98 b	114 r	130 ¦	146 ´	162 ¢	178 ²	194 Â	210 Ò	226 â	242 ò
3 ¦	19 ¦	35 #	51 3	67 C	83 S	99 c	115 s	131 ¦	147 ¦	163 £	179 ³	195 Ã	211 Ó	227 ã	243 ó
4 ¦	20 ¦	36 $	52 4	68 D	84 T	100 d	116 t	132 ¦	148 ¦	164 ¤	180 ´	196 Ä	212 Ô	228 ä	244 ô
5 ¦	21 ¦	37 %	53 5	69 E	85 U	101 e	117 u	133 ¦	149 ¦	165 ¥	181 µ	197 Å	213 Õ	229 å	245 õ
6 ¦	22 ¦	38 &	54 6	70 F	86 V	102 f	118 v	134 ¦	150 ¦	166 ¦	182 ¶	198 Æ	214 Ö	230 æ	246 ö
7 ¦	23 ¦	39 '	55 7	71 G	87 W	103 g	119 w	135 ¦	151 ¦	167 §	183 ·	199 Ç	215 ×	231 ç	247 ÷
8 ¦	24 ¦	40 (	56 8	72 H	88 X	104 h	120 x	136 ¦	152 ¦	168 ¨	184 ¸	200 È	216 Ø	232 è	248 ø
9 ¦	25 ¦	41)	57 9	73 I	89 Y	105 i	121 y	137 ¦	153 ¦	169 ©	185 ¹	201 É	217 Ù	233 é	249 ù
10 ¦	26 ¦	42 *	58 :	74 J	90 Z	106 j	122 z	138 ¦	154 ¦	170 ª	186 º	202 Ê	218 Ú	234 ê	250 ú
11 ¦	27 ¦	43 +	59 ;	75 K	91 [	107 k	123 {	139 ¦	155 ¦	171 «	187 »	203 Ë	219 Û	235 ë	251 û
12 ¦	28 ¦	44 ,	60 <	76 L	92 \	108 l	124 ¦	140 ¦	156 ¦	172 ¬	188 ¼	204 Ì	220 Ü	236 ì	252 ü
13 ¦	29 ¦	45 -	61 =	77 M	93]	109 m	125 }	141 ¦	157 ¦	173	189 ½	205 Í	221 Ý	237 í	253 ý
14 ¦	30 ¦	46 .	62 >	78 N	94 ^	110 n	126 ~	142 ¦	158 ¦	174 ®	190 ¾	206 Î	222 Þ	238 î	254 þ
15 ¦	31 ¦	47 /	63 ?	79 O	95 _	111 o	127 ¦	143 ¦	159 ¦	175 ¯	191 ¿	207 Ï	223 ß	239 ï	255 ÿ

9 VIRUSES, WORMS, TROJANS, HACKERS

"Sincerity and loyalty make for good neighbours"

9.1   A menagerie of beasties

I f your computer is attached to other computers via any sort of communications medium, or is open to data input via the serial ports, parallel ports or floppy disk drive it is liable to attack and infestation by computer viruses, worms, logic bombs and trojans.

A virus is a malicious self-propagating software program that attaches itself to another program or programs stored within the computer or lurks in computer memory. The purpose of most (but not all) viruses is to either disrupt the normal working of the computer for malicious reasons, or to display some sort of political, personal or offensive message. Viruses attach themselves to programs or to the boot sectors of floppy disks and are spread by passing around disks between computers.

FIGURE **9.1**

Virus descriptions in 'Disinfectant'
for the Mac

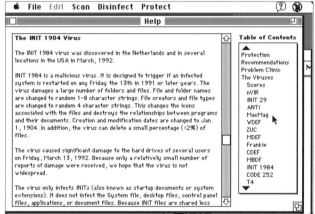

A modem link is a great way to pick up a virus-ridden file, as is passing floppy disks around your friends, and enemies.

A worm is a specific type of program that is distributed around networks of computers and consists of several segments or processes that keep in touch with each other through the network medium. When a segment is lost (perhaps through detection) the remaining segments attempt to re-establish the lost part on another workstation or take revenge by replicating two or more segments to replace the lost one.

A logic bomb is a program that takes unauthorised explicit action at some point in the operation of computer or computer program, and a trojan (horse) is a program that looks like another but does not produce the functions of the original. Using a modem is a great way to pick up infected files from bulletin boards.

Files imported through the serial port often bypass anti-virus programs which only check the floppy disk drives. If you have a modem attached to your system you really must have anti-virus software installed too. If you don't you must expect to lose data through virus attack, at some point. But then you do keep regular backups, don't you?

Early nasties

One early description of a malicious self-propagating computer program was described in Gerrold's 1972 book *When Harlie was One* in which an infected computer dialled telephone numbers at random until it found other machines into which it could spread. A 1975 novel called *Shockrider* (Brunner) described a prototype worm program. The first major 'real' virus outbreak was discovered in 1987 at Jerusalem University. A virus infected many PC files, causing them to grow longer. The virus was discovered because a bug in it caused the files to be re-infected. The virus was designed to slow down the processing speed of the PCs on certain Fridays and to erase all data on Friday the 13th.

Towards the end of 1988 a worm program arrived within the American Internet network and spread itself around the system by searching for mailing addresses in personal mailing lists. It took a massive amount of time and finances to eradicate the worm from the network. Today's viruses are much more sophisticated than they were in early days and many now employ 'stealth' techniques (named after the American bomber that is supposedly invisible to normal detection) to defeat existing protection methods.

FIGURE **9.2**

'Form' virus found on a PC disk by 'F-PROT'

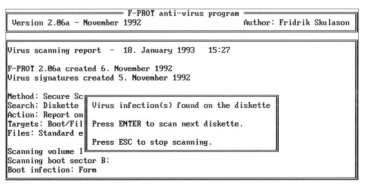

```
═══════════════ F-PROT anti-virus program ═══════════════
Version 2.06a - November 1992          Author: Fridrik Skulason

Virus scanning report  -  18. January 1993   15:27

F-PROT 2.06a created 6. November 1992
Virus signatures created 5. November 1992

Method: Secure Sc┌──────────────────────────────────────────┐
Search: Diskette  │ Virus infection(s) found on the diskette │
Action: Report on │                                          │
Targets: Boot/Fil │ Press ENTER to scan next diskette.       │
Files: Standard e │                                          │
                  │ Press ESC to stop scanning.              │
Scanning volume I └──────────────────────────────────────────┘
Scanning boot sector B:
Boot infection: Form
```

First aid

The media has latched on to viruses and worms as a matter of course but malicious computer programs are much more prevalent in the pages of the tabloid press than in real life. However, the author's research shows that 10 percent of all corporate computer users who exchange or receive data on a regular basis will come across a virus at least once a year.

Viruses are by nature machine specific, and all computer types are targeted at some stage by the writers of viruses. The sensible approach is to make sure that your machine has up-to-date virus-protection software installed in it to block memory and write-able disks from infection. There are hundreds of anti-virus programs available for all computer types and many shareware versions can be downloaded from bulletin boards. These are often as good, if not better than many commercial offerings. You must also make a firm policy of checking all imported disks and files for infection, before using them.

The general corporate viewpoint in Britain is that virus infection can be prevented by locking off the floppy drives from the users, and forbidding the ad-hoc use of modems. But removing the use of any personal computing facilities is a sad policy, especially when there are so many effective virus protection methods available.

Viruses survive and prosper because people cannot be bothered to install anti-virus software or are ignorant about prevention procedures and solutions. You no longer have ignorance as an excuse!

9.2 The gentle art of the hacker

Hacking, the intriguing art of investigating the complexities of other people's data-handling systems is now a pejorative term, although prior to the milestone legal case of The Great Prestel Hack of 1984 hacking was considered to be an intellectual game.

The Great Prestel Hack was perpetrated by Steve Gold and Robert Shifreen who 'broke into' HRH Prince Philip's unused Prestel mailbox. They were actually allowed into the system after a programming change at a Prestel computer displayed a system manager's ID number instead of the usual log-in prompt. Our anti-heroes used the ID made available to them to look around the system and eventually came across the mail-box of Prince Philip, amongst other interesting features. They subsequently exploited the weaknesses of the system to publicise the security problems of Prestel, and landed in deep mud as a result. Robert Shifreen's phone line was tapped ('intercepted' in BT parlance) and the pair were arrested in March 1985 after BT decided that it had enough evidence to prosecute them, in the form of reams of printouts generated by the tap on Shifreen's phone. Scotland Yard charged the pair with 'uttering a forgery', in lieu of finding anything better to make charges stick.

After numerous court cases, during which BT's standing as a guardian of private information was shot to pieces, the hackers were found guilty. An Appeal Court in the House of Lords decided that no crime had been committed and overturned the judgment. The costs of the case were put at £1.8 million.

The consequences were that it was declared not illegal under British law to enter a computer system without authorisation, as long as there was no theft, fraud, criminal damage, or access to official secrets. Clearly something had to be done to re-address the balance in favour of the commercial operators of computer systems.

The Computer Misuse Act

Unauthorised access to a computer is now a crime in the UK under the 1990 Computer Misuse Act, a piece of legislation seemingly brought in to make up for the deficiencies of corporate and commercial computer operators, and operators who want 'secure computer systems'. The simple fact that someone will wander in if you leave a door unlocked, goes unnoticed in the Act.

The Act attempts to define the thin line between an electronic prank and a criminal offence. There are three levels of offence: unauthorised access to computer material, unauthorised access with intent to commit or facilitate the commission of further offences, and unauthorised modification of data. The bill was introduced by MP Emma Nicholson who, in an interview said entering somebody's computer system, corrupting it or simply looking at it 'is dangerous for the well-being and security of one's fellow citizens'.

The wording of the Act, and especially terms like 'intent to destroy data' and 'unauthorised' are ambiguous. If you were caught outside a jeweller's shop with half a brick in your outstretched arm you would have difficulty disproving your intent. Simply dialling up a remote system to which you have an inadvertently published phone number and password could not possibly be construed as 'unauthorised access'. Or could it?

The net result of the Computer Misuse Act is that the authorities now have a very large stick with which to beat 'unauthorised' computer users, although there is as yet no legal definition of the term 'unauthorised'.

9.3   Summary

If you load data into your computer from any source you are open to attack from viruses. You must take measures to keep your systems secure – after all you wouldn't dream of going out and leaving your front door open, and you should apply the same philosophy to your computer data.

■ YOU MUST HAVE ANTI-VIRUS SOFTWARE INSTALLED ON YOUR COMPUTER AS A MATTER OF COURSE. DON'T WAIT FOR AN ATTACK TO HAPPEN, OR TELL YOURSELF THAT IT WON'T HAPPEN TO YOU. THERE HAVE BEEN INSTANCES OF VIRUSES FINDING THEIR WAY ONTO SHRINK-WRAPPED COMMERCIAL SOFTWARE. THERE ARE OTHER INSTANCES OF VIRUSES FINDING THEIR WAY ONTO THE SET-UP DISKS SUPPLIED WITH COMPUTER MOTHERBOARDS. ANY DISK OR FILE MUST THEREFORE BE REGARDED AS A POTENTIAL THREAT UNTIL IT'S CHECKED.

■ PUBLIC DOMAIN AND SHAREWARE SOURCES HAVE GOOD ANTI-VIRUS SOFTWARE FOR YOUR COMPUTER AVAILABLE FOR THE PRICE OF A PHONE CALL OR A FLOPPY DISK.

Modems and computer security

If you have a modem connected to your computer, then in theory your machine is open to investigation and manipulation.

■ THE AUTO-ANSWER FEATURE ON THE MODEM SHOULD BE TURNED OFF (ATS0=0 ON HAYES MODEMS) UNLESS YOU SPECIFICALLY WANT TO ALLOW OTHERS TO RUMMAGE AROUND YOUR HARD DISK OR NETWORK. MOST EXTERNAL MODEMS HAVE A LIGHT ON THE FRONT PANEL WHICH SHOWS WHEN AUTO-ANSWER IS ENABLED, BUT USERS OF PORTABLE AND CARD MODEMS CAN OFTEN ONLY GUESS WHETHER THIS FEATURE IS TURNED OFF ON THEIR MODEM. ATS0=0 SHOULD BE SENT TO THE MODEM BY YOUR COMMS PACKAGE AT START-UP. YOU CAN CHECK IF THIS IS SET BY LOOKING IN THE MODEM CONFIGURATION SECTION OF MOST COMMS PACKAGES.

■ BEWARE OF MODEMS WHICH ALLOW REMOTE SETTING OF THEIR PARAMETERS FROM THE OTHER END OF THE VIRTUAL LINK. YOU SHOULD CHANGE THE PASSWORD WHICH ALLOWS THIS FEATURE AS SOON AS YOU GET THE MODEM AS MANY OF THE DEFAULT REMOTE ACCESS PASSWORDS ARE WELL PUBLICISED.

■ EASY ACCESS TO CORPORATE SYSTEMS AND NETWORKS VIA MODEMS IS VERY COMMON, AS ARE STUPID

CORPORATE PASSWORDS. SOME SPLENDID EXAMPLES ARE ENGINEER, GUEST OR FIELD SERVICE FOR BOTH LOGIN AND PASSWORD, USED ON MANY VAX, IBM AND NOVELL SYSTEMS. TRY THESE ON YOUR SYSTEM NOW. IF IT WORKS THEN YOUR SYSTEM MANAGER IS NOT TELLING THE TRUTH WHEN HE SAYS YOU HAVE A SECURE SYSTEM. COMMON CORPORATE PASSWORDS ARE THEBOSS, SUPER, FRED, ME_AGAIN, EXTERNAL, FIXIT, QWERTY, 123, 007, PASSWORD, SECRET AND THE NAMES OF AMERICAN STATES FOR SOME REASON. OTHERS ARE CAR REGISTRATION NUMBERS, SPOUSES' NAMES AND BIRTHDATES, FOOTBALL TEAMS AND NAMES OF PETS. ALL ARE EASY TO BREAK SIMPLY BY MAKING AN EDUCATED GUESS.

FIGURE 9.3

An open Novell network with no passwords set. There are thousands of open sites like this.

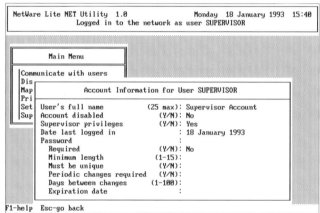

■ PASSWORDS MUST BE A MINIMUM OF SIX CHARACTERS LONG AND CONTAIN AT LEAST ONE NUMERICAL OR PUNCTUATION CHARACTER TO BE EFFECTIVE. THIS SUBTERFUGE PREVENTS HARRY HACKER FROM SQUIRTING THE CONTENTS OF AN ASCII DICTIONARY FILE AT YOUR SYSTEM TO GAIN ENTRY. PASSWORD ATTEMPTS SHOULD BE LIMITED TO THREE TRIES BEFORE THE USER IS LOCKED OUT. MACHINE GENERATED PASSWORDS SUCH AS PAWMRKX OR TREBSFGH ARE OFTEN USELESS – IF THEY CANNOT BE REMEMBERED EASILY THEY WILL ALWAYS BE WRITTEN DOWN, OFTEN IN A CONSPICUOUS PLACE. IT'S MUCH BETTER TO USE AN EASILY REMEMBERED PASSWORD AND THEN SUBSTITUTE PUNCTUATION MARKS, AS IN 'M*DEMUS&R'.

■ YOU SHOULD BE AWARE THAT IT IS MUCH MORE COMMON FOR PEOPLE TO STEAL AN IDENTITY THAN IT IS FOR THEM TO TRY TO 'BREAK' A PASSWORD SYSTEM. STAFF AT EXHIBITIONS AND DEMONSTRATIONS OFTEN GIVE AWAY PASSWORDS BY TYPING THEM OUT IN FRONT OF THE PUBLIC AT LARGE, OR BY WRITING THEM ON POST-IT NOTES WHICH ARE THEN STUCK TO THE SIDES OF TERMINALS. IF YOU DO LEAVE THE DOOR OPEN IN THIS WAY THEN SOMEONE WILL WALK IN. YOU MAY THEN HAVE TROUBLE BRINGING A PROSECUTION UNDER THE COMPUTER MISUSE ACT.

■ ONE EASY WAY OF GAINING FULL ACCESS TO A COMPUTER NETWORK THROUGH A MODEM LINK IS TO UPLOAD A NEW FILE TO THE HOST SYSTEM. THIS FILE CONTAINS THE EXISTING USER-DATABASE, PLUS A FEW NEW PHANTOM USERS. IT OVERWRITES THE ORIGINAL FILE AND OPENS UP THE SYSTEM TO THE HACKER WHO

OWNS ALL OF THE NEW ACCOUNT DETAILS. SYSTEMS SUCH AS NOVELL NETWARE KNOW ALL ABOUT THIS APPROACH AND TAKE APPROPRIATE MEASURES, BUT SOME OF THE MORE STODGY MAINFRAME OPERATING SYSTEMS KEEP ALL OF THE ACCOUNT DATA IN ONE SINGLE FILE, OR SPREAD THE DATA AROUND THE USERS WORKSTATIONS IN THE FORM OF ADDRESS BOOKS. THESE FILES OR THE DIRECTORIES IN WHICH THEY LIVE SHOULD BE MADE READ ONLY AT THE SERVER TO PREVENT UNAUTHORISED OVER-RIDES BEING SENT IN VIA MODEM. A SIMILAR SITUATION EXISTS ON MANY RECREATIONAL BULLETIN BOARDS WHERE IT'S POSSIBLE TO UPLOAD A NEW AUTOEXEC OR OTHER BATCH FILE TO OVER-WRITE AN UNPROTECTED FILE OR DIRECTORY AND THUS GAIN ACCESS.

Remember that sloppy housekeeping will almost certainly leave a door open on your system, somewhere. Every corporate IT manager should read *The Cuckoo's Egg* by Clifford Stoll, and *The Hacker's Handbook*, edited by Steve Gold, for eye-opening accounts of just how easy it is to get into many corporate and academic installations. One of them might even be yours.

10 TRANSPORT MECHANISMS

"He treads on the tail of a tiger which does not bite him"

10.1 What is a transport mechanism?

Transport mechanism is the name given to the combination of protocols and standards used to move data around on a network. A network, for the purposes of this book, is a number of interconnected computers or clusters of computers.

A Wide Area Network (WAN) is a series of linked computers in different geographical locations. When you use your modem to connect your computer to a remote system you become a part of the larger network. You have become a 'node', in the jargon. Large computer networks have many thousands or tens of thousands of nodes. A node can be a large mainframe in a university, a smaller mini-computer in an office, or a personal micro-computer in the back bedroom of a suburban house.

It is usually not easy to tell from looking at your screen how large (or small) the computer at the other end of the link is. The distinction between large and small computers has become blurred over the last five years. If you have a modern Apple Macintosh or a 486 PC you may be surprised to learn that your computer is capable of running many more program instructions per second than some of the mainframes still used in major corporations, although it's unlikely that you will have quite so much data storage space available to you.

For the purposes of accessing the dial-up networks of the world, all computers are created more or less equal. Computers are bound together (and sometimes limited) by the transport mechanisms they use to talk to each other.

The largest common transport system we have in the world today is the voice telephone network, called the Public Switched Telephone Network (PSTN). You can use the PSTN to put a voice call through to anywhere else in the world that is equipped with a working telephone receiver. Naturally if you plug your computer into the phone jack you can use the phone network to talk to a computer located anywhere else, as long as the receiving equipment at the other end matches your own. The size or type of the computer at the other end of the link doesn't matter.

But what if the receiving equipment doesn't match your own? What if you want to send a message via your 300bps modem and your personal computer to a machine on the other side of the world? You probably would not know whether that machine has a modem with error correction available, or whether it uses the same data format as yours.

The answer to this conundrum lies in transport mechanisms. If you use a standard-

ised form of transport mechanism you can talk to wherever you wish, with a few pro-
visos. There are dozens of different transport mechanisms available to computer users.
Almost all of them are provided by PTTs or by large international commercial companies who rent out their equipment to users.

Many of the commercial companies also 'add value' – other services and products, to
the transport mechanisms they provide and become Value Added Networks (VANs).
A typical value added product is electronic fax capability for people who don't have a
fax machine. You send your fax as electronic text via your modem. Equipment at the
service provider's end re-formats it as a fax and transmits it to the fax machine of your
choice. We are going to have a look at some of the more common transport mechanisms, i.e. those used by people with personal computers and modems.

10.2 Mercury

Mercury is a PTO – Public Telephone Operator in the jargon. In Europe PTOs are
called PTTs – for Post, Telegraph and Telephone operators. PTT is the term generally used in this book. Mercury provides a great number of services, including packet
switched and other services. You can get a full list of theses by calling Mercury's sales
office, the number is in Appendix 5.

One of Mercury's more widely used services is that of cheaper long distance calls.
Mercury itself reckons that trunk class calls made over these lines are around 20 percent cheaper than those from BT, but it is hard to justify these figures without seeing
itemised bills from both parties for identical calls.

To access Mercury you need a Personal Identity Number (PIN) available for around
£9.00 per annum. This PIN can be inserted into your dial-up software by putting it
into your dial command prefix line. You will need to prefix the PIN itself with 131,
the number that connects BT's lines to those of Mercury. A second option is to have
Mercury fit a 'smart socket' in your home, which automatically routes long distance
calls via the Mercury service. Smart sockets cost around £100 and can now be bought
in blister packs from office supply companies to plug into your existing phone socket.

If you want to find out whether you have a Mercury service available in your area –
dial 131. If you hear a dial tone you can use Mercury once you have a PIN. If you
want to use Mercury for voice calls too, you can often program your PIN into the
memory of many modern memory phones. That way you don't have to buy a phone
with a blue Mercury button to access the service.

10.3 Packet Switching Networks

Packet switching (PS) is not what happens at the Post Office at Christmas, but is a method of sending error-free data across a data network.

One of first PS systems was the ARPANET, developed in 1969 for the US Defence Advanced Research Projects Agency (DARPA). The system used mini-computers as packet switches and communicated over dedicated 50kbps lines. Since then a great many other PS networks have sprung into being, and almost every country in the world now has PS access. (The term 'PS system' is used here to avoid confusion with PSS – which is British Telecom's name for Packet Switch Stream, another PS service).

PS systems primarily came about in order to bypass the 'physical circuit link' overhead that exists when networks are use. If, for instance, you make an analogue voice call to Australia from England, a real-time, virtual 'physical circuit' is created for you via the switches, satellite links and cables that eventually end up in the destination country. This is fine for short voice calls, you only pay for the amount of time that the link exists, not the amount of data passing through it. Setting up such a link for computer data is wasteful, more time would be used (and charged for) in maintaining the virtual circuit than would be used for actual data transfer.

PS works in a different way. You send your data to a Packet Switching Exchange (PSE) with your dial-up modem or a direct link. On arrival the data is chopped up into smaller pieces of 128 bytes and control information is added to the packet to denote its destination address, amongst other things. Your packet is then multiplexed, along with lots of packets belonging to other people, and routed to its destination address. When it arrives the control information is read and stripped and the packet is reassembled in the correct order with all the other packets you have sent. It is then fed to the destination computer along either an analogue PSTN line or via a dedicated packet switching terminal unit.

The boxes at the Packet Switching Exchange which do all of the chopping and reassembling at both ends are called PADs – Packet Assembler/Disassembler.

The benefits of Packet Switching

The benefits of PS are that you pay only for the amount of data traffic you generate, not the amount of time you spend using the service. The disadvantage is that the system does not always maintain its full speed for the duration of the link, although PS system usage is normally transparent to the user and appears as a 'real-time' connection.

You may have spotted that there has to be some sort of equipment at the receiving end of the link waiting to correspond with you – it's not (usually) possible to place a PS call directly from point to point as you would do with a dial-up PSTN link. The receiving computer has to be on-line and attached to a PAD before it can answer you. In practice this means that PS is mainly used by commercial companies who need to feed large amounts of information to users.

Most VANs allow PS access to their mainframes and database systems, as do many private and public UK Companies. To get over the point-to-point dial-up problem many PS providers now provide a value-added auto-answer service that can provide PS calls to unattended remote equipment connected to the PSTN. PS service is great for accessing large computers located anywhere in the world as it provides error-free and almost real-time connections. If you access a PS node it's difficult to tell that you are not directly wired to the host computer at the other end of the link.

You can talk to a PAD at the packet switching exchange using your own computer and modem. PADs are intelligent animals and recognise an asynch modem when they hear one.

The CCITT recommendation in use over the PS network is X.25 and such networks are often referred to as X.25 Packet Switching, for that reason. X.25 services were often called Public Data Networks (PDNs) when they were first introduced and PDNs are to be found in almost every country of the world.

One major advantage of PS networks is that charging is for the amount of data transferred, not the connect time, which makes these systems much more cost effective to use than point-to-point links. PS links are now acting as gateways to other services, the CompuServe UK PS access is a good example.

Talking to PS systems

Communicating with PS systems was a frustrating business up until quite recently. The communications between packet switching exchanges has always been error-corrected and so data coming from a computer connected to PS via a PAD was always error free up to the PSE. When the data left the PSE and hit the analogue voice lines it was often corrupted, making a mockery of the entire process. Nowadays, lines from the packet switching exchange are error-corrected to V42 standards so that the link is error-free from end to end.

As PS is a commercial service it does not kowtow to its users, and you would normally have to come to grips with acronyms a such as NUA, DNIC and NUI. Luckily many PS service providers have recognised this approach as being unfriendly and almost all of them now provide a 'value-added' friendly front-end to hide this odd world of acronyms. If you do feel a burning need to learn about NUIs and NUAs then BT provides an admirable publication free of charge. It's called *First Steps in Packet Switching* and is available from the Dialplus sales office (Number in Appendix 7).

Packet switching systems are a universe of their own, and could easily take up the entire contents of a couple of books the size of this one. As in most things, using PS becomes easy with practice, and you can use the same computer, modem and software that you use to talk to recreational services. BT, Mercury and AT&T all market PS services.

Frame relay

The future holds changes for PS services too – a much faster packet switching mechanism called frame relay is already here and will be expanding rapidly in the next couple of years. BT already markets frame relay services under the banner ExpressLane and will be adding high speed access up to 2Mbps.

Value Added Services on PS networks

Most of the information providers now have PS nodes available for dial-up users. If you regularly access services such as Dunn & Bradstreet, Telecom Gold, Infocheck etc., you should be using a PS account in order to save money on connect charges. Connecting to these services is now as easy as connecting to a recreational BBS. You don't need to know anything about NUAs or NUIs if you use a friendly front-end such as Dialplus.

You will of course need a subscription to the particular service you wish to access and you may find that the PS service provider can arrange this as part of the bundle. If you're an information provider, that is you have data or information that you wish to re-sell to the community at large, you will find that connection to a PS system will make for easy global access to your data.

File transfer via PS

Files can be transferred over PS systems in the normal way by initiating the transmit routine at the host, and the receive routine at the remote. File transfer via PS is not likely to be particularly fast, but as the link is error controlled you can use a streaming protocol such as ZMODEM to collect data. If you don't have any error checking across the PSTN link as would be the case if you used an older V22 bis modem you should use an error-checking protocol such as Kermit or XMODEM to effect the transfer. It's likely that the world will eventually move away from X.25 towards ISDN but the process will not happen overnight. It's already taken ISDN 22 years to achieve a reasonable level of market penetration, it could easily take X.25 the same amount of time to disappear completely. Because PS is such a useful way of accessing remote data services there's a list of all of the local UK PS nodes in Appendix 7.

10.4 X.400 Messaging

Electronic mail and office automation are the current buzzwords in the corporate IT sector. Not every company IT director is sure what the full implications of these words mean, but he (or she) will be sure that the company must work towards these goals, at some point.

If you install a proprietary E-mail system you will be able to transmit mail across your office LAN (Local Area Network), or even across the PSTN or a leased line to a branch office. Until recently what you couldn't do with your commercial E-mail system was to send mail to anywhere else which didn't have access to the same proprietary system that generated the data. The CCITT came to the rescue with a whole series of Message Handling System (MHS) recommendations called X.400.

X.400 permits the interchange of E-mail between systems which conform to it. X.400 is also linked to a global directory structure called X.500 and the two together should make it possible for a compliant system to be able to talk to any other compliant system. The Value Added Network providers have been quick to seize on X.400 messaging and they can already hook your X.400 compliant E-mail system into their global data networks with little fuss. X.400 MHS is now being incorporated into so-called office automation products. Office automation (OA) is a buzzword that really means very little but any system worthy of the title should have X.400 capabilities available to most of its internal functions.

Through an X.400/X.500 compliant OA system it is possible to send messages attached to binary 'documents' such as spreadsheets, graphical data and reports. Other enhancements include X.400 voice mail and messaging. At the time of writing there are some hundreds of office automation solutions around for the corporates to spend money on but only systems which have demonstrable working hooks into X.400/X.500 MHS should be considered for the title of office automation. Failure to recognise this could mean that non-compliant systems are locked out of the world's growing telecomms and E-mail revolution.

10.5 Internet

The Internet is a collection of interconnected computer networks which spans the world through 56 or 64Kbps links. Virtually all the world's academic institutions are connected to the Internet, as are many American government offices. Internet offers the possibility of real-time on-line text and binary file transfer between nodes, and a global addressing mechanism allows hundreds of thousands of different nodes to interact.

Access to the Internet has not been too easy for non-academics in the UK, but an enterprising UK company called Demon Internet Services has started to make Internet working possible for anyone with a personal computer and a modem. The Internet is not a recreational service, nor is it only for academic use. It is mainly used by people doing work of some kind, such as researching a book, communicating with distant co-workers or managing an academic project. At the time of writing there are more than 750,000 computers connected to the Internet, and more are being added every day. If you need research data of any kind you can find it on the Internet, the only problem is knowing where to look. The system is already so large that producing an accurate catalogue of Internet services and connections will be nearly impossible.

Internet transport mechanisms

The primary method of transferring files over the Internet is called FTP – File Transfer Protocol. It is not to be confused with the file transfer protocols used in asynchronous communication packages, although it fulfils the same function. FTP can ferry data around the Internet at around 10Kbps if both ends of the link support it.

Anonymous FTP allows file transfer to take place from hosts to any connected inquirer without the need for rigorous management of user accounts. Archie (archive) sites hold data-files and details of anonymous FTP sites, description databases and information documents located on the Internet, together with lists of frequently asked questions (FAQs).

Telnet

Telnet is a protocol which allows connection to a remote machine or terminal on the Internet. It allows work to be carried out on remote sites by a distant user. It is possible to Telnet to a computer and use applications stored on the remote machine, or access files and data stored there. As there are no real standards associated with Internet, access routines and methods vary between nodes and getting into a site can be a hit and miss affair. The system is tremendously useful in spite of this limitation because of the huge amount of data stored within it. There is a full discussion of Internet in chapter 16.

10.6 PS access examples

PS services are now much easier to use than they were and, if you are a subscriber, you will in all probability find that the destinations to which you need to establish calls, are all ready set up for you in menu form by the service provider. You can also place 'reverse charge' calls via PS services if you have an account with a service provider at the other end of the link. This is a useful feature as you only pay one bill, (plus your phone bill) at the end of the day, and you may get your PS access at local call rates.

You try out a packet switched service for free by dialling British Telecom's GNS Dialplus service. Dialplus offers a front-end to packet switch services and through it you can connect to information services anywhere in the world that use packet switching.

For this example we are going to have a rummage through Hostess, a GNS Dialplus information service connected to the outside world via packet switching.

■ SET YOUR TERMINAL EQUIPMENT TO 7 DATA BITS, EVEN PARITY AND 1 STOP BIT, AND V22 BIS (2400/2400BPS) TTY OR VT100 TERMINAL EMULATION CAN BE USED.

■ DIAL ONE OF THE DIALPLUS LOCAL ACCESS NUMBERS LISTED IN APPENDIX 6 YOU MAY NEED TO SEND A COUPLE OF CARRIAGE RETURNS WHEN CONNECTED TO WAKE THE SERVICE UP.

■ ENTER **GUIDE** WHEN ASKED FOR YOUR PASSWORD. GNS DIALPLUS WILL CONNECT YOU TO HOSTESS FREE OF CHARGE. (YOU PAY FOR PHONE CONNECT CHARGES ONLY.)

■ HOSTESS PROVIDES INFORMATION ABOUT GNS DIALPLUS SERVICES IN THE FORM OF DOCUMENTS DISPLAYED ON-SCREEN AND IT WOULD BE USEFUL TO TURN ON YOUR SCREEN CAPTURE (DISK LOGGING) OR PRINTER BEFORE YOU ENTER THE SERVICE.

■ TO ESCAPE THE CLUTCHES OF HOSTESS TYPE **BYE** AT ANY POINT.

■ YOU MAY ALSO FREELY ACCESS ELECTRONIC YELLOW PAGES VIA DIALPLUS BY TYPING **YELLOW** AT THE PASSWORD PROMPT.

■ TO GET THROUGH TO COMPUSERVE VIA PACKET SWITCHING TYPE **UKCNS** AT THE PASSWORD PROMPT, AND **CIS** WHEN ASKED FOR THE HOST NAME. FROM THAT POINT YOU WILL BE CONNECTED TO COMPUSERVE'S SYSTEM.

CONNECTING TO PACKET SWITCH STREAM

FIGURE 10.1

Set up your communications...

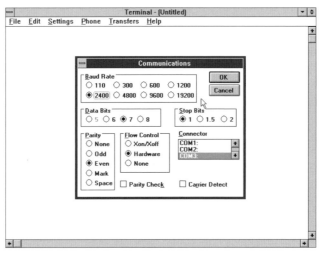

FIGURE **10.2**

...and terminal parameters...

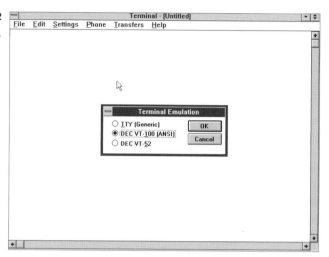

FIGURE **10.3**

...and dial. You should get the Dialplus Welcome screen.

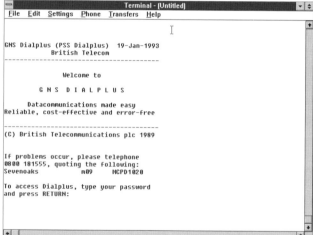

11

INTEGRATED SERVICES DIGITAL NETWORK – ISDN

"Do not despair at the prospects of change"

11.1 ISDN

Ask yourself a question. What is wrong with the telephone system we have today? If you are realistic you will say that the system works tolerably well – considering its size, there are not too many wrong numbers these days, and there are few times now when calls are interrupted by clicks and noises from other users.

This isn't an accident – the UK telephone system has been virtually fully replaced in the last 20 years, resulting in all the benefits mentioned above. Virtually all Britain's telephone trunk cables carry digital signals down fibre-optic cables (perhaps they should be called 'pipes') to and from digital switching equipment. It is this mammoth re-wire that has brought the advantages and the UK telephone system can now carry both voice telephony and data. But punters at the 'local' end of the line are still largely using analogue equipment, the basics of which were designed in 1876. It is high time for us to catch up with 20th century technology, in the form of Integrated Services Digital Networks (ISDN).

ISDN basics

To introduce ISDN we must go back to 1937 when an engineer called Alex Reeves conceived Pulse Code Modulation (PCM). This was a technique applied to analogue telephone lines to rid them of the distortion and electrical noise common in all analogue transmission systems.

PCM (in telephony) works by sampling an analogue signal at 8,000 times a second and encoding the result into one of 256 levels. The signal can then be represented by an 8-bit 'bandwidth' and analogue speech is converted to a 64Kbps digital signal in this way. The benefits of digital PCM networks were soon realised, and most of the trunk cables and switches in the UK and North America were converted to digital operation in the 1980s. Many of the trunks were replaced with fibre optics during the process, and Britain now has over ten million miles of fibre optic cable installed.

The main trunks have long been able to carry voice or data at 64Kbps but the 'local loop' – the pair of wires that comes from the switch to your house, has remained as two copper wires. This has some advantages – copper can carry digital or analogue signals, and can also carry current which may be used to power telephony equipment. It's why your telephone continues to function when there is a local power cut. In the UK after the great storm of 1987 many telephones continued to function for up to ten days in areas where lines were left intact – the power came from stand-by batteries in the switch-rooms.

In reality ISDN represents the conversion of the analogue local loop to digital, as all BT digital switches have the inherent capacity to carry ISDN. The UK conversion of local loops to ISDN was started by British Telecom in June 1985, after the 1984 CCITT 'Red Book' recommendations were adopted. In 1988 the CCITT introduced their 'Blue Book' recommendations and these led to the implementation of internationally accepted standards for ISDN.

ISDN will become the standard exchange line of the future for both domestic and business users. It won't be a case of consumer choice – all new lines will be digital when the conversion process at the switches is complete. This is likely to be towards the end of this century in the UK, the process is already happening in parts of the USA and on the Continent.

ISDN and you

An ISDN 'line' actually comprises three parts: two digital 64Kbps B channels (B for Bearer), which can be combined to provide 128Kbps throughput, and a separate 16Kbps channel called the delta channel. The delta channel is currently used for synchronisation and call set-up signals although there is a suggestion that it may also become available to X.25 users. The existing telephone pair of wires is used, and the three channels are multiplexed down it to the switch. Voice is encoded onto the B channel using a standardised form of pulse code modulation (PCM).

The delta channel (D channel) is sometimes referred to as a 'bit pipe' by our American cousins, as data can be squirted down it and retrieved with little needed in the way of protocol conversion. It's likely that laboratory, banking and remote sensing equipment will eventually use the D channel as easily as we use the voice telephone today. The security and intruder alarm manufacturers are already casting an interested eye over the capabilities of ISDN.

If you are a corporate user then you may be interested to know that ISDN usage can usually be justified on a one year payback basis if your company has a total fax/modem usage of just two hours a day. But if you are the Man on the Clapham Omnibus then ISDN is probably still too expensive for domestic use. Compare the cost of current ISDN phones with the costs of compact disc (CD) players when they were first introduced. CD players cost £500-plus at launch, which equates to the current cost of ISDN phones. Now CD players are available in the sub-£100 price range, which is where ISDN equipment will eventually end up.

The key to the current acceptance of ISDN for domestic use lies in its pricing structure. At the moment an ISDN2 line costs three times as much to install as an ordinary analogue line, but you get two virtual telephone connections for the price. And you need either an ISDN telephone, or a terminal adapter with analogue capabilities so you can use your existing equipment over an ISDN line.

At the time of writing there are a considerable number of ISDN adapters under development or in BABT labs, and a good number have made it through the approval process and are now available from dealers.

11.2 Using ISDN

It is important to emphasise here that whilst ISDN technology is still evolving (as is technology for the standard telephone service) ISDN is here now and is usable straight 'out of the box'. If you believe that you have an application for using point-to-point modems in a business environment, then you should check out ISDN before you spend any money on modems. You will probably find that ISDN is a quicker, cleaner and easier to use alternative. It may also be cheaper.

What you need for ISDN

First of all, let's dispel any myths that ISDN needs expensive hardware at both ends of the link before it can be used. ISDN lines equipped with an analogue port will accept normal telephonic equipment such as telephones, answering machines and Group III faxes. Terminal adapters, (the boxes which plug into an ISDN line) equipped with analogue ports give backwards compatibility with existing equipment.

If you want to use ISDN just for data transfer then you don't have to junk your existing modems or fax machines. You won't get the full benefits of ISDN by using your old equipment but then you don't have to fork out immediately for new ones as soon as ISDN hits your office or spare bedroom. If your major requirement is for personal data-communications then all you need is a suitably equipped ISDN terminal adapter for your computer and an ISDN line.

ISDN hardware

ISDN is terminated at the customer's premises with an NTE (network terminal equipment) box. This is a white box about 20 centimetres tall by ten centimetres wide, and it has what appears to be two ordinary phone sockets on the front. Each socket contains connections for each of the two ISDN channels. You simply plug your ISDN terminal adapter into the socket, as you would a telephone. That's all there is to it.

Each NTE can communicate with up to eight different devices attached to it, and each of these devices can communicate simultaneously with any other two. This makes the use of an ISDN NTE for a mini local area network possible, although this area hasn't yet been fully explored by manufacturers.

There are currently two levels of ISDN: ISDN2 gives two 64Kbps channels per NTE for the smaller business or domestic user; and ISDN 30 offers 30 or more 64Kbps channels per NTE connection. At the computer end you will need to install an ISDN adapter, either as an internal card for your computer or as a stand-alone box. The stand-alone types plug into the RS232 port and run data at around 38,400cps, the internal types can reach the maximum full throughput of 64Kbps or 128Kbps using both D channels at the same time.

Software is needed to talk to your ISDN terminal adapter if you are going to transfer data files in the traditional sense. This will normally come with the device, and is currently available for PC and Mac computers. Stand-alone ISDN adapters currently cost less then £400 – about the same price as a decent V32 bis modem.

ISDN numbering

ISDN numbering is the same as for analogue PSTN lines. There is a number allocated for each pair of ISDN2 channels connected to your NTE. You can have a separate number for each channel as an option. This is useful if you are a small business and want a separate fax and phone number – you only pay for the one ISDN line. This dual channel facility suddenly makes ISDN appear much cheaper.

The one number per channel may also be needed in some cases if you want to use both D channels simultaneously for data transfer. User features ISDN is able to detect automatically a data call and put it through to the correct piece of equipment. Calls connect almost instantaneously as there is no need for end-to-end negotiation to determine a common speed, as there is with modems, and ISDN equipment can discern between voice and datacalls, so only one terminal adapter will be needed. The prospect of a combined voice phone, data 'modem' and fax machine in one box is interesting, especially to equipment manufacturers who are already gearing up for the fray.

11.3 ISDN features

- **CALLING LINE**
  A subscription feature (you don't get it for free) where the callers number is displayed on the phone or terminal adapter of the recipient. CLI is the subject of much current debate about the possibility of its misuse when used to identify personal data associated with a telephone number.

- **TERMINAL PORTABILITY**
  Allows a call to be interrupted and then resumed. This is useful for 'timing out' data calls if no data is being transmitted. ISDN resumes the virtual connection as data flow re-commences.

- **NUMBERING OPTIONS**
- One exchange number with hunting across the channels. This is the default option.
- One exchange number for several ISDN lines. Up to 30 lines (60 channels) can be connected to one number.
- One number per ISDN channel. May be needed if you wish to use both channels together for a 128Kbps link.

11.4 Other ISDN advantages

ISDN also has many advantages over the existing packet switched networks, not the least being the ability of ISDN to maintain the full 64Kbps throughput for the duration of the call. This is vital for real-time data links and cannot currently always be met by existing packet switching arrangements. The bandwidth of the service is also large enough for the real-time video phone to become a reality and there are models already on the market.

There is still more development on the horizon for ISDN. 64kbps is regarded as being too slow for purposes such as high-definition television, computer aided design and suchlike and Broadband ISDN (ISDN-B) is currently evolving. It's very likely that ISDN-B service will be fully compatible with ISDN2 and ISDN30 services – and would-be purchasers should not be put of from making decisions to install ISDN just because 'yet another standard' is just around the corner.

ISDN and Wide Area Networking

ISDN integrates easily with digital computer equipment. There is no need to convert binary data into noise and then back again to send it thorough the phone network as there is with analogue systems, and you don't need a modem to couple to an ISDN NTE. You do need an ISDN terminal adapter which couples your computers digital signals to the ISDN bearer (B) channel. These adapters are coming down in price all the time and an ISDN data adapter now costs less than a decent V32 bis modem.

For the corporate user ISDN is now the best way to couple an internal local area network (LAN) to the outside world, either to provide LAN services to users working from remote sites, or to couple a LAN to other networks (bridging). This LAN bridging facility is especially useful if levels of data traffic do not warrant a continuous 64kbps link as ISDN can be made to interrupt calls when data traffic stops, and resume when traffic starts. You are then only charged for the actual call duration.

The low costs of the service make ISDN useful for backing up Kilostream and other networks, or even replacing them altogether.

The Homeworker

ISDN is ideal for corporate teleworkers. You need an ISDN line installed into your home and an ISDN line installed onto a gateway PC on your employer's network. Both the gateway machine and the remote PC have a terminal adapter installed in them. Software in the remote PC automatically communicates with the local gateway PC which in turn connects you to the LAN.

ISDN can be told to 'time out' when no data traffic is sensed and the time-out facility is used in this example to 'disconnect' the remote user from the LAN gateway after ten seconds of no data flow. If the remote user then re-accesses the LAN the connection is made almost instantaneously and the user does not notice the disconnection. This process actually reduces call costs to below those for a comparable link using modems – with a modem link the re-dialling and connection process is so tedious that disconnecting for a brief period is never contemplated.

Remember that the actual connection process is entirely transparent to the user — there are no telephone numbers to remember, no special software to run each time you want to make a connection (other than the network and ISDN start-up sequence) and no need to get involved with terminal emulation software or hard-handshaking once the system is set up. As far as users are concerned using the ISDN link is almost as fast as being directly connected to the LAN, and there is the added advantage that voice can be carried over the same link.

ISDN needs no complex routine to send and receive data-files, the process is carried out by clicking on an icon or using the DOS Copy command and the file is received within seconds by the recipient. Other possibilities include the real-time transmission of files from one live system to another, along with person-to-person voice links. This is ideal for help desk operations, computer applications training, E-mail systems, Executive Information Systems (EIS) and much more.

ISDN and personal data

ISDN equipment is able to display the number of the caller on the receiver of the recipient. The feature is called Calling Line Identifier and is touted as being the greatest deterrent to nuisance callers yet devised.

While having this facility may seem no great shakes (many digital exchanges already offer it), the possibilities of infringement of personal data security will be greatly increased by the mass introduction of ISDN. Information from ISDN appears as a digital data stream and this information can be directly hooked into a computer to trigger instantaneously a database listing of personal information. This could be a print-out of your credit references, the council tax rating and therefore probable value of your home (from the postcode), your marital and income status, and whether or not you have a criminal record or an unblemished driving licence.

While this can be done already with slower means, such as dial-up modems or X.25 links, ISDN will open the way for credit reference databases to be instantly accessed by anyone who can afford the equipment.

The standard response to this from people marketing personal information is that, if you have nothing to hide, there is no harm in collecting information about you. The danger is that ISDN will make it ever easier for personal information to be collected and collated by unlicensed and unchecked bodies and misused in a variety of ways. If you phone a company you have never heard of via ISDN they will be able to address you directly by your name and title, and decide whether or not you are credit-worthy before you have given your name. It will be possible to track down the telephone number of your workplace, and the phone numbers of your friends, simply by pushing a button to log the information when you call. The possibilities for misuse of personal information are endless and ISDN makes life easy for those who choose to use it in this way.

At the moment there is much consternation about the publication of massive amounts of personal details in electronically readable form. It's possible to credit-check anyone in the UK who holds a bank account, credit cards, telephone number, postcode, mail order account, credit account of any sort, mortgage, household insurance policy, driving licence or anyone who fills in a register of electors or poll/council tax form. This information is freely available, often at zero cost and is pooled by information providers for resale. Once all this information is collated, cross-referenced and stored, it can be accessed automatically by merely asking ISDN to feed incoming phone numbers into the computer as a search key. It's debatable whether this is a feature which the public at large regards as desirable.

In the USA, a joint marketing venture – between USA information supplier Equifax and Lotus Development Corporation – to supply data on 120 million people, backfired when a large number of people wrote in demanding to have their personal data removed from the database. We British are a tad more phlegmatic than that (and not so well-informed) – we make very few enquiries to information holders under the Data Protection Act, for instance and many people are not aware of their rights under this piece of legislation. If you are worried about the misuse of Calling Line Identification (CLI) then rest assured that BT and the other UK PTT's have made this feature optional for ISDN users. You have to specifically order CLI before it operates from your phone. It's the ISDN equivalent of an electronic unlisted number and this move is to be wholly welcomed until firm legislation is brought in to curb the potential misuse of 'public' information.

There is probable EEC legislation in the pipeline to force PTTs to make CLI optional on all ISDN services.

Where do I find out

You can contact BT or Mercury directly for prices and details of ISDN installation. If you want to know about networking applications such as the example outlined above then any of the ISDN equipment suppliers listed in Appendix 5 will be able to point you in the right direction.

And remember that ISDN isn't future technology, it's here now, as are the applications and solutions – there are currently more than 100,000 ISDN channels in use in the UK.

ISDN INFORMATION

BRITISH TELECOM:

- DIAL 152 AND ASK FOR AN ISDN INFORMATION PACK.
  BT IS CURRENTLY QUOTING TEN DAY LEAD TIMES FOR INSTALLATION OF ISDN TO YOUR PREMISES.
  BT ISDN HELPDESK: 0800 181514

- USEFUL PUBLICATIONS FOR THE ASKING FROM THE ABOVE NUMBER:
  ISDN: MANY APPLICATIONS, A SINGLE TOOL
  ISDN: YOUR TECHNICAL QUESTIONS ANSWERED

- DEFINITIVE TECHNICAL READING ON ISDN:
  ISDN EXPLAINED BY JOHN M GRIFFITHS
  ISBN 0-471-93480-1

MERCURY ISDN SERVICES

- 0500 500 194.

12 THE BULLETIN BOARD SYSTEM

"The wise man withdraws into himself and conceals his true quality"

12.1 BBSs

A bulletin board system (BBS) is an interrelated system of software and hardware which coexists to provide electronic mail (E-mail) and file handling services to its users. A BBS may be nothing more than a small personal computer which runs a simple electronic mail package, or it can be large mini or mainframe computer dedicated to providing a wide range of value-added services. For our purposes a BBS is defined as a recreational dial-up service. A service run for commercial profit is defined as a Value Added Service (VAS).

BBSs have been around since the birth of the first personal computers in the late 1970s. Many of the early systems were programmed entirely in assembly language – prior to the efforts of one Mr Gates there was little around in the way of affordable high-level languages for small computers. One of the first BBSs was put together by Ward Christensen of XMODEM fame. It was written entirely in assembler, ran under CP/M (Control Program for Microcomputers) and was called the Computer Bulletin Board System (CBBS). It's still running today. BBSs were thus born in the States – the name comes from the ability of a BBS to accept messages 'posted' for all to see, as on a pin-board.

The birth of the IBM PC brought systems written in Microsoft Basic on to the market and the grand-daddy of those, called RBBS, is still available today although in a much advanced form.

The birth pangs of UK BBSs in the early 1980s were drawn out and painful. Many public authorities saw the intellectual and social freedom they brought as being subversive, for no reason other than the fact that BBSs were a new phenomenon and were not subject to any kind of legislation. Rumours about the use of BBSs by criminals, hackers, drug smugglers and child molesters circulated in the tabloid press although much the same was said during the Citizens Band radio debacle a few years later.

Media hysteria was subsequently brought to a head in the mid-1980s by the Great Prestel Hack and by a series of hysterically funny live demonstrations on BBC television in which silhouetted 'hackers' apparently raided the secrets of British Telecom's Prestel service. As far as the British Press was concerned, bulletin boards were the haunt of evil and socially maligned computer freaks.

One of the first, and ultimately most notorious British BBSs was the Peoples Bulletin Board Service (PBBS), which ran from a large house in a suburb of Guildford. PBBS was designed to be an open system in the true nature of American BBSs. The system operator (sysop) didn't force censorship of any sort on his users and there was complete freedom of discussion about any and all matters under the sun. There was no registration of users and the use of pseudonyms in place of real names and addresses was common. During the height of the media anti-hacker campaign, PBBS was closed down and its sysop grilled by Scotland Yard because of allegations about child pornography and the like. The accusations mainly stemmed from a self-sustaining media interest which was kicked off by the BBC's Cook Report programme which happened to be investigating pederasty that week. No arrests or charges were ever brought but the board ceased to function from that time.

About the same time in the USA, 'hackers' and their equipment were being seized by a paranoid FBI, mainly on the grounds that there was subversive material available on the BBSs, or that undesirable personalities had hacked their way around computers connected to the huge ARPANET network. The FBI's approach was to surround a sysop's house with armed police, and then take away all 'evidential' material, such as video recorders, TV sets, books, personal letters and, of course, computers. Much of this material was never returned although few charges were ever brought.

One such victim was Steve Jackson, a writer of computer games. An innocuous remark by a staff member (of Jackson's company) who ran a BBS brought the US secret service into Jackson's house, where they removed all the computer disks, records, personal possessions and drafts of a book he was writing at the time. Again no charges were brought but Jackson's private and business life was badly affected as a direct result of the 'bust'.

Sysops in the UK and USA consequently lived in trepidation of authoritarian bully-boy tactics for some years and many BBSs became the victim of self-imposed over-regulation by paranoid sysops.

This is one of the reasons why it is almost impossible to find a 'free' BBS in the UK these days. Many sysops now ask for details such as personal phone numbers and dates of birth before allowing access in an attempt to prove that their boards are above suspicion. Suspicion of what is never clearly stated but, if asked, they will say that these procedures are to keep out nuisance callers and hackers. The great age of the free unregulated bulletin board was stillborn, at least in Britain.

There have been a few exceptions. A BBS called Corrupt Computing (CCBBS) attained a brief spell of press notoriety in the late 1980s by publishing details of phone hacking techniques, 'interesting' Prestel and Telecom Gold IDs, and recipes for largely ineffectual home-brew explosives. A recommended sport was 'trashing'; a process which involved up-ending the dustbins outside telephone exchanges and BT offices to look for useful tid-bits, un-released telephone numbers, and technically challenging print-outs. There were fashion articles too. These described what the would-be lurker should wear after dark to avoid detection by the constabulary.

One day Corrupt Computing BBS disappeared without trace, perhaps because of a self-inflicted chemistry experiment, or possibly through the intervention of men in big boots. We shall never know the reason.

In late 1992 the Federation Against Software Theft (FAST) ran a press campaign against a number of bulletin boards who were alleged to be spreading pornography, virus programs and pirate software. Quite why FAST, an organisation funded in the main by commercial software vendors, decided to start a campaign to protect us from each other's sexual preferences wasn't made clear. Bob Hay, the President of FAST was quoted as saying "We have found pornography and recipes for making LSD". One can only wonder what this outraged moral stance has to do with protecting the commercial interests of software producers. The Thought Police are at hand, it seems.

On the Continent the Business Software Alliance (BSA) took action against a number of bulletin boards supplying copies of 'illicit commercial software' in the same period. Twenty-five BBSs in Belgium and Berlin were closed down and their owners prosecuted.

But you will have to look hard to find anything so exotic on the majority of British BBSs. Most of them are morally sound, conservative (with a small 'c') and about as exciting, from an anarchist's viewpoint, as watching paint dry.

FIGURE 12.1

The 'Golly' BBS on 0734 320812

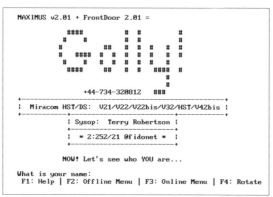

The contemporary BBS

Some of the first bulletin board systems were built around Altair and North Star hardware, many others were put together in kit form around the S100 bus and Zilog's powerful Z80 CPU chip. An early home-brew BBS often consisted of a system of lashed together electronic breadboards, connected to the outside world via an ex-PTT 300 baud modem.

Modern BBSs now run almost exclusively on small fast personal computers and are often kitted out with gigabytes of bolt-on hard disk storage. CD-ROM has also brought benefits, it's now possible to fit a CD-ROM drive to a PC and still have enough change left from £200 to buy 430 Mbytes of data to feed it with.

The best BBSs tend to be those that have definite themes, such as support for a particular type of computer or sphere of human activity. Unfortunately the phone lines of many popular BBSs are often engaged until the small hours of the morning making both access and 'brand-loyalty' difficult. Some of the more well-heeled boards now have pooled modems and multi-line access to overcome the problems associated with being highly desirable.

FIGURE 12.2

Dortec's support BBS on
0297 24469

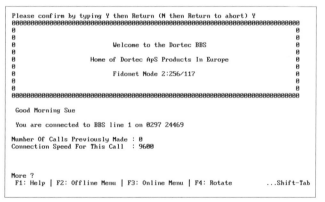

```
Please confirm by typing Y then Return (N then Return to abort) Y
000000000000000000000000000000000000000000000000000000000000000000000000
0                                                                      0
0                                                                      0
0                        Welcome to the Dortec BBS                     0
0                                                                      0
0                 Home of Dortec ApS Products In Europe                0
0                                                                      0
0                        Fidonet Node 2:256/117                        0
0                                                                      0
0                                                                      0
000000000000000000000000000000000000000000000000000000000000000000000000

  Good Morning Sue

  You are connected to BBS line 1 on 0297 24469

Number Of Calls Previously Made : 0
Connection Speed For This Call   : 9600


More ?
  F1: Help | F2: Offline Menu | F3: Online Menu | F4: Rotate      ...Shift-Tab
```

In the halcyon days of 1980 it was possible to log onto a bulletin board and stay there for as long as you could afford to, but nowadays most sysops impose a time limit of 30 to 60 minutes a day. This time limit can be increased by uploading distributable files onto the system or by leaving messages for others. It's a useful way to build up the board.

As in all things, there are good and bad sysops and the more authoritarian of these sometimes impose draconian access restrictions. Much of the original altruism of the BBS is now lost behind a barrage of requests for credit card details, personal questions and 'verification' of your phone number by persons or methods unknown.

Finding the perfect BBS

Which is the best BBS for you? If you are a recreational user then the best BBS is the one that either provides you with special information, or gives you access to other people who share your particular joys. The easiest way to find out is to ring around a few BBSs and ask questions: "Hi, I'm new here – does anyone know where I can get extra strong elastic in 400 yard lengths?". You will receive dozens of suitable replies from crazed, computer-literate bungee-jumpers.

If you have a specific computer interest then you will be spoiled for choice. Some of the better computer-hardware oriented BBSs are Apple Crackers, Mactel, 01 (and 061) for Amiga, and BEEB-TEC. There are dozens of boards now dealing specifically with the PC, although not a few of them have succumbed to Mammon and charge real money for their services. One of the more informed is the PC Independent User Group BBS, who will at least let you have a look round the system before extracting cash from you.

FIGURE 12.3

The Mactel BBS on 081 543 8017

For those of a more inquisitive bent there are boards called Hobbit's Armpit, Alternative Reality and Madness BBS. If you have an interest in matters litigious you will take special note of the splendidly named Non-BABT Approved BBS in Essex.

Connecting to a BBS

Connecting to a BBS is relatively easy. Most of the commercial information providers use 7-bit data with even parity, one stop bit (7-E-1), while recreational BBSs use the new fangled 8-bit data, no parity setting, 1 stop bit (8-N-1). Most BBSs have quad or faster modems with error correction and it's now rare to get garbled data on a dial-up connection.

One possible area for error during the connection phase is feature-negotiation. Some modems do not latch properly on to modems from another manufacturer and if you have a problem connecting to a BBS using V32 or V32 bis this may be the reason. If you get this sort of problem where your modem tells you that there is a 4800bps connection, or a 'Negotiation Failure' message appears you should check the 'Negotiation Fallback' setting on your modem. This is register S36 on Hayes modems.

If you have problems with V32 connections (not V32 bis) try setting S36 to 4 with 'ATS36=4' [enter]. This disallows the speed buffering feature which can sometimes cause erroneous connects at 4800bps on V32 hosts. If you still have problems you should disable the speed buffering and feature negotiation at your modem and reset your DTE speed to match that of the service you are calling. Mostly though, you should have few problems as modern CCITT modems are very compatible with each other, especially if they are BABT approved.

BBS user interfaces

Most BBSs are now simple to access and tend to use menu driven 'front-ends'. The front-end comprises the screens of information presented to the user while he or she is on-line. Menu driven front-ends are easy to learn and use.

Some systems use a Command Line Interface (CLI), where you have to know the correct command to make the system do something before you can use it. The well-known CIX BBS is a good example. CLI based systems are generally an anachronism, dating back to the days of large computers. They have no real place in today's personal computing environment, other than for occasional housekeeping tasks. However, some people feel that learning 40 different word commands by rote for each BBS that they use is a worthy achievement. These people will defend Command Line Interfaces to the death (against all reason) and are known as Command-Line Diehards.

FIGURE 12.4

The Hawks Castle BBS on
0344 411621

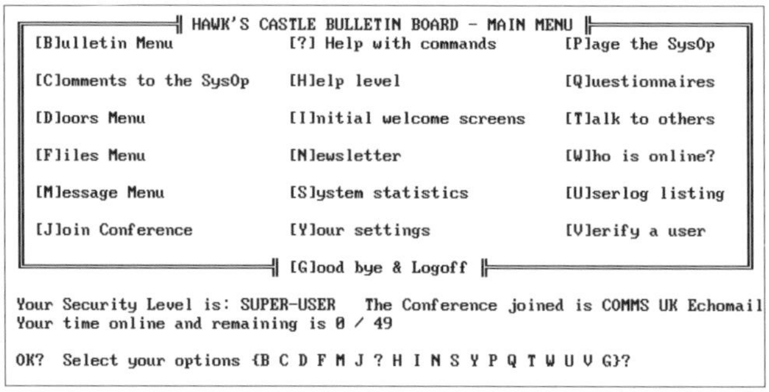

```
                      ┤ HAWK'S CASTLE BULLETIN BOARD - MAIN MENU ├
   [B]ulletin Menu           [?] Help with commands       [P]age the SysOp

   [C]omments to the SysOp    [H]elp level                 [Q]uestionnaires

   [D]oors Menu               [I]nitial welcome screens    [T]alk to others

   [F]iles Menu               [N]ewsletter                 [W]ho is online?

   [M]essage Menu             [S]ystem statistics          [U]serlog listing

   [J]oin Conference          [Y]our settings              [V]erify a user

                           ┤ [G]ood bye & Logoff ├

   Your Security Level is: SUPER-USER   The Conference joined is COMMS UK Echomail
   Your time online and remaining is 0 / 49

   OK?  Select your options {B C D F M J ? H I N S Y P Q T W U V G}?
```

Command Line Diehards (CLDs) decry the use of automatic gearboxes on cars and prefer to wash their clothes by taking them down to the river and bashing them with a rock. User-friendly presentation is unheard of among CLDs.

Alas, most CLDs are professional computer programmers.

The GUI Revolution

Many commercial systems are replacing CLIs with menus or Graphical User Interfaces (GUIs) which is to be welcomed. Some, such as CompuServe, now have their own intelligent front-end software which uses the processing power of the receiving computer to draw menus and process mouse clicks. The computer systems of the corporate and academic worlds are not yet in the era of the GUI and if you access USENET, JANET or INTERNET you will come across stuffy CLIs that will leave you gnawing at your feet, or those of a close friend, with frustration.

The only way to approach a CLI is to download the instruction manual, (if there is one), log off, and read it at your leisure. You can needlessly spend a lot of your money on connect time if you try to learn 'experientially', that is, by poking in commands and learning what the results do. People who provide CLIs on dial-up systems have found a great way of soaking up other peoples money, especially if the service they are providing charges you for on-line time in addition to your call charge.

Corporates have now discovered that CLI-based systems cost them a lot of money in terms of user training, and many of them are rapidly moving away from CLI based systems towards menu driven or GUI front-ends. Would-be commercial BBS operators take note!

On-line editors

Beware the editor, my son (daughter). On-line editors are the things you use to edit a text or mail message at the remote end of the virtual link, and if you are using one at the remote end of a telephone you are clocking up call charges.

Many BBS editors now equal the text editors you would expect to find on your personal computer but others don't, especially the editors found on systems which still use CLIs. Some older CLI editors are so bad that you should log off and edit your text off-line to save money. Commands like LINE NO: SUBST/OLDTEXT/NEW-TEXT/ are not the easiest things to remember, nor should their use be encouraged. There are good editors around and many are transferable between different BBS systems. If you don't like the editor that lives on your favourite BBS then don't be afraid to tell the sysop. You're the one that's paying to use it.

Conferencing

Conferencing is a BBS feature which allows a user to set up a corner of his or her very own and invite other users in for a chat. Conferences are divided into sub-conferences, usually called Topics. A conference called Bungee Jumping might have topics called Elastic Suppliers, First Aid and Next-of-kin. Conferences with computers or computer software as a focus will often have a 'Files' topic in them, where you can upload and download data and text files. Moderators are the people who run individual conferences on a BBS under the auspices of the sysop.

Most sysops welcome suggestions from would-be moderators, especially if they have specialist knowledge of some kind. Closed conferences often exist, you can often only gain access to these by pleading with the moderator. Some of these closed conferences discuss matters of a socially steamy nature, others merely keep the public out of trade or commercial conferences. On some older systems conferences are called Special Interest Groups, or SIGS. Closed User Groups are called CUG's. Operators are called SIGOPS or CUGOPS.

Flaming communications

The manual for one famous commercial conferencing system used to state that 'opinionated conference users' are welcomed, as these vociferous people generate ideas and mail from others. The reality is often different. Many people are seemingly not made welcome on conference systems if they voice opinions which are considered by other members to be at all revolutionary or go against majority opinion.

The reasons for this social phenomenon were studied by two eminent American sociologists, Lee Sproull and Sara Keisler. They found that people who use anonymous electronic conferencing do not acknowledge or are not aware of the social or official status of other conference members because the more usual social barriers and cues are missing. Sproull and Keisler believe that this phenomenon leads to greatly impassioned self-expression, brought about by the perceived freedom from physical, social or intellectual limitations.

A second, less-popular hypothesis is that people who like to use computer systems in this way are childish and unruly, and get pleasure from taunting others.

FIGURE 12.5

Phoenix BBS on 0249 817704

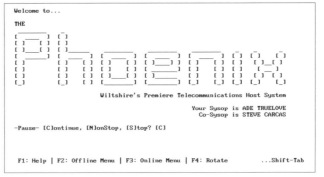

The act of attempting to obliterate or modify the opinion of another by supplying an even stronger (though not necessarily more accurate) counter-argument is called 'flaming'. It comes, perhaps, from the expression 'to shoot down in flames'. This social phenomenon is especially prevalent on conferencing systems with a large number of users, where each contributor tries to correct or add information to a topic in play. The net result is one of overall dilution, as arguing each point through takes a very long time and the original subject gets bogged down in a sea of alternative opinions and unqualified statements. It takes around four times as long to reach a democratic decision in this way, compared with direct face-to-face discussions.

As this is a practical guidebook you may care to sample this (un)social phenomenon for yourself. Log onto a system and grumble loudly about antiquated CLIs or editors, or make positive statements about the superiority of one operating system over another. A good subject to try is 'long live the mouse, the keyboard is dead.' Another is

'UNIX programmers don't understand computers'. You will almost certainly be 'flamed' by huge numbers of people who feel an urgent need to modify your thinking or logic processes or, in extreme cases, your physical appearance.

This aggressive behaviour often puts people off from using conferencing systems, but on the other hand such systems are occasionally the source of useful information. If you are of a sensitive nature the moral is to tread carefully, as not all moderators are fussy about the use of socially unacceptable language in their conferences, or the unjustified intellectual battering of their members by others.

Dissent and the BBS

It used be considered that bulletin boards were forums where free speech and thought were commonplace. Sadly this is no longer generally true, especially in advanced countries like the USA and the UK. Commercial and recreational bulletin board operators constantly exercise censorship of one form or another, often in covert ways.

Prodigy, an American service set up by Sears and IBM to provide an on-line meeting place for computer users, found itself in hot water in 1990 when users pointed out that messages critical of Prodigy's charge rates were being covertly removed from conferences. Prodigy subsequently admitted that messages, and entire conferences pertaining to sexual matters, were sometimes removed on the grounds that Prodigy was a 'family' service. The vast majority of users disagreed, they wanted freedom of speech and no censorship.

In the UK a large conferencing system came under fire in mid-1992 when many users started complaining of dropped lines during log-in procedures and downloads. One computer journalist was threatened with disconnection after complaining about the problem in a public forum. Many other similar complaints were simply put down to 'user problems' by technical staff.

Similar 'disruptions' of service have led to litigation in the States. Revlon, the cosmetics firm, was brought to a standstill by a software company, who remotely disabled the software that managed Revlon's product distribution network. The software house claimed that it had every right to do so as Revlon had declined to honour a payment. Revlon claimed that this was an act of commercial terrorism and extortion.

The corporate BBS

At one time it used to be the in-thing to have a corporate BBS to provide in-house news and electronic mail. Corporate BBSs have largely gone out fashion these days, along with phrases like 'in-thing'. Most PTTs now provide proprietary or X.400 based messaging systems which offer many more facilities than most current BBSs and are easier to use and to integrate into the corporate computing environment. A typical corporate E-mail system will run over a local area network, and will provide file attachments to messages, global directories and much more. The poor old personal computer driven BBS cannot usually compete.

But small dial-up BBSs have their uses among the suits and ties and funny mannerisms of the business world. They can be used for point-to-point file transfers from representatives in the field, or for sending international E-mail for only the cost of the call. In general, most corporates with more than 20 or so employees do better to look at the messaging services provided by VAN suppliers if they need anything more than occasional message transfer. Small BBSs start to need an increasing amount of daily maintenance as they grow larger which often outweighs the convenience of keeping them running.

One interesting use of an in-house corporate BBS is to allow employees to let off steam. A go-ahead (but now defunct) VAN called One-To-One had an in-house BBS called The Bitch. Employees were allowed anonymous log-ins and utter freedom of speech, much to the delight of the lower minions. There are now few company directors who would welcome such freedom of speech among employees.

Going abroad

BBSs don't stop at Dover – there are several thousand of them in the USA of course, and several thousand more in Europe, and in each of the continents. You can generally access any of these (regardless of how far away they are) with a good error-correcting modem and a bottomless money box to pay for the call charges.

Long distance point-to-point data calls often fail because an operator in some forgotten part of the world interrupts to ask you for information. If she finds herself talking to a modem she is likely to hang your call up. But you can generally get through on a direct dialled call with no trouble to most of the Continent, USA, Australia, Middle and Far East. The main trouble spots for dial-up comms are places where there is a war going on, or Third World countries, such as parts of Africa, South America,

India, Indo-China.

Them and Us – International BBS and the Law

Accessing a foreign BBS is fun. You can find all sorts of information that is simply not available on UK BBSs – either because the UK systems are much more conservative or because we have different cultural and legislative ideas. In Britain we have stringent copyright laws which exist to prevent copying and distribution of almost any form of created work without permission. Many other countries don't and it's possible to find copies of major commercial programs on BBSs in Saudi Arabia, Czechoslovakia and Russia. Naturally, if you download prohibited items from these systems you are importing them into the country and could in some circumstances fall foul of UK legislation.

Many overseas BBSs also carry image files portraying sexual matters which are considered as pornography by the courts (and by some righteous individuals) in this country. Again you could fall foul of the law or, more importantly, the tabloid press, if these are imported – even by the indirect means of a modem.

Using a recreational dial-up BBS

Remember to set your comms package parameters to 8-N-1. That's eight data bits, no parity, one stop bit (many commercial systems use 7-E-1). If you encounter connection problems the fault will almost certainly be at your end of the link, so double-check before harassing the sysop.

REMEMBER THE GOOD PIGGIES' CODE

- DON'T HOG THE LINE ON A SINGLE MODEM SYSTEM – LET OTHERS ON BY BEING BRIEF.

- DON'T JUST LOG ON SO YOU CAN DOWNLOAD A DOZEN FILES ('TROUGHING') AND THEN LOG OFF. INTERACT WITH OTHERS BY LEAVING MESSAGES OR JOLLY COMMENTS, AND HELP BUILD THE BOARD UP BY CONTRIBUTING FILES, MESSAGES OR TEXT. A BOARD IS ONLY AS GOOD AS ITS CONTRIBUTORS.

- DON'T LEAVE THE GATE OF THE STY OPEN BY DROPPING THE LINE AT YOUR END. THIS CAN OCCASIONALLY CAUSE PROBLEMS AT THE OTHER END, AND IS BAD BAD BAD. DISCONNECT BY USING THE 'GOODBYE' OPTION ON THE BBS, WHERE POSSIBLE.

■ IF YOU DON'T KNOW WHAT YOU'RE TALKING ABOUT – SHUT UP. (ENGAGE BRAIN BEFORE OPENING MOUTH.)

■ RESPECT THE OPINIONS OF OTHERS, THEY MAY HAVE A DIFFERENT VIEWPOINT FROM YOU, AND ARE ENTITLED TO IT. ASK YOURSELF WHY YOU FEEL A NEED TO DIVE IN AND MODIFY SOMEONE ELSE'S OPINION BEFORE YOU GO AHEAD AND DIVE IN. UN-OBJECTIVE EXCHANGES OF USELESS OPINIONS WASTES EVERYONE'S TIME AND MONEY.

OLRs

Many systems now have Off-line Readers (OLRs) available. An OLR is a software package which interacts with the remote system to get your mail, update your message base etc. It does this by downloading the data to your computer and doing the housework there, instead of at the remote system. OLRs therefore save connect time and money.

If the BBS that you are using supports an OLR you will almost certainly find a copy in the files directory. If no OLR is available for your favourite BBS you can usually have your comms package automatically write a script to get your messages and send any mail you may have written while off-line. Most comms packages feature an 'auto-learn' feature which will do much of the hard work for you.

12.2 Starting your own BBS

Any one can run a BBS. You need three essential things:

■ ENDLESS PATIENCE

■ A SPOUSE OR PARTNER WITH ENDLESS PATIENCE

■ ALL THE TIME IN THE WORLD, PLUS A BIT TO SPARE

A computer, printer, phone line and modem are useful too.

Before you set up a BBS you should consider carefully whether you have the time available to dedicate to it, and whether your nearest and dearest will object to you being plugged into the thing ten hours a day (running a BBS is addictive). Most BBSs need some daily maintenance, even if it is only by way of replying to mail. If you stay away from the keyboard for too long your users will eventually leave you – if you spend too long at the keyboard your partner will leave you. A sysop (f.'sissop') has to strike a balance between his or her private and public lives. It's not always easy.

BBS hardware

The sort of computer you need is not generally important as long as it has a serial port that can keep up with the modem you are going to use. A large-ish hard disk will be useful in later stages as the board grows in size, but you don't need very much at all in the way of equipment to get you off the ground. Almost any personal computer equipped with a hard disk and a fast serial port will start you off, as will a cheap quad modem with error correction.

As your user base grows you will need a faster modem to attract the punters and enough hard disk area to store all the files and messages as they come in. Some popular systems are now so full that the messages are deleted after they are a few weeks old, which is a pity as a message base is a living history of users and changing ideas – a valuable social document in its own right.

If you do use a PC for your BBS bear in mind that MS-DOS, the operating system for the PC, is over-fussy about the length of filenames it uses. If you run a section for MAC or Amiga users on your PC based BBS you will find that perfectly ordinary file names such as GERRALOAD_OF.THIS will be objected to by the PC. Some BBS software gets around this limitation by truncating file names to the eight letter prefix and three letter suffix that MS-DOS uses. An easy way to get around this problem is to use a Mac or an Amiga computer as a base for your BBS. These machines have the advantage that they don't get cross and bitter about long filenames, and their serial ports don't get migraines when running at 38,400 bps. The Mac and the Amiga also multitask properly – you can use a word-processor to update your text files or perform backups without having to take your BBS down to do so as you would with a PC. The disadvantages are: there is less BBS software around for the Macintosh and the Amiga than there is for the PC, additional disk space is likely to cost more pounds per megabyte for these machines, and the purchase price is liable to be slightly higher than for a similarly equipped PC because of this.

Modems

Most BBS users want access to files, and a large software base is likely to be the biggest inducement you can provide, at least in the early stages. You will also find that most of the uploaders, the people who send you files, will be using fast modems, so you should make the fitting of a sextuple mode V32 bis modem a priority as soon as funds allow. But track down your BBS software before you buy the modem and get recommendations from other sysops first. Some BBSs are fussy about the way that they talk to modems and don't always work with all modems. Early Wildcat! software and early Pace modems refused to talk nicely to each other, for instance. Many modem manufacturers offer special purchasing deals for sysops, and both Hayes and Courier will sell you a modem at a good price if your BBS has been up and running for some time. There are commercial companies who deal in sysops' sundries too, and having a good dealer behind you can make a lot of difference to the number of facilities available on your BBS.

BBS software

There are around 150 different commercial BBS software packs around. Most if not all of them will have message and file handling built in, some will also have 'doors' – a feature that allows users to run live programs on-line. Many FIDONET systems have multi-phone line control and global messaging built in.

FIGURE **12.6**

A 'Fidonet' BBS; messages can be left for other Fidonet boards.

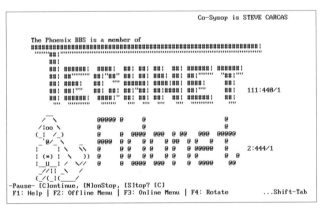

You should choose your software carefully by studying other boards and evaluating their features. Your BBS is almost certainly going to become an extension of your personality and you should look for software which is not only going to fulfil the needs of your users but your personal needs too. Most BBS software is shareware. You can try it before you buy it.

Some boards are much easier to set up than others and Wildcat!, by Mustang

Software for the PC is one of the easiest to set up and operate, although it lacks a few of the more esoteric BBS features. One useful source of BBS shareware is the Hayes BBS, among others. It has a CD-ROM available to users which contains over a dozen BBS systems.

Part-time BBS

There are dozens of BBSs which only run part-time. This causes problems for people who want to log-in to the boards as lines are more likely to be engaged if they are only available for a couple of hours. The sysop will also be plagued by calls from modems out of hours and it's much better not to run a part-time board with a published number, if you can help it. A useful alternative is to become a partner in a BBS, either by setting up a joint venture with some one to share the bills and the glory, or by becoming a Special Interest Group Operator (SIGOP) or conference moderator.

Publicising your BBS

You've plugged in the computer and modem, installed the software, and spent hours on setting up to give your BBS a personality. Up until now though the only person who has called in has been you! How do you publicise a BBS?

The easiest way is leave messages on other BBSs. Out of courtesy you should ask the sysop of the receiving BBS if you may do that thing. There is nothing worse than having the competition (for that's what you are) come round and stick up a poster without asking. When you do ask you will be pleased to find out that sysops are a friendly bunch and will almost certainly welcome you in. You should aim to do this on at least five other BBSs in your geographical area, and exchange the compliment by publicising other boards on yours. You should also be prepared to advertise in the press, especially if you run a BBS that deals with specialist subjects like knitting socks for sailors (or bungee-jumping).

One surefire way of not generating any calls is to sit staring at your BBS wondering why no-one phones it. Bear in mind that it takes around six months for a UK BBS to become popular, and that the most popular boards have friendly, active sysops who return messages and do the housekeeping on a daily basis.

The most unpopular BBSs are run by domineering fascisti who need to know every aspect of your private life before they will give you access to their out-of-date file and message bases.

Going commercial

Once your board becomes successful and reaches say, 50 callers a day you will almost certainly be tempted to install more phone lines, extra modems and more disk space. This all costs money and you may decide to extract a proportion of the required sum from your users to enable you to effect modernisations.

Before you go commercial you should think carefully about the reason why your board has become popular. If you have any common sense you will realise that this is because you are providing an interesting service at no charge. The emphasis is on the words 'no charge'. If you do go commercial you will enter into competition with other commercial services such as CIX and CompuServe and you will have make sure that the service you provide warrants the fees you propose to charge. You may also become liable for tax on any profits you make, and could be classified as a business by the Revenue, your landlord, mortgage provider or insurance company, despite your plaintive pleadings to the contrary (see the chapter on Teleworking).

Some people do make a great success out of going commercial, but others make a complete mess of the entire thing. You should remember that being successful does not necessarily equate with making a lot of money, and that the original philosophy behind BBSs is a simple one...

The Data Protection Act (DPA) and the BBS sysop

To put it simply, if you keep any more than name and address data concerning your users on a computer system then you are potentially liable to be required to register your BBS under the DPA. Such additional data includes the familiar requests on some bulletin boards for details of your name, age, address, voice and data line numbers, the type of equipment you are using and details of your place of work. If this information is stored on computer then the operator may be liable for registration. The rules are somewhat different for clubs and associations.

The Act is a complex one and you are advised to contact the Data Protection Registrar for a friendly natter concerning your intentions before you actually set your board up. (The Data Protection Registrar's office is often staffed by human beings).

The number is in Appendix 5. Don't be put off from making that call by information coming from other sysops, who might tell you that there is no need to register a BBS. Check for yourself. It only takes one disgruntled punter with a grudge against your BBS to bring the law down upon your head. You should Be Prepared, as they say.

12.3 CIX

It's hard to wave goodbye to this section on bulletin boards without having a glance over CIX.

CIX is Compulink Information Exchange, a BBS set up in the late 1980s. For reasons not readily apparent, CIX has become that wonder of wonders, a successful commercial bulletin board.

CIX suffers from all the grumbles voiced earlier about Command Line Interfaces and line editors seemingly devised by Lucrezia Borgia -although one saving grace is the excellent CIX user manual. It comes with a subscription, as does the seemingly endless patience of CIX support staff. Perhaps these are some of the reasons that people flock to CIX, and the system is now the UK's most popular recreational service.

The year of 1992 was a vintage year for CIX. The service implemented a great number of changes, and installed a fax gateway (a facility whereby faxes can be sent using ordinary modems and the services of a third party), and ISDN and packet switch access. This latter feature makes it possible to access CIX from most places in the world, although the main core of CIX users are as British as Union Jack underpants.

In November of 1992 CIX implemented a gateway facility to the Internet, a move which was greeted with much metaphorical bell-ringing by the denizens of CIX. This feature finally gave CIX what it desperately needed – access to the huge trans-world network of computers connected to the Internet. The gateway offered CIX users the chance to finally correspond with other computer users all over the planet, for no more than normal connect charges.

Social anthropologists will find much of interest on CIX. BBSs bring out the best and worst in people and CIX has a fair cross-section of all types. There is occasional wisdom in its conferences and CIX's low fees make the service an interesting proposition for any computer and modem user.

CIX is now a national institution amongst its followers. You can find out by joining

CIX online with virtually any sort of modem.

SEE THE SPECIAL OFFER COUPON OVER THE PAGE

CIXs true position is probably that of a club for people who have a computer interest. Its regular members evangelise its value way above its true importance, which is low cost providing E-mail and Internet services to the masses. If only the many thousands of Prestel, AT&T and BT Mailbox users were as enthusiastic then many more modems would be sold in the UK.

FREE REGISTRATION TO CIX WORTH £25.00

Offer ends 1st August 1994

For readers of the PCPLUS Modem and Communications Guidebook, Compulink Information Exchange (CIX) have waived their normal registration fee. To become a member of CIX and take advantage of this offer, follow the instructions below.

SET YOUR COMMUNICATIONS PACKAGE PARAMETERS TO 8 DATA BITS, NO PARITY, 1 STOP BIT (8N1).

SET YOUR MODEM TO THE FASTEST SPEED IT CAN DO AND DIAL ONE OF THE CIX MODEM LINES:
- 081 390 1244 UPTO V22BIS
- 081 390 1255 UPTO V32BIS
- 081 399 3468 ISDN
- PSS NUA: 2342 1330 0310

Once connected to CIX follow the prompts. You'll be asked for your name, address and credit card details, and then the 'special code' which is future. Please make sure that you enter future in lower case. After completing the registration you will receive a user manual in the post.

Once registered, regular monthly and hourly rates will apply. If you want further advice or information prior to registering:

TELEPHONE 0492 641961 OR FAX ON 0492 641538

Alternately, write to:

COMPULINK INFORMATION EXCHANGE LTD
LONDON HOUSE
ANCASTER SQUARE
LLANWRST
GWYNEDD LL26 OLD
WALES

Once registered and on-line, queries can be answered by sending E-mail to cixadmin.

13 TELEWORKING

"Companionship begins with those at the gate"

13.1 Teleworking

Teleworking isn't a new phenomenon. As long ago as 1982 electronic teleworking schemes were being set up both in Europe and in the USA.

Teleworking (working 'at a distance') usually involves producing work away from the main workplace, and then sending that work off, either as electronic mail, or as some form of binary data. Computer programmers, analysts and writers all fit this description.

In many ways teleworking is a return to the ways people used to work before there was large scale employment in the cities. It was only after the industrial revolution that spending potentially productive hours on trains, buses and motorways became 'normal' behaviour. Prior to that people mainly lived near to their place of work, or commuted a small distance to work by foot or by horse. It's only now that people are beginning to understand the folly of spending four hours a day travelling in order to do six hours work at some distant location.

For the purposes of this book teleworking is defined as 'working from home', not necessarily for an employer, and this chapter is to warn you of some of the pitfalls that teleworkers encounter.

There are over 600,000 teleworkers in Britain today and the vast majority of them are self-employed or run small businesses. Only a few of them work directly for companies. This is due to many factors – not the least being that British managers tend not to have an enlightened attitude to what is considered to be work and what isn't, and many see teleworking as a threat or as a soft option. It is also taking time for the unions to fully accept teleworking and, as you will see in the first of our three examples of teleworkers below, there are good reasons for this. But, the times they are a-changing, as somebody famous once said, and managerial attitudes towards teleworking are slowly becoming more reasonable.

What equipment?

The equipment you need to start teleworking will vary depending on your chosen metier but will usually include some form of word-processing equipment, a phone and a device for electronic communications. If you have read this book up to here you should now have enough knowledge to equip yourself with a fax machine, or a modem or both. Would-be teleworkers should also consider acquiring an answerphone to prevent frustrated callers from passing their business elsewhere, or for irate managers to leave bad-tempered messages on. But your first priority as a teleworker is to deal with the masses of paper-work occasioned by your decision to work from home, and to find somewhere where you can actually be productive. Don't rush out and spend money on computers and fax machines before you have read the rest of this chapter.

Where to work

If you are to work from home then it's absolutely vital to have somewhere in the house that you can exclusively call your own, no matter what material aspect of domestic life you have to sacrifice to achieve it. You should earmark a room or a corner of a room where you will not be disturbed for any reason other than actual emergency. If you don't start as you mean to go on, you will find that a lot of productive time can be lost with good-natured family interruptions; offers of cups of tea, and friendly heads poked round doors to 'see how you are getting on'. Some people do manage to work from the kitchen table but these people are above mere mortals. For most of us the spare bedroom or garage is pressed into service and becomes the UK national office of whatever empire we imagine ourselves to be in charge of.

If you have children you may find that you have to make your 'office' out of bounds for some of the time, as there is nothing more disruptive to mental flow than anguished toddlers. This will not always be possible but many working parents do manage to get a full day's work done in between school drop-off and collect times, and somehow find time to run a house and a family.

How can telecomms help the teleworker

If you have ever used the telephone to sort out a problem (most of us have) then you have experienced the sort of beneficial effect that using a mass telecommunication system brings. If you think how that process can be applied to your work then you will soon realise that teleworkers can often be as effective using electronically carried text of some sort, as they can with their voice. It follows, therefore, that if you had direct or indirect access to the text and paper handling systems of other people you would become more efficient in those areas too.

Electronic mail – E-mail

There are two main formats in which information is transported electronically around the world. One of them is our old friend ASCII, the other is a binary file. A binary file is information stored on your computer in machine readable form such as an application program or database file. To use E-mail services you'll need to be familiar with the both types. These file type have already been covered in this book but for the sake of bookshop browsers here's a refresher.

■ ASCII

Most word-processor programs and memory typewriters have an option for copying your text to an ASCII file. Some systems use the phrase 'print to disk', which usually means the same thing. ('save to disk' usually means save the data in the native format of the word-processor as a binary file). An ASCII text file can be read by most electronic systems, including electronic mail systems and those host systems run by commercial companies. Your ASCII file can be translated into a fax, telex or electronic mail document by these commercial companies without you needing to do anything other than send it to the host in the correct format.

■ BINARY FILES

A spreadsheet or other non-ASCII file is usually called a binary file, as it contains only binary information. A binary file cannot be read by simply displaying it on the screen of a computer or terminal, but must go through some conversion process first. Binary files cannot generally be handled as ASCII text files by E-mail systems.

Using a third party data bureau

If you are working from home on a tight budget and cannot afford a fax or telex machine, then using a third party to carry and translate your ASCII text could be the ideal answer. Using a third party to move your electronic mail around (as you would do if you posted a letter) is usually faster and often cheaper than surface or air mail. The only disadvantage is that the recipient must have access to the same system that was used to carry the message, so he can retrieve it.

Third party Value Added Networks (VANs) that cater for exactly this need are numerous, to say the least. Using one of them to carry text and receive mail from customers and clients can be worth its weight in gold. In many cases it is still cheaper for individuals and small companies with a low data throughput to use a modem to access one of these carriers, than it is to try to set up and send data via a point-to-point dial-up link.

The great advantage of electronic mail is that it is machine readable, and an ASCII file or spreadsheet can be imported straight in to the recipient's word-processor without conversion. A received paper fax containing similar information would not (generally) be machine-readable in the same way. All VANs can carry binary files such as drawings and spreadsheets with the same ease as they handle ASCII text.

Some of the largest VAN's in the world are GEISCO, BT TYMNET, AT&T ISTEL, US SPRINT, and CompuServe, and all of them can be accessed simply and easily with almost any dial-up modem.

FIGURE 13.1

CompuServe Mail being created, can be sent as E-mail, fax or paper all by modem.

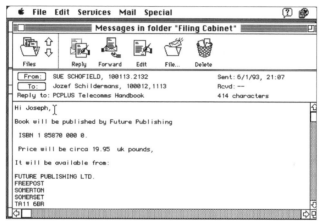

If you wish to communicate to your employer's office from your home with E-mail and your employer has a Local Area Network set up than you will normally find that there is a 'gateway' through to the LAN to allow mail to come in from an external VAN. The gateway will normally be an X.400 compliant Message Handling System (MHS), through which E-mail passes onto the corporate file server or gateway server.

Point-to-point E-mail

A point-to-point (PTP) connection is the linking of two people, modems or fax machines via a straight through dial-up link. Point-to-point communications can be quick and easy to use, but suffer the disadvantage of needing dedicated on-line equipment running at the receiving end. A point-to-point dial-up link using two modems and a host computer can be useful for sending and receiving small amounts of E-mail on an irregular basis and is sometimes cheaper than using a third party VAN. But you can only send data to one location via a PTP link, which isn't so useful if you want to communicate regularly with a dozen people in four branch offices.

One of the easiest occasional PTP links to set up will use a simple comms program running in Host mode at the receiving end. Another sort will use an electronic Bulletin Board System (BBS), possibly hooked into a larger computer or file-server. Both of these systems need regular management, which is why they tend not to be popular with large corporates who usually choose to use VANs for the purpose.

International PTP links are prone to the same sort of problems associated with voice calls – wrong numbers, crackling lines, and irate non-English speaking operators. But PTP links can be useful as an interim or temporary measure while other systems are being set up or strategic planning is taking place.

PTP links are in use by many NGOs – Non Governmental Organisations – a euphemism for charities. PTP links are popular because the equipment needed is simple to operate and cheap to install. But many of the NGOs find that using PTPs is self limiting for the reasons above, plus the fact that not all developing countries have reliable telephone networks. At the end of the day it's still often cheaper and easier to send a fax or a telex from remote parts of the world than it is to get your modem to try and make a connection directly.

13.2 Rural teleworking

In the mid 1980s teleworking was seen as a major way of regenerating some of the more remote and rural areas of Britain. In fact this has turned out to be as much of a myth as the paperless office. The major problem is not one of technology, but providing enough of a social infrastructure in the form of schools, hospitals and shops to lure people away from the cities and towns.

There have been some good attempts to utilise the brave new world of teleworking – the telecottage movement is one example, where computers, modems and fax machines are made freely accessible to those living in rural communities. The Scottish Highlands and Islands Enterprise board and British Telecom jointly launched the Highlands and Islands Initiative in 1990 to implement the high quality telecomms infrastructure seen as being politically desirable by the Conservative Government.

It may well be that the project attracts people to the wonders of Teleworking – but industry is a key player in the conversion of workers from office-bound slaves to rumbustious country rustics, and the migration rate of capital investment to the Highlands is still woefully slow. The English ACRE (Association of Community Councils of Rural England) has also taken an interest in teleworking but few of the plans for national teleworking schemes will succeed until industry agrees to initiate and can afford to fund such schemes. And teleworking is seen by many as a poor relation to finding people 'proper jobs' despite all of the prognosis of sociologists who predict that proper jobs will have ceased to exist by 2010. There simply won't be enough of them to go around. Teleworking might not yet be recognised for its true value, but it will become increasingly important in the next few years. If you are involved in any aspect of teleworking then you will find membership of the National Association of Teleworkers valuable.

Cabin fever – the curse of the teleworker

The first reaction of the teleworker to his new environment is one of elation. He is free from the mindless treadmill of commuting, he can spend more time with the children, and myopic face-to-face meetings with his office peers are finished, for the most part. But there are many psychological problems to trap teleworkers – there is often no real perceived break between domestic and work life, and teleworkers tend to work longer hours and at weekends because of this.

There is also the probability that some form of social deprivation will result – many teleworkers complain of a lack of communication between themselves and their office-bound colleagues – a telephone conversation is no real substitute for being there in the flesh and interacting with people face-to-face.

In many cases corporate teleworkers also become paranoid that their career prospects are being undermined, or feel that being 'at home' for the entire day is somehow undermining their status back in the office. Company executives who are quite capable of running their businesses from a single telephone will travel miles to the office each day just to enforce their authority. And our social culture makes it impossible for a homeworking executive or manager to be taken seriously, whilst it's much more acceptable for a writer or a programmer to work from the back bedroom.

If you are considering teleworking then you must give some thought to what effect staring at the same four walls every day will have upon you. You could try teleworking for only part of the week to break the routine, or working from a different place on occasions. People who can comfortably spend months at a time doing the same thing in the same place without social interaction are few and far between.

It's often useful to build your own routine to mirror that of the corporate office. You should stop work for a few minutes each hour to make tea or coffee, or pick up the newspaper. You should have meals at regular times each day, and try to avoid working at weekends if possible. It's much better to keep a couple of days a week free for leisure activities. Teleworkers should also beware of the Random Snacking Syndrome, a hole in the space-time continuum into which entire packets of chocolate biscuits disappear in the space of just a few hours.

If the opportunity occurs to move yourself and your family to a remote part of Britain it's vital that you consider the needs of your family. They will have to provide that part of the social interaction you would normally receive from your office colleagues and this added strain coupled with adapting to new surroundings often proves be too much for many.

The location you choose is important. It's very common for teleworkers to move out to some rural idyll and then find that having to drive 40 miles each way to the nearest supermarket (or hospital) is a huge strain. Many of them move back to the cities after a couple of years.

How do teleworkers succeed without going mad? Many of them do by making sure that 'the job' doesn't occupy any more time than it would do if they were office bound. The successful teleworker also seems to have the self-discipline to know when to call it a day and put his/her feet up.

13.3 Case studies

There are three distinct types of teleworker: the Quiet Mouse, the Self-Employed and the Corporate Home-Worker and we begin by having a look at the particular needs of each.

Case 1 – The Quiet Mouse

Liz is an employed teleworker. She spends two days a week in her employer's office in London, and three days a week plus quite a few weekends working from home. Her job entails working with long technical and legal documents and her home office is equipped with a PC-based word-processor, and a fax machine. She has converted the top room in her house to an office and can work comfortably there for reasonably long periods. The two days a week spent at her employer's office sometimes seems a bit of a drag, especially as she has to commute over a 90-mile return journey to get there and back, but on the whole she is reasonably happy with her lot. Her employer doesn't have a pre-determined policy for teleworkers so the agreement between the two parties is not formalised in any way. Neither does her employer contribute to heating, lighting and other expenses directly incurred in the production of work at Liz's house, but as the arrangement suits Liz she doesn't want to rock the boat by complaining. She says that she would find it hard to go back to a 'proper' job in an office, despite the fact she quite often works through weekends in addition to working a 40-hour week.

Case 2 – The Self-employed Teleworker

Tony is a computer freak. He's always been interested in electronics and moved into computer programming when the IBM PC was launched. He used to have a 'proper' job, but was made redundant and has now found that the freedom of making his own independent decisions suits him. Tony will work all the hours it takes to get a job done or see a project through.

Tony enjoys technology for its own sake and communicates with his clients by fax, letter, and E-mail. He has converted a part of his house into an office and workroom and often holds court there to some important paying clients. He has thought about making his business into a limited company, but is fairly happy as he is. He claims a tax allowance for using part of his home as an office, and off-sets part of the heating and lighting bills against tax. He has an accountant too, but is not over-enamoured of the advice he sometimes gets. Tony is typical of the many small business owners that work from home.

Case 3 – The Corporate Homeworker

Sally is 34, has a degree, two small children and a dog, and lives in the country. When her children started school she considered going back to work as a programmer/analyst but a full-time job would have disrupted her family life too much. She contacted the personnel department of her old computer company and was delighted to be told that the company had a teleworking scheme that had been in operation for two years, and that they would be pleased to welcome her back to her old job, with the prospect of promotion thrown in.

She accepted the offer and within a few weeks a terminal with a dedicated phone line was installed in her home, and a second telephone line was installed by the company. She also had a meeting with her union representative who explained that the company's home-working scheme was fully supported by the union, who had negotiated extra payments for heating and lighting bills.

Sally has been a home-worker for two years now, and teleworking allows her to watch her children to grow up while she holds down a full-time and well paid position. She was promoted to Project Leader after six months and now spends two days a week travelling to meetings. Her company keeps her in touch with office events with a monthly newsletter, and there are frequent office based social events organised especially so the teleworkers do not feel isolated. The scheme is judged a success by all.

Paperwork and the teleworker

The above three examples are taken from real life. All three people have different problems directly caused by teleworking: Liz has only a tacit unwritten agreement with her employer which could fold at any minute; Tony sometimes finds the strains of being a parent conflicts with his clients needs for instant results; and Sally is about to be offered more promotion which would mean her losing her home-worker status. But by and large these people are happy with their lot.

So. If you are thinking about becoming a teleworker there are many things to consider, apart from which computer and fax machine you should buy. You first of all have to deal with one or two administrative matters.

Planning permission

You will become involved with the invariably overworked planning department of your local authority if you change the main use of your house from residential to business use. For most home-workers this doesn't apply – but you might be called to account by upset neighbours if delivery vans continually call at your house, or you have a trade vehicle parked in your drive. You may even find that a small nameplate above your letter-box which says 'F Bloggs Programmer' will constitute an advertising sign which could land you in hot water.

Tenants

If you are a tenant of a property you should get written agreement from your landlord that you may use the premises for the purpose of 'working from home.' Many tenancy agreements are worded (sometimes unworkably) in 18th century legalese and their clauses do not differentiate between working from home and running a business or trade. When (not if) you check your tenancy agreement you should look for clauses which expressly forbid "the carrying on of any business or trade". Working from home for an employer is not normally construed as running a business in law, (although it might be by the Inland Revenue), but the forbidding and ill-informed dragon-lady who acts as your landlord's agent may lend her own interpretation if she needs a reason to terminate your tenancy. This does happen. You should therefore get an agreement in writing between you and the landlord that working from home, for an employer, is acceptable to all parties.

Mortgaged properties

Funny things mortgage companies. They give you all the money you need to set up home and then tell you what you can and cannot do there. Some mortgage companies have a clause in the mortgage agreement which says that the loan may only be made for the purposes of "securing a domestic property." You should check your mortgage agreement carefully for such wording. Again, this point can be clarified by writing to the mortgage provider and explaining that you will be working from home, not running a business.

Mortgage companies are also very concerned about house (not contents) insurance because in real terms it's usually their loan that you are paying the insurance premiums on. Correspondingly if you contravene your house buildings insurance policy your mortgage provider will want to know, especially if there has been a 'change of use' from a domestic to a commercial property.

Insurance

The contents of your home will normally be covered by household contents insurance. If you suddenly install a couple of thousand pounds worth of computer and telecomms equipment you may have trouble convincing your insurance company that these items are not for business use. If your house burns to the ground the loss adjuster who comes round to assess the remains (and the size of the subsequent payments) will not be pleased to find what appears to be commercial equipment on the claims form for a domestic property.

One solution is to advise your contents insurance provider that you have a certain amount of 'home-working' equipment. But, sadly if you write to your insurance company with a simple note explaining that you are working from home, then 30 percent of British insurance companies will write back asking you to pay a higher premium. (Source: 'Which?' magazine).

You can get small business insurance for any equipment, such as computers, filing cabinets etc, associated with your teleworking enterprise direct from some of the larger insurance companies. The costs are much lower than you might think and many companies will provide additional cover which you may not have realised you need. For example, Commercial Union provides a Small Business policy which offers rapid settlement of claims, and replacement of lost data, including the re-keying of replacement data into your system. The cost is around £150 per £10,000-worth of cover. If you're searching for such insurance it's probably best to phone the insurance company direct rather than go through a broker.

Some brokers, in the author's experience, classify teleworkers as small businesses and charge high rates accordingly. Quotes for premiums obtained through brokers in 1992 varied from £250 to £600 per annum for less cover than that offered by the Commercial Union policy. The best advice is to shop around. If you are in the position of Tony in our example and have more than a couple of thousand pounds worth of equipment then you must insure it under a small business policy.

Tax and the VAT man

Both the Inland Revenue and Her Majesty's Customs and Excise are aware of the teleworking phenomenon but seem to judge each case on its own merit when deciding what is and isn't considered to be correct. They also tend to be fairly nebulous about the small but important differences between self-employed and employed status and will quite often make an arbitrary assumption as to what your status is – unless you can persuade them differently.

There have been a number of cases where companies have changed the status of their workers to teleworkers and fallen foul of the Revenue's definitions – particularly where a self-employed person does a lot of work on a long term basis for a single client. This is often the case with computer analysts and programmers. Computer contract staff who obtain work without going through an agent are often penalised in this way. If you are in this category it is better to sort out just what your actual tax status is earlier rather than later.

You may also run into problems with definitions at the hands of the DHSS who have been known to classify employed teleworkers as self-employed for the purposes of paying NI contributions. This can lead to the ludicrous position of you being classed as employed by the Revenue, and self-employed by the DHSS.

It also takes a lot of time and trouble to sort these problems out due to the sheer size and inefficiency of the DHSS. The author has a prize letter from the DHSS in Newcastle (she lives in Sussex) telling her: "We cannot tell you what your contributions record is to date as we are updating our records." The letter was received three months after posting the enquiry.

The moral of course is that you should have an accountant who will sort these things out and do battle with the Revenue on your behalf if there is any hint of the self-employed stigma about you. Your own feeble protestations may tend to carry little weight with the DHSS, and Inland Revenue, even if you are absolutely correct in a technical sense.

Contracts of employment for teleworkers

It's quite possible that the Revenue will decide that you are a 'sub-contractor' to your employer if your contract of employment as a teleworker differs considerably from that of your office-bound colleagues.

The differences between contracts of employment for office-bound and home working staff doing similar work are often very noticeable. They shouldn't be. The Equal Opportunities Commission (EOC) publishes a Code of Practice for home-working employees, as they are properly called, which says among other things, that home-workers should receive the same pay as other workers, that career paths should be kept open, and that all expenses should be paid. The report, published as early as 1982 as The New Homeworkers, by Ursula Hews, is available from the EOC.

Trying to convince an employer that they should take notice of people like the EOC is often a difficult matter. You may find that you are labelled as 'bolshie' if you start to make a fuss about pay differentials for home-workers. The sad reality is that many home-workers regard themselves as being fortunate if they are allowed to work away from the office and this is exploited by too many employers.

If you do feel that you are being treated differently from other staff members as a result of your home-working status then your first stop is an appeal in writing to your personnel department director or manager. If this brings no success then you should either consider joining a trade union who will fight the case on your behalf, or taking your own case to the EOC. The EOC will be unlikely to take direct action against your employer in the courts (they are too busy sorting out cases of racial and gender discrimination) but they may be able to write to your employer explaining current guidelines for teleworkers. If that fails you may be able to bring legal action if you can prove that your contract of employment has been breached in some way, or your employer refuses to negotiate a new one on the grounds of your new teleworker status.

VAT

If you have decided to become registered for VAT then you will be able to reclaim the VAT content of a proportion of your domestic utility bills (including the phone bill) if you work from home. The decision as to what constitutes a 'reasonable amount' is best left to your accountant. VAT inspectors are especially trained to gain the upper hand in any discussion about what constitutes fair practice and prefer to deal with other finance professionals. Life is less emotional that way.

If your turnover (as opposed to earnings) exceeds a certain amount you will be liable to become VAT registered by default. The threshold level varies at the Chancellor's whim but is currently set at something in excess of £30,000 turnover per annum.

The VAT departments of the Customs and Excise like to affirm that they are there to help the small business man or woman to run their business as smoothly as possible, but woe betide you if you register for VAT and then fail to keep your paperwork in the way desired by the VAT inspector. Remember too that VAT inspectors are often on the look-out for a phenomenon known as 'hobby-farming' – a situation where a business becomes VAT registered to claim back the VAT on its many purchases, but produces little in the way of VAT-able income. You may well have perfectly reasonable reasons as to why your business has spent £10,000 on computer equipment during a year when your turnover was below £5,000, but it's worth remembering that VAT inspectors are not trained to be 'reasonable' at all times. A reputable medium sized firm of accountants is often your only defence against the often subjective opinions of income tax and VAT inspectors.

Capital Gains Tax

If you claim tax relief on part of your mortgage payments on the basis that part of your house is used for work you may find that you are liable for capital gains tax when you come to sell the property.

In the past many accountants would advise their clients that this ploy was best avoided. But as legislation and the UK economic position changes rapidly it may well be that this no longer applies. House prices in many areas have fallen, and as CGT is based on the increase in the sales price of the property over the price paid (while disregarding inflation) it may be that claiming part of your mortgage payments against tax will be useful.

You should of course consult your accountant first.

13.4 Conclusions

It is time to return to the fortunes of our three teleworkers, in the light of all of the above.

■ LIZ
Poor Liz has no formal teleworking agreement with her company and the equipment loaned to her is not technically insured. Liz's house has been burgled and Liz has found to her horror that she is liable for the cost of the full replacement value under her existing contract of employment.

Her company is trying to forge a claim against Liz's own insurance company which will fail because the property was not explicitly covered by that policy. Liz will have to pay for the lost equipment. She will also be shocked to learn that as her employer has paid for her travel to and from the office twice a week the Revenue has decided that Liz will be taxed on her travel allowance – an item which Liz does not believe is a perk.

■ TONY
Tony on the other hand is being sued by the local council for turning his residential premises into a business office after complaints about 'the noise from delivery vans' by the (deaf) old lady across the way.

Tony's mortgage provider is awaiting the outcome with keen interest – the main interest being that charged at a higher rate on a commercial loan than on a domestic one.

Tony's solicitor doesn't think he stands much of chance of winning the case as Tony has converted part of the house into a large office and workshop and subsequently claimed a tax allowance on his mortgage payments. This has had the effect of bringing the property under the jurisdiction of the Department of the Environment's 'Practice Note' regarding collection of the business rate. This paper intimates that conversion of part of a domestic residence 'adapted or structurally altered for the purposes of carrying on a business' will render the alteree liable for payment of the business rate, as well as for payment of any personal community charge liable. Tony has asked his accountant why this was not pointed out to him but his accountant has not replied to any of Tony's letters. Poor Tony.

- **SALLY**
Sally is still doing rather well for herself. She has signed a hand-over letter which states the type and location of the equipment and its serial number, and which confirms that the equipment is installed at the risk of the company, although she agrees to take reasonable care of it. The letter also tells Sally what to do if the equipment is stolen or damaged and gives the phone number of the insurance company concerned, and the policy number.

Her company pays her PAYE and a portion of her heating and lighting bills, and submits details of all payments regarding heating and lighting to the Revenue. Her mortgage provider finds nothing to complain about either, as Sally's insurance policy was bought through the mortgage provider, and all the necessary provisions are there.

Morals

Are there any morals to these three stories? There are:

- DON'T TAKE ANYTHING AS READ FROM YOUR EMPLOYER REGARDING TELEWORKING. YOU NEED ALL AGREEMENTS IN WRITING, OR AS AMENDMENTS TO YOUR CONTRACT OF EMPLOYMENT, WHICH AMOUNTS TO THE SAME THING.

- DON'T IGNORE THESE PEOPLE:
THE INLAND REVENUE
THE DHSS
THE CUSTOMS AND EXCISE VAT DEPARTMENT

YOUR LANDLORD OR MORTGAGE PROVIDER
YOUR HOUSEHOLD INSURANCE PROVIDER
YOUR LOCAL AUTHORITY

All of them will have an interest in your status as a teleworker, whether you decide that this should be so, or not.

If your employer does not pay PAYE or NI on your behalf you will probably be cited as being self-employed by the Revenue. If this is the case you need access to a accountant with a qualification from at least the Institute of Chartered Accountants, and a personal recommendation from one of his or her long-standing clients.

14 EUROCOMMS

"He distinguishes himself from his neighbours"

14.1 Europe? Where's that?

As you tuck into your roast beef, with your faithful bulldog, Margaret, by your side, and your Union Jack underpants steaming gently on the top of your warm modem, your mind drifts into a reverie. Is there electronic life on the other side of La Manche? What do all those 'foreign' people over there do for electronic entertainment? How on earth would you ever contact these people, should you want to?

The answer is that Europe, of which Britain is a small part, boasts the biggest telecommunications network in the world, apart from North America. France in particular shines out as an example to us all; there are more computers connected to phone lines in France, than there are in all of England, Scotland, Wales, Ireland, put together.

For the main part we British ignore these huge continental telecomms networks. We are not at all interested in what the French say to each other on the several million calls placed daily to the Minitel system, nor are we generally concerned about what goes on in Torino or Basle. But to ignore this huge Eurocomms network is a folly, as many of our corporate bodies who are trying to sell to Europe are now beginning to realise.

So, we are going to have a look around Europe, using the dial-up services available to us. We shall be looking at just the services provided by the national PTT in each country, otherwise we shall get bogged down by sheer numbers. (If you think that Britain is doing well with over 1000 recreational BBSs available then remember that there are over ten times that number available to you in Europe.)

Most of Europe's PTTs use viewdata as a means of presenting computer information to users and viewdata is a very popular way of transferring data around on the Continent. Virtually all the European videotext services carry information such as White and Yellow page directory services and many of the national systems are hooked into each other via 'gateways' so that you can hop across national boundaries with ease.

It's now possible to search through most of Europe's phone directories from the UK with relative ease, and the information you will come across will sometimes amaze you. The French are much less secretive about the private telephone numbers of their politicians than we are, as are the Swedes and Danes. All you need to access many of these systems is the relevant phone number, a smattering of the national language concerned, and a decent terminal emulator that knows about electronic Euro-speak, or videotext as it's called.

How Videotext works

Videotext is the generic name given to computer data displayed on a TV screen. If the data appears via the telephone line it is known as viewdata, and if it arrives by a broadcast medium such as television it is called teletext. In the UK we have Prestel, Oracle and CEEfax, all of which are examples of videotext systems. There are many more. The commercial sector uses videotext for information distribution as the terminal equipment is cheap, easy to install and use. Many local libraries make use of videotext services to provide on-line indices to books, and there are dedicated videotext networks for schools, local government offices, car dealers and travel agents. A prime example of a dial-up viewdata system is British Telecom's Prestel service.

Videotext information is held in a database containing graphical and text information. The graphics are decidedly low resolution when compared with normal medium resolution computer output but the system has the advantage of not requiring huge amounts of bandwidth (and therefore transmission time). Videotext systems can operate efficiently over fairly slow dial-up links, often using 1200/75bps connections.

As we have seen, there is no such thing as a standard 'standard' in telecomms and there are at least two major and a dozen minor implementations of videotext standards available world-wide. The UK, France and Germany all use the simplest form of 72 x 80 pixel videotext graphics, called Alpha-mosaic. This service provides chunky block graphics of the kind we see on Prestel. 'Alpha-geometric' graphics have a much higher resolution, and can provide true curves on screen. A third implementation called 'Alpha-photographic' can send high quality images of 250 x 512 pixels over a phone network in around four seconds using screen-draw instructions and data-compression.

Accessing EuroComms

You can access most European videotext (EuroText) systems using a standard comms package and modem as long as the software supports the correct viewdata terminal type. For the UK a Prestel terminal emulator will work on most public services, for continental use you will often need Teletel (sometimes called Minitel) or BTX emulation in addition. Many of the continental viewdata systems support more than one emulation. Some of the services will actually change their emulation during a session as you move from one gateway to another and a comms program that senses the remote emulation and changes your terminal configuration automatically to match is useful. Setting up your exotic V32 bis modem to accept V23 is not so easy. Many of today's modems feature speed buffering, feature negotiation, data compression and error correction, all of which gets in the way when you are trying to make your modem talk at speeds first used in 1983. The best approach is to turn all these features off on your modem before you even start to dial out around Europe. Hayes modems need the command 'ATB2' to turn them into V23 modems.

FIGURE 14.1

Rencomm Plus

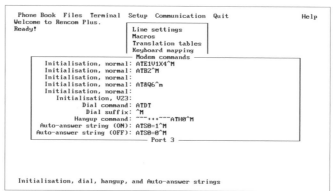

A good tip is to start with the V23 Prestel service as it's available as a local call to many places in Britain. If you cannot connect to Prestel your chances of getting through to the rest of Europe are fairly slim. The German service is difficult to gain access to, simply because the modems there seem to reject any attempt at feature negotiating; conversely, the Spanish system seems to accept almost anyone. The modem settings used to access the services shown in this chapter are displayed in FIGURE 14.1. If you do decide to use the excellent Rencom Plus for the PC as your comms package remember that the V23 speed setting therein is a true split rate speed for non buffering V23 modems. It may be prefarable to set your modem and DTE speed to 1200bps if your modem has any speed buffering capabilities.

Accessibility

Most of the EuroText services make money by charging users for the time spent connected to the service. This works if you are calling the service from within the country concerned, but it's not (generally) possible for trans-national charging to occur, as yet. If you call Minitel France from London or Edinburgh you will therefore only be allowed access to a limited service, as Minitel has no way of charging you for full access. You will pay only the call charges for your local PTT. This limitation will probably change as more European PTTs get together and implement cross-boundary charging, a feat which is already possible with packet switching networks.

If you just wish to browse through EuroText services many services offer a 'Guest' log-in which lets you look around, but not much more.

User IDs

There are two methods of charging you for your time spent on the system. The first is User Identification where you will be required to register with the supplier before being allowed onto the system. Prestel is such a system. You cannot gain full access to Prestel until you have filled in a form, and waited some days for your registration details to arrive. Contrast this with CompuServe where you call a toll-free number, and are given an immediate registration number together with 15 days free time on the system. And both CIX and CompuServe allow on-line registrations.

A 'kiosk' system allows callers directly into its innards without the need for cumbersome form filling. You are charged only for the amount of time spent connected to the system. This is made possible by digital trunks and subscriber lines – your phone number and billing information is available to the videotext supplier (usually a PTT) and connect charges are simply added to your phone bill in an orderly fashion. Many EuroText kiosk systems also allow 'foreign' users to register so that bills can paid by credit card debit. Kiosk systems should become common as ISDN takes hold in the UK. On the Continent it is already possible for EuroText users to be able to hop around from country to country while on line to a single gateway by this means. Each different kiosk system simply adds its charges to your bill as you go along.

EuroComms software

The comms package used in producing this section of the book is called Rencom Plus and comes from a company called Dortec, based in Copenhagen. If the name seems familiar to you it may be because you have used Procomm or Odyssey on a PC, both of which use viewdata emulations from Dortec. Rencom Plus was used because there are very few comms packages available in the UK which know about both Minitel and BTX emulation, and have a multi-lingual user-interface.

The program has a number of other unique features, such as the ability to select items with a mouse with any remote system that offers choice from an on-screen menu, and the ability to switch automatically from one type of viewdata emulation to another. The program also stores viewdata screens in colour for later access. You can access many of the EuroText systems with the Prestel emulation found on many other communications packages, but not all services conform exactly to the Prestel standard and you may see some screen errors as a result.

14.2 The Grand Tour

We are going to use Rencom Plus on our Grand Tour of Europe and the first stop will be…

The United Kingdom – Prestel

Well, what else did you expect? In the UK we have several videotext services, the best known being Prestel. The service was launched in the UK towards the end of 1977 after a gestation period in the hands of the UK Post Office.

Prestel was originally conceived to use a push button telephone as the interface between the user and the remote computer – in 1975 when the system was conceived no one had foreseen the coming explosion in the numbers of home-based personal computers. Early Prestel was a poor system by today's standards: the system was based on large numbers of menu screens which quite often led the information seeker off at tangents or into cul-de-sacs.

FIGURE 14.2

Pretel

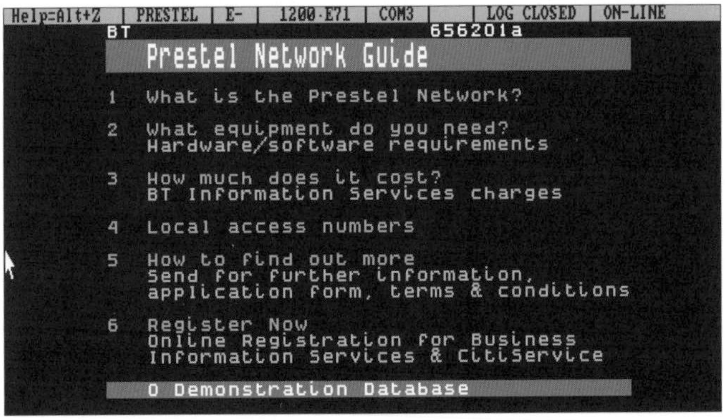

```
Help=Alt+Z | PRESTEL | E- | 1200·E71 | COM3 |    | LOG CLOSED | ON-LINE
          BT                              656201a
              Prestel Network Guide

         1  What is the Prestel Network?

         2  What equipment do you need?
            Hardware/software requirements

         3  How much does it cost?
            BT Information Services charges

         4  Local access numbers

         5  How to find out more
            Send for further information,
            application form, terms & conditions

         6  Register Now
            Online Registration for Business
            Information Services & CitiService

            0 Demonstration Database
```

Prestel security and administration was laughable in its early days and the system was publicly 'hacked' on many occasions. Since then Prestel has grown up and become respectable under the auspices of BT, and is now comparable in quality, if not in breadth, to many other EuroText services. Prestel caters mainly for business services but has gateways to other information providers. There is a demo access available on 071 618 1111. Many exchanges have a local charge-rate access for Prestel – try dialling 7311 with your modem.

- MAIN NUMBER: 071 618 1111
  EMULATION: PRESTEL DATA: 7-E-1
  SPEED: V23, V22, V22 BIS

- ACCESS: ENTER 'DEMO' OR A USER NUMBER OF 4444444444, WITH A PASSWORD OF 4444

Austria – VTX

The Austrians allow access to VTX via a demo account. Simply type a 0 (zero) to gain entry. You can start a search with the hash (#) key.

- MAIN NUMBER: 010 43 51 258 45 84
  EMULATION: BTX DATA: 8-N-1
  SPEED: V23, V22, V22 BIS

France – Teletel

The French have taken videotext to heart with their Teletel service which was introduced as an experiment by France Telecom in 1981. Minitel started off as an electronic telephone directory and every telephone subscriber in France was offered the chance to own or rent a Minitel terminal at a very low price. The result was mass acceptance of videotext into peoples homes. In later days Minitel has become a national hobby and is minting money for some of the information providers (IPs) who now offer value added service of every shape and variety. A new Irish-French joint venture company is now marketing Minitel services in the UK. Watch out BT, the marketing professionals are coming...

There was a national outcry in 1991 about the huge increase in the numbers of 'personal services' (a euphemism for erotic or pornographic) pages on Minitel. This paralleled fears in the UK over the use of premium rate pay-as-you-go 0898 numbers by persons pedalling similar wares.

Statistics for the service are staggering: in France alone Minitel subscribers generate 105 million hours of service a year, from 1.7 billion calls (source Transpac). Minitel is expanding rapidly, there are new services opening up in the USA, and there is a joint Franco-Irish Minitel project under way. Transpac, the French PTT has aggressive marketing campaigns now running throughout Europe and including the UK, and looks set to become a force to be reckoned with in the future. New services include electronic payments from the Minitel terminal and provision of specialist business services such as credit check and information marketing. Even Prestel has joined onto Minitel. Prestel subsribers now have access to some of the Minitel directory services.

FIGURE 14.3

Teletel France

If you wish to access Teletel through PSS or outside France you can contact Intelmatique SA in Paris. They will allow full access through PSS when you register.

■ MAIN NUMBERS
010 33 36 42 13 13 FOR TELETEL 1
010 33 36 42 14 14 FOR TELETEL 2

The English version of the French telephone directory on this number. Type ED for British, ETB for German, GTE for Spanish.

■ 010 33 36 42 15 15 FOR TELETEL 3
FRENCH TELEPHONE DIRECTORY: 010 33 36 43 11 11
EMULATION: MINITEL
DATA: 7-E-1 SPEED: V23

■ ACCESS: TYPE 'MGS' FOR AN ON-LINE GUIDE TO THE SYSTEM ON ANY OF THE MAIN NUMBERS.

Germany – Bildschirmtext

Bildschirmtext (screen text) has been around almost as long as Prestel and is a large system. It uses the BTX viewdata standard, which technically is called CEPT Profile 1. When you access the main telephone number Bildschirmtext displays a Guest log-in number on the Welcome screen. Pressing [enter] gets you into the system. You will need to register to get full access to the system. Bildschirmtext has a number of links to other countries, notably the USA via INFONET, and has multilingual capabilities. Bildschirmtext is fussy about the sorts of modems it connects to and does not seem to like data compression or error correction being present.

Entering *1401# from the main menu makes the system speak English.

■ MAIN NUMBERS: 010 49 69 19304 V22 BIS
010 49 69 19300 V22
010 49 69 19100 V23
EMULATION: BTX DATA: 8-N-1
GUEST ACCESS NUMBER: 000829017874

Italy – Videotel

This system doesn't give free access and you need a 'codici d'accesso' (user-number) to get in. The system provides all three viewdata standards and contains the Italian telephone directory.

■ MAIN NUMBER: 010 39 2 54 678 (MILANO)
EMULATION: BTX DATA: 8-N-1
EMULATION: PRESTEL DATA: 7-E-1
EMULATION: MINITEL DATA: 8-N-1

Luxembourg – Videotext

Another multi-lingual system that speaks French, English and German. Videotex doesn't have an official demo facility but there is an interesting way available of entering the system as a guest. Full details are in the Dortec Guide to Viewdata Systems. The system will throw you off if you cannot convince it that you have a correct access number.

■ MAIN NUMBER: 010 352 0711
EMULATION: BTX DATA: 8-N-1

FIGURE 14.4

VideoTex Luxembourg

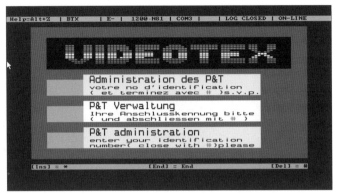

Netherlands – VideotexNet

This is a large system which contains a number of access points, both from inside the Netherlands and from other European systems. Videotex Nederland is a kiosk system; it detects your phone number and then bills you accordingly. This service is not available from UK PTTs as yet and correspondingly there is little to see on the service from the UK. This is unfortunate as there is much there of interest. The service also uses Minitel and ASCII for some gateways. You can get to Videotex Nederland from the Belgian RTT Videotex system.

FIGURE 14.5

VideotexNet The Netherlands

- MAIN NUMBER: 010 31 6 7100
  EMULATION: PRESTEL DATA: 7-E-1
  SPEED: V23,V22

Norway – Teledata

A Scandinavian system with a guest log-in available. To gain access type 000000 (six zeros) and six zeros again as a password.

FIGURE 14.6

Teledata

```
Help=Alt+Z | MINITEL | E- | V23-E71 | COM3 |     | LOG CLOSED | ON-LINE


                   Velkommen til Teledata



           ┌──────────────────────────────────────┐
           │  Brugernummer: ■                       │
           │                                        │
           │  Password:                             │
           └──────────────────────────────────────┘

           Hvis password er mindre end 8 cifre/
           tegn afsluttes med <ENTER> eller (#)




    [Enter] = Send        [↑] = Previous      [↓] = Next
    [Home] = Index        [BkSp] = Correction  [F1] = Guide
    [F2] = Repeat         [Del] = Cancel      [End] = Local/connect
```

■ MAIN NUMBER: 010 47 5 32 14 09
EMULATION: BTX DATA: 8-N-1
SPEED: V22, V22 BIS

Portugal – SPV

Another large system with international gateways to other services. SPV is undergoing lots of development at the time of writing.

■ MAIN NUMBER: PSS ONLY FROM THE UK.
NUA 9268005400100
EMULATION: BTX/MINITEL/PRESTEL (TRY BTX FIRST) DATA: 8-N-1
SPEED: V23 AND PSS

Spain – Ibertex

One of the few systems that does not restrict UK callers. A good place to try out your holiday Spanish, too. The service is often busy and it's best to call in the morning. To see the Ibertex guide type:

*GUIA# at the main menu.

FIGURE 14.7

Ibertex Spain

FIGURE 14.8

Ibertex services directory

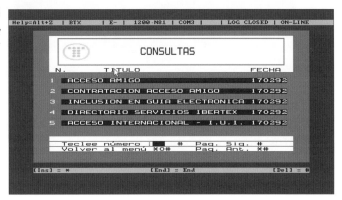

■ MAIN NUMBER: 010 34 1 801 90 31/32/33

. TELEPHONE DIRECTORY ON THE 33 NUMBER

EMULATION: BTX DATA: 8-N-1

SPEED: V23

Sweden – Videotex

This system has demo facility, which is useful if you can read Swedish. It also supports both the Prestel and BTX emulation on two different phone numbers.

■ MAIN NUMBER: 010 46 31 84 47 55 (BTX – 8-N-1)

SPEED: V23

ACCESS: ENTRENUMMER: 488069669, MEDABONNENT NUMMER: 1234, LOSENORD: 'DEMO'

Switzerland – VTX

The Swiss have spent some of their loose change on VTX, a large multi-lingual video-text service. The service speaks English, French and Italian. The telephone directory is available to guests by typing:

*ETB# for the German language directory

*F*ETB# for the French language directory

*I*ETB# for the Italian language directory

■ MAIN NUMBERS:
010 41 47 01 11 11 – V23
010 41 46 05 11 21 – V22
010 41 46 05 11 24 – V22 BIS
EMULATION: BTX DATA: 8-N-1

More EuroText information

Dortec, the company that makes Rencom Plus, has produced a Guide to European Viewdata systems which lists full information and gives registration details for the services above. Rencom Plus is fully supported in the UK by Shareware Marketing in Seaton, Devon. See special offer coupon at the back of this book.

Viewdata and the future

Viewdata systems are starting to look a little dated by today's standards. The screens are slow over V23 links, and you may have to wade through half a dozen menus and password options before you find the information you require. The user interface in particular changes from system to system. This is indictable on services run by different information providers (IPs), where each IP has implemented a different log-in and log-off sequence, despite running over the same carrier. The AT&T UK Travel Service, run for travel agents is good example – some IPs use 90#, others have a different exit code. This makes using the service on an ad-hoc basis tiring and unpleasant.

What can surpass viewdata as a means of providing computer information to the future masses? The answer is probably multimedia – a 1991 buzzword which means 'combined graphics and sound from a single source'. At the moment multimedia is in its infancy but already it has the capacity to provide photographic quality graphics and digital sound, using a basic 16-bit computer as the transducer. Connect a multimedia station up to an ISDN line and Voila! – the death of viewdata is nigh. Existing videotext services will probably still be with us for the next decade, which is sad because the standard will not have moved forwards in 20 years by that time. Already V23 looks slow and cumbersome. In the year 2002 it will simply not be acceptable.

14.3 Practical EuroComms

Your flight bag is packed, you have a fortnight's supply of cheese sandwiches and brown ale in your suitcase, and the airline has confirmed your flight to Milano. Have you forgotten anything else for your fortnight in the sun? Ah yes, the computer.

You have decided that you will not succumb to the filthy foreign habit of relaxing while on holiday and you are taking your laptop computer and modem with you to prove it. But a shadow crosses your pale untanned face. Will the modem work in these far off countries? Will you be stopped at the airport for exporting Britain's trade secrets? Will your wife ever forgive you for being such a heartless basket of a workaholic?

If you do decide to take a computer and modem abroad you will almost certainly run into difficulties of one sort or another. The first problem will be at the airport, where you will be asked at the airline check-in desk to unpack any equipment containing batteries that is packed away into your suitcases. Airlines do not like boxes containing wires and batteries and if you decide not to tell the check-in clerk that there is 'something' in your main luggage remember that it will show up on the X-ray equipment behind the airline desk. Your embarrassment in this case will be more than complete. You should take all computer and battery-operated equipment through as hand baggage, where it will be manually searched and X-rayed.

There is a lot of consternation about the effect of X-rays on computer equipment – the airline security people will tell you that there is no effect on equipment, as will the equipment manufacturers. However the author's NEC laptop did not survive being X-rayed at Barbados Airport in 1990, and there are other similar horror stories about. All you can do is to check that the machine is working before and after it goes through the equipment, and if you find any problems you must complain there and then, even at the risk of holding up the flight.

EuroModems

It's a vain hope to expect to use your modem in Europe without taking some special precautions before you leave Blighty. Your first problem will be getting your British Telecom jack plug into the sockets of our Continental cousins. It won't fit. Of course you can buy adaptor leads for each country you visit, but until we have our PanEuropean Approvals procedure you will almost certainly be breaking some regulation or other if you attempt to make a direct connection to the phone line.

The best solution for travelling modem user is to use a pocket modem fitted with an acoustic coupler. This device looks a little like a pair of Walkman headphones – one end slips over the phone mouthpiece and the other over the earpiece of the phone handset. The end with the plug on it goes into a socket on the modem or onto the end of the phone lead which would otherwise go into the phone socket.

Acoustic couplers used to be unreliable, especially in the days when most of us had carbon-phones fitted to our telephones. Modern electronic phones tend to use electret microphones which are much clearer, and don't suffer from the in-built crackle of loose carbon granules. A number of British modem manufacturers make modems with an acoustic coupler connection. Some of these devices also have a normal lead and plug connection for UK use.

Our American cousins seem to be able to plug almost anything into their telephone networks without fear of litigation, and a number of BBSs in the States carry details of travel kits for the travelling communicator, together with instructions on how to use them. These travel kits consist of collections of small pieces of wire, RJ11/RJ14 phone connectors, test meters, needle nosed pliers and such like. The idea is that if you are armed with a sufficiently flexible tool kit you can tackle any sort of telephone socket, no matter where. In reality of course you need a certain amount of technical knowledge to hardwire your modem to the back of a hotel room phone socket, and the procedure cannot be recommended. If you are tempted to start levering the tops off Continental phone sockets then you should at least remember that the voltage used to ring telephones is much higher than the 50 or so volts used to drive the speech circuits, and these voltages can kill in some circumstances.

So forget the tool kits, the suitcase full of phone connectors and the hassle of carrying computers and modems halfway around the world to find that they don't work. Go buy yourself an acoustic coupler.

Adaptor leads

If you do happen to have a correctly approved modem but find that you have the wrong connector on the end, you should be able to pick up the correct lead in most major cities. (Except in Italy, for no good reason). Most modems terminate their incoming phone lead into an RJ11 or RJ14 connector, sometimes referred to as an American phone jack. In most European countries it is possible to buy the correct lead from an electronics store. In Paris the BHV is a good place to start looking, in Holland try the Pavilioensgracht in the Hague, or at any Primfoon outlet. In Germany and Belgium the leads or adapter plugs are often available at the large supermarkets that sell telephones, as is the case in Spain.

In Britain…? Well, a good starting place is your local Tandy store.

Euro dial tones

Not all dial tones are the same. Not all modems are the same. Not all modems recognise all dial tones, and the same goes for ringing tones, and busy signals.

Much of Europe is being converted to DTMF (Dual Tone Multi Frequency) dialling but there are many countries where pulse dialling is still the norm. You can easily check if pulse dialling remains by tone dialling a single digit from your modem. If the dial tone remains then the system is using pulse dialling.

You can make your modem pulse dial (unless it's an acoustic coupler) by using the command ATDP[number] or by putting the P in your modem initialisation string in whatever comms package you are using. Acoustic coupler users will have to dial manually, and then use ATO[enter] (O for Originate) to go on-line when they hear the answering modem. If you get a NO DIALTONE response from your modem, even though there is dial tone present then you can tell your modem to ignore dial tone with ATX4[enter], in many cases. The reality of travelling in Europe with a modem is that you will have little success with a direct-connect modem not actually bought in the country in which you intend to use it, unless you are prepared to change leads and plugs, and fight with Hayes commands. But acoustic couplers do give you a half decent chance of getting through, especially in France, Belgium and Germany.

The Italian phone network is undergoing massive development at the moment and it often seems to be a case of some phones work with modems, others don't. Spain and

Portugal seem to be rewiring the entire Iberian Peninsula and again, reports from those two countries are mixed.

The svelt Euro-communicator

You should bear in mind that the successful Eurocomms user is a fluent speaker of the local language and can deal with irascible hotel telephone operators. This peculiar breed (distantly related to Homo Sapiens) often wonder what those strange noises are coming from the phone, and consequently summon the manager or the police, and occasionally, the army. Bear in mind also that hotel phone bills in Europe are often twice or three times the going rate for pay-phone access, and not everywhere will accept plastic cards in payment, especially if you have upset the dragon on the switchboard.

And remember that a smattering of the local lingo turns you from being a filthy foreigner in the eyes of the locals, to becoming a half-civilised European. The English habit of shouting at Continentals to make them understand no longer works. It is we who are foreign, not they.

15 COMPUSERVE

"Enjoy your neighbours, without boasting of your riches"

15.1 CompuServe Incorporated

CompuServe is one of Europe's largest information providers, after Minitel. It runs from computers in Columbus Ohio and has about 20,000 European users at present. CompuServe came into being in 1969, initiated by Harry Gard, a Columbus businessman. The service was originally started as a data processing business for Harry's insurance company and became CompuServe Information Service in 1979. The company was acquired by H&R Block a year later and has continued to grow ever since. CompuServe rapidly gained popularity among its native Americans for the strength and quality of the financial services it provided. It has today become one of the most popular single network entities on the planet, providing news information and support to over a million global users.

CompuServe is the largest coherent information provision system in the world. Why is the service so popular? Probably because you don't need any special equipment to access it other than a terminal and a modem, it's available to all with few administrative restrictions and CompuServe offers something for everybody. The main attraction to many is the fact that CompuServe is truly a global service. News, opinions, knowledge and facts come in from all round the world.

FIGURE 15.1

CompuServe – the service

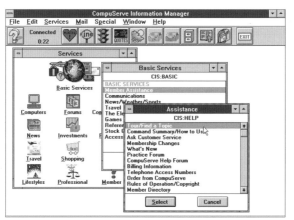

The latest additions to the service are access nodes in Hong Kong and Israel, and it's now possible to gain access from 120 countries. If the global village exists it exists in the cabinets of CompuServe's 37 DEC KL and System Concepts SC-30 mainframes. The medium is certainly the message.

What's in CompuServe for me?

The glib answer is 'lots'. The proper answer is communication and support with 1.2 million other people. That's more people than there are modems in Britain, by the way. If you have almost any sort of hobby, commercial or professional interest you will find others on the service to share it with. This differs radically from the concept of the recreational bulletin board where specialised interests tend to rule the message areas.

Sticking a pin into the CompuServe Forum Index comes up with: ABC World Wide Hotel Guide, Bacchus Wine Forum, Contact Lens Supplies, Fine Arts Forum and so on. For Z try the Zagat Restaurant guide. CompuServe is getting to be like The Hitchhikers' Guide to the Universe concept, only bigger. And you can carry it around in your pocket if you have a palm-top computer and a small modem.

FIGURE **15.2**

A few of the 400 forums available

CompuServe's powerful research and E-mail facilities were invaluable in the production of this book as you may have read in the Preface. Those same facilities are open to you, whether you are writing a book, researching a thesis or trying to out-smart your Open University tutor. One useful aspect of the service is its global appeal – you are just as likely to get an answer to a question from Japan or Australia as you are from the UK or USA – the service is used by so many people.

This spread of culture makes CompuServe seem very open to those who use it and there are few preconceptions or bigots in the forums, everyone is interested in everyone else. Accessing CompuServe is like stepping into a different country – the views of other contributors reflects the global diversity of people's opinions and cultures. If you do have friends or business contacts in other countries CompuServe is the ideal way to keep in touch. It's generally cheaper to send global mail by CompuServe than it is either to post it or use a dial-out point-to-point link with your modem.

What do I need to access the service?

You need a modem, a terminal or computer and a CompuServe Membership Kit. The kit includes CompuServe Information Manager (CIM) for the Mac, DOS or Windows platforms, a new members guide and a $25 usage credit. The kit can be obtained by telephoning 0800 289 458 in the UK or using the coupon in the back of this book. If you have a credit or charge card you can sign up straight away and be given an interim password and account over the phone. The call is free, by the way. CompuServe often market special membership deals, and these can be found in the UK computer press when they appear.

CompuServe is connected to a number of other networks and transport mechanisms throughout the world. In Britain you can gain access either via direct dial numbers in Birmingham or Manchester, or via the GNS Dialplus packet switch network. The Mercury 5000 packet switch network now connects to CompuServe too. If you go by Dialplus/Mercury 5000 you will be charged a small amount for the packet switch connection which will be added to your CompuServe bill by the reverse billing features of the Dialplus/Mercury 5000 network.

FIGURE 15.3

CompuServe settings for a 2400bps modem

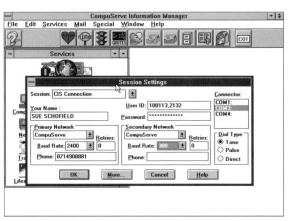

If you are calling from other countries within Europe you can access CompuServe through the Infonet and Datex-P networks in many European countries. For access set your comms software to 7-E-1, full-duplex. You can use speeds from V21 (300bps), V22 (1200bps) V22 bis (2400), or V32 (9600bps). V32 bis is likely to be added in the near future. If you have ISDN access you should find that CompuServe will offer UK ISDN connections as soon as the market starts to demand it. A good guess is towards the end of 1994. Remember that charges are higher for faster connections and a good place to start is with V22 or V22 bis as the displays are adequately fast at this speed. If you intend to download files and have a V32 modem you will find that setting your connection speed to 9600 produces cost effective fast downloads.

CIM for Windows works well at 9600 on a fast PC, it's possible to set a stream of downloads going while you continue to use the forum messaging and mail services. Conversely if you use the CB simulator, then as the amount of data being transmitted is so low you should find that a 300 bps connection is the most cost effective. If you live miles away from London or Reading you should go through the Dialplus/ Mercury 5000 PS network to access CompuServe. When you connect to Dialplus or Mercury 5000 you will be asked for a password which is UKCNS, and a host name which is CIS. From there you will be connected to CompuServe by the Packet Switch network and you will need your User ID.

CompuServe and CompuServe Information Manager

CompuServe will squirt raw ASCII at you by default. This ploy makes the service available to virtually any terminal in the world but falls foul of the sentiments previously expressed in this book about unfriendly command line interfaces. CompuServe has recognised that raw ASCII is about as appealing as raw liver for breakfast and has done something about it. The result is called HMI/CIM. HMI is Host/Micro Interface. HMI sends codes to your computer based terminal to tell it to generate menus and windows, and to automate many of the key-pressing processes into mouse clicks. The software which sits on your computer and translates of these codes is called CompuServe Information Manager or CIM. CIM is available for PCs and Macs, and a Windows 3.x version is now here.

The Windows version is particularly notable as it performs background tasks with ease – it's possible to set CIM to download files in the background while you check out your mail or look around a forum. CIM is also bundled (given away) with many of the special offers and membership deals that CompuServe offers from time to time.

All versions of CIM can be downloaded from CompuServe (type `GO CIM`) and they generally come with a credit for usage time – i.e. you pay for the software but are compensated in full for using it on the service.

If you have previously been used to using ASCII or ANSI based systems and you switch to CIM you will be amazed at the functionality it provides. The software uses the processing power of your computer to provide a real graphical user interface comprising windows and pull-down menus. CompuServe comes alive as a result. ASCII based CompuServe is still provided for some of the services such as billing, but CIM turns CompuServe into a powerful menu and event driven tool for business and recreational users. You shouldn't be without it. The Windows version has loads of functionality, including off-line message reading and preparation. Commercial BBS sysops who are still running command line interfaces should take note!

OLRs

CIM isn't yet available for Atari or Amiga computers but many off-line readers (OLRs) are and these can be downloaded from CompuServe. An OLR is a program which effectively transfers whole chunks of CompuServe to your hard disk. It will let you read your messages and prepare replies off line, they can then be dispatched at cheap call and connect rates to CompuServe.

If you use CIM for your front end to CompuServe you may not need an OLR, but if you work a lot within the forums you will find an OLR invaluable. OLRs either save money by reducing connect times, or provide an increase on usage for the same connection costs. Many OLRs for CompuServe are either public domain (free usage) or shareware (you pay a small fee for use after an evaluation period).

15.2 Looking around CompuServe

So. You have your User ID, your password and you have picked an access number local to you. Let's dial-up CompuServe and have a rummage around its insides. Our first stop will be CompuServe Mail. In all of the following 'how-to-do-it' sections it will be assumed that you are using CIM on a PC. You can access the same features without using CIMs GUI feature or with non-PC computers of course, but as CIM is so user-friendly we should be using it.

E-mail

E-mail is the sending of documents and files by means of electronic data transfer. CompuServe manages to do rather well with its implementation of E-mail. This is because you can use CompuServe Mail features to:

■ SEND AND RECEIVE E-MAIL TO USERS OF :
COMPUSERVE, MCI MAIL, INTERNET, AT&T MAIL, AT&T EASYLINK, NOVELL NETWARE MHS USERS.

■ SEND PAPER MAIL TO ANYWHERE IN THE WORLD

■ SEND TEXT TO ANY FAX MACHINE

■ SEND TEXT TO ANY TELEX MACHINE

You can send ASCII text messages of up to 50,000 characters per message, and binary data files of up to 512k in length. If you use CIM you will find that all the send options are presented to you in a series of impossibly friendly menus, and you can build your own address books and filing cabinets of contacts and letters. As E-mail includes the ability to send data (binary) files the E-mail service is great for corporate support teams and for marketing or for sending copies of the new shoot-em-up game you have just written to friends across the world.

CompuServe Mail makes setting up and receiving a call over a point-to-point modem link look difficult, and is generally a much cheaper and reliable way to get mail and data around the world. CIM even makes the process simple enough for company directors and CEOs (Chief Executive Officers) to understand, which says a lot for its ease of use.

CompuServe Mail was used extensively during the preparation of this book to mail data and files to Don Milne, the author of Odyssey in Aberdeen, to correspond with Denis Dornoy of Dortech in Copenhagen and various people in the USA. The service provides an almost instantaneous transfer of data to the recipient's mailbox and on a number of occasions mail was replied to whilst the author was still on line. Is that fast enough for you?

CompuServe has hooks into the USA 'snail-mail' (postal) service, which despite the disparaging term used here, seems remarkably efficient. If you select the Postal Mail option CompuServe prints out your electronic text onto white bond paper, seals it into an envelope with your return address at the top and posts it via first class mail.

This is a good way of sending international letters around the world without having to leave your office or workplace. It's also ideal if you are housebound and don't wish to rely too much on other people. Paper mail sent in this way was often received by the recipient the following day.

E-mail for the corporate user

CompuServe's mail service via the CIM front-end software is probably one of the easiest of all to use to use. This makes it ideal for the corporate environment where training users costs time, and therefore money. If you are an IT manager or director you will know from bitter experience that giving staff awkward tools to use invariably means that they won't use them. It's a fact of life.

CompuServe and CIM together are arguably the best solution to many of the needs for ad-hoc global E-mail that exist within corporates: the service is supported and maintained by a third party at no extra cost to you, it runs 24 hours a day, the plug cannot be pulled out by the cleaners, and thousands of other companies worldwide have access to the system. If your in-house users are on a Novell LAN then mail can be forwarded to and from CompuServe via the CompuServe Mail Hub, which operates in conjunction with a modem and a Netware MHS gateway PC on your LAN. This system is easy to operate and requires little in the way of additional capital investment to set up. If you already have a Novell LAN and MHS then you can set up a global E-mail option within your company for the price of the gateway PC, a V32 modem and a CompuServe membership.

One prime example of a corporate need for global E-mail occurs when a UK company with affiliated offices in Europe, Australia and the States needs to send end-of-month accounting figures to all offices. This is often done by fax, or even courier, but E-mail makes it possible for those figures to be sent as electronic spreadsheet or database files. This saves endless amounts of time spent in re-keying the data by the recipient, and of course CompuServe is utterly confidential.

If you do use this method to mail confidential matter around the world then remember that most spreadsheet and database files can have a password encrypted into them should you happen to mail them to the wrong person by accident. If you send other confidential matters then PKZIP and alternative file compression programs also have password encryption built in. Finally, CIM allows messages and files to be copied to other users by means of a 'CC' option. This is selected with a couple of mouse clicks, so one simple operation is all that is needed to mail all the offices in this example. It's a snap, as our cousins across the pond say.

15.3 Technical support services on CompuServe

You have just taken delivery of a new expensive PC. It is supposed to run its 8 Mbyte of internal memory in something called Extended Mode, but the instruction manual for your favourite word processor tells you that the program needs Expanded Mode. What does all of this mean? And who can you turn to for help? (It's Saturday afternoon).

CompuServe offers a multitude of areas dedicated entirely to technical support for virtually every computer system still in operation. (This includes the author's ten-year-old Tandy laptop). These areas are called forums (pl. forums or fora) and they are areas where people meet and exchange files, opinions and ideas. Many of the forums are run by commercial companies, and it's very often possible to receive help not just from the sales manager for that company but from the actual programmer who wrote the code.

FIGURE 15.4

Computer support extends to user reviews of hardware and software

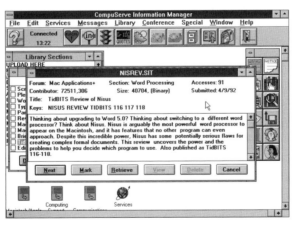

In our example above you would go into the MS-DOS forum by typing 'GO MSDOS' and then use CIM to search for files with the keyword 'MEMORY'. CompuServe would bring you a list of suitable files, together with a small description of each, and you would certainly find a text file detailing the use of and updates to a system driver called EMM386.SYS – an expanded memory driver for MS-DOS machines. If you wanted a little more information you could search through the messages in the forum. Many companies also place software updates in the File Libraries and these can be downloaded directly to your computer for instant use. This makes the service invaluable for both corporate and domestic users.

15.4 CompuServe forums

Forums (GO FORUMS) are special services on CompuServe. They put you directly in touch with other people who have similar interests. Forums are places where people can meet and exchange information across town or around the world. CompuServe offers over 350 forums and each one is dedicated to a special interest like cooking, investment, computers, auto racing, health, software programs, law, travel, and word processing. You can join as many as you like. Each forum is like an online club where everyone is welcome.

Forums offer an exceptional opportunity to explore new interests and meet others who share those interests – experts and novices alike. You will find that each forum has its own personality. Some lean toward shoptalk, others toward casual conversation. But in any forum, you are certain to find people who are willing to share whatever they know about the topic at hand, whether it is choosing a wine or using a computer.

How forums are organised

Each forum contains three main areas:

- MESSAGE BOARDS
  Here members correspond with one another by posting messages. You can find person-to-person notes, answers to questions, and ongoing discussions.

- LIBRARIES
  These are resource areas that contain program and text files. You can find reference materials of all kinds, plus transcripts from on-line conferences. You can read these on-line, or download them to your computer. You also can find a variety of useful software (public domain, shareware, and freeware) that you can download and add to your personal computer software library.

- CONFERENCE ROOMS
  Here members gather on-line for 'live' conversations. You can participate in unsched-

uled chats, formal meetings, or special conferences hosted by guest speakers.

Who takes care of a forum?

Each forum has at least one person who oversees that forum's activities. He or she is called the forum manager or sysop (short for SYStem OPerator). Sysops welcome new members, host conferences, provide help, and maintain the message boards and libraries. Although they usually are not CompuServe employees, sysops work closely with CompuServe to ensure that the forums operate smoothly.

FIGURE 15.5

One of many human interest forums

How to find a forum

CompuServe offers several ways you can find a forum you like. The menu below, for example, can help you find a forum that matches your interests. To get to this menu, enter GO FORUMS.

```
1       Aviation Forums
2       Education Forums
3       Science/Technology
4       Entertainment/Games Forums
5       Financial Forums
6       Hardware Forums
7       Media/Electronic Publishing
```

```
8       Home/Health/Family Forums
9       Professional Forums
10      Software Forums
Enter choice or <CR> for more !
```

To see more forum categories, press the carriage return key. This key is usually denoted by the symbol <CR>.

```
11      Sports Forums
12      Travel Forums
Last menu page, enter choice !
```

After you select a forum category, CompuServe displays a menu of forums. If you select Financial Forums, for example, CompuServe will display this menu on your screen:

```
FINANCIAL FORUMS
1       Investors Forum
2       NAIC Forum
3       Javelin User's Forum
4       The World of Lotus
5       Monogram Software Forum
6       Instructions/Fees
Enter choice !
```

To visit one of these forums, enter the number beside its name. You also can use the FIND command to find a forum that matches your interests. For an alphabetised menu of forums and their quick reference words, enter FIND FORUM. To access a forum directly, use the GO command and the forum's quick reference word (for example, GO IBMNEW). The quick reference word appears at the top right corner of a forum's introductory page. Forums are the heart and soul of CompuServe. If you cannot find an answer to a question here, the chances are you won't easily find it anywhere.

15.5 Modem gaming

No, modem gaming isn't something that uses pocket modems instead of roulette chips. It's a whole sub-class of in-home entertainment where you do battle with your human opponents over a modem link. Here's what New Yorker Mike Shoenbach says about modem gaming:

"Modem-to-modem gaming is a feature of a growing number of computer games that enables you to link up and play micro-computer games with other people. These games typically support one or more of the following implementations:

Null-modem connection

This allows local players to connect their computers together with a null-modem cable for head-to-head play. Often, these connections are cross-platform (ie one player using an Atari ST and the other an Amiga). The advantage of a null-modem connection between two computers over a standard single-computer multiplayer game is most apparent in complex multi-screen games, particularly flight simulators. Each player has access to his or her own full keyboard, mouse, and/or joystick, and can explore and engage in play while in separate areas of the game's electronic world. The action comes to head when the two players enter the same domain and confront each other.

File-based competition

Two players can engage in competition by saving and transferring the game scenario to their opponent for response. Similar to an electronic play-by-mail game, this form of modem-to-modem play is mostly used in turn-based games. The main advantage of a file-based competition game is that the players do not compete in real-time, thus allowing each player to participate in the competition according to his or her convenience. Additionally, connect-time between the two computers is minimal because only a simple file transfer is necessary to support the multi-player competition.

Direct modem (head-to-head) connection

This allows two players to connect their computers via modem to engage in head-to-head play. Characteristically similar to a null-modem connection, games that support a direct modem connection can practically turn the world into one giant video arcade as your opponent can be located across the street, across the country, and yes, even across the world! You can play against anyone who has a telephone line, a Hayes-compatible modem, and a copy of the game.

Modem-to-modem gaming is perhaps one of the most dynamic forms of computer gaming currently available. It is very attractive because it combines the sophistication of today's computer games with the social interaction made possible through advancing telecommunications technology. These games have bridged computer gaming – often charged with being an anti-social form of entertainment – with traditional gaming by adding back that important missing quality of social interaction. The numbers indicate that computer users see the value and advantage of bringing their work online and sharing information with other real people via electronic bulletin boards and information services.

Messaging with modem games

Modem games not only allow people to meet and play with other people from all over the world, but playing a traditional (graphics) computer game with another person adds a whole new dimension to the actual game play. Because each player brings to the game his or her own personal experience and skill, each game session becomes much more unpredictable and consequently much more challenging.

Many of these modem games also support a messaging function that allows the players to chat back and forth to each other in between the action. This messaging feature has proved to be one of the most popular components of these games as it allows both players to share human responses in reaction to gaming manoeuvres. If the two players established contact through an electronic bulletin board or information service, the messaging function also enables the players to get to know each other.

As a result of this feature, many valuable personal and professional relationships have developed in between exploding F-16 missiles, checkmates, volcanic eruptions, and conquering tank artillery.

Games services on CompuServe

To help modem-to-modem game players get in contact with each other, the CompuServe Information Service offers three services to serve players' needs. The Challenge Board (GO CHALLENGE) is an electronic directory of modem game players. Participants profile themselves in this directory so other games can easily search for them as opponents for most commercial, shareware, and freeware games that support the modem-to-modem feature.

Additionally, the Modem Games Forum (GO MODEMGAMES), an electronic special interest group, is available for members to discuss all aspects of games that support modem play. The forum features an electronic bulletin board for message correspondence, data libraries for file exchange, and conference rooms for real-time interactive discussions. The Modem Games Forum contains one of the most complete collection of freeware and shareware modem-to-modem games available.

The most recent addition to CompuServe's expanding modem-to-modem gaming coverage is the Modem-to-Modem (MTM) Gaming Lobby. The MTM Lobby allows players to connect their direct-connection, modem-capable games to opponents through the CompuServe network. The MTM Lobby affords players the convenience of staying on-line for all aspects of modem gaming, connects them to domestic and international opponents at reduced CompuServe connect charges, and offers both players anonymity since neither party needs to give out their phone number to connect.

Instructions on using CompuServe's modem-to-modem gaming services, including complete directions on how to connect most popular games, is available free-of-connect-charges by using the GO MTMGAMES command."

Thanks Mike. Mike Shoenbach seems to enjoy MTM gaming, but then he should. He is the sysop of the MTM conference, and half a dozen others on CompuServe. You can say "Yo" to Mike on 76703,4363.

15.6 Executive Information Services (EIS)

EIS is an acronym used by company executives to baffle the operatives of corporate Help Desk departments. A director will go to a luncheon run by some purveyor of modems, or network services or computers, and come away enthused with the idea that, regardless of what EIS actually is, he must have some. A directive is then issued to the hapless IT departments, who then have to implement this nebulous concept.

In reality EIS is the presentation of information and news services, and the implementation of the mechanisms needed to provide that information. EIS needs differ from company to company, but most directors of large companies need information regarding stock market performance, international news feeds, and indications of how well, (or how badly) their competitors are doing. This information often comes from disparate sources and generally needs subscriptions to several different information providers.

Setting up a complete EIS solution in this way is time consuming and expensive. And teaching a company director how to use dial-up comms and a modem to access half a dozen services, each of which needs different passwords and log-in routines, is a difficult process and one best avoided.

CompuServe has recognised this need and set up their Executive Service Option, a service which provides much of what is needed in an EIS, from a single source. The Executive Service Option also gives access to CompuServe's Executive News Service (ENS) which offers news from Reuters, United Press International, and Associated Press, together with featured articles from the Washington Post, and The Times, among several other sources.

ENS makes it possible to select your own news feeds and items of interest via keywords, which are then scanned. Any resulting 'hits' are placed into a folder for retrieval at a later date. This is a useful feature which saves much time and effort when compared with systems run by other EIS providers. CompuServe's intelligent newsroom will automatically fill your folder with relevant information for collection on a day-to-day basis.

FIGURE 15.6

Personal finance support

There is also a huge amount of investment information available on CompuServe, not surprising when you consider the origins of the service. Much of it USA generated, but there are also areas devoted to UK prices and financial information. At the moment there is no on-line brokerage available for UK users but the service is constantly being updated.

Finally, if your company director is one of those who always wears beige suits, drives a Jaguar coupé and sports a perpetual suntan then he will find the CompuServe on-line weather maps of the UK, USA, Continental Europe, Pacific Rim, and Australia to be of special interest. CompuServe's provision of extensive airline and hotel booking arrangements makes it possible for directors to spend more abroad time on 'business trips' than ever before.

15.7 Other services

Got an old Apple or Commodore Pet in the loft that you don't know what to do with? CompuServe makes it possible to keep your 'unusable' computer equipment going. There are files and support forums for just about every popular micro-computer that's ever been made, and a few unpopular ones too. The 1983 Atari 800XL was a popular home micro in its time but like many computers it died a death when the IBM PC became popular. But there are still people writing software for the Atari on CompuServe, and there are more than 4,700 files available for this machine alone on the service.

Much the same goes for the Tandy 100. There is so much support for this machine that one wonders why Tandy ever made it extinct. Apple, Zenith, and DEC machines are all supported on CompuServe, as are many other veterans.

FIGURE 15.7

Support for the ten year old
Tandy 100

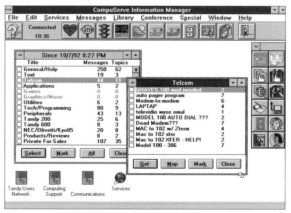

CompuServe is now so large that it's impossible to document every single service that it offers. But there is certainly something for everyone here. Non-computer based forums include fine art, the Audio Engineering Society, Aviation Forum, the Citizens Band simulator, a legal forum, much information on medical matters, pets and animals, scuba diving etc. There are suppliers like Sears who allow you to go shopping on-line and the number of forums is increasing all the time.

It's fair to say that CompuServe is so big that you are unlikely to be able to use it fully for a while. It seems to take most users a week or two to get the hang of it, but CompuServe does its bit to make life easier for neophytes. If you are looking for information on a particular topic then the FIND command should be your first stop, followed closely by a visit to the PRACTICE forum, where you can polish your skills before you go out into the big wide world of CompuServe.

The PRACTICE forum is also a genuinely useful place to meet people, and has a special atmosphere to it as everyone knows as much (or as little) as everyone else. CompuServe is also fully supported, both on-line and by an efficient customer service department. All new members receive a copy of the New Member's Guide, a wholly useful publication which gets you into the service with little fuss.

15.8 Is CompuServe for you?

If you have a real need for information in your work or professional interest then CompuServe seems to be unassailable in its ability to come up with the right information, time after time. For recreational use there is also much of interest, the only slight drawback being the size of the system. It takes time to navigate, and therefore incurs connect charges. But most recreational users explore CompuServe after 7pm, when call and connect charges are at their lowest.

CompuServe have introduced two useful billing options. Standard Plan charging gives you as much connect time as you need for a flat fee of $7.95. Alternate Plan charging means that you pay as you go. And you can switch between plans at your leisure.

Is CompuServe really so useful? The unequivocal answer is YES! If you have a lifestyle where you need interaction with other people, or access to accurate technical, financial or social information then CompuServe is one of those things that you wish you'd discovered years ago. If you have kids then CompuServe is probably one of the best educational presents you could ever give them, second to a computer and modem. Doesn't it make more sense than buying them video games?

FIGURE 15.8

Science topics on CompuServe

There are a few flies in CompuServe's ointment. The first is that the rapid growth of the serivce in Europe has lead to transport throughput problems over the data lines that link Europe with the States. This is the one major reason why CompuServe still doesn't offer V32 bis (14,400 bps) connections as they are unable to readily increase the service bandwith to cope. CompuServe are looking seriously at the problem, but it's unlikely that there will be much action before the end of 1993. And when V.FAST modems hit the streets the year after that then CompuServe will be faced with the same problem all over again, unless their planning staff are already listening to people like Hayes and all the other modem manufacturers who are planning for 28,800 bps throughput.

CompuServe's second problem is cost. The service is expensive enough in the UK to put it out of reach of many recreational users. Charges are also increased by the need for users who cannot access local nodes in London or Reading to have to go through the PSS network, increasing costs still further. Because of this CompuServe is slowly becoming something of an elitist service, availible only to those who can afford it . Whilst there is no doubt about the value the services it provides many UK comms users are becoming increasingly disillusioned with monthly bills of thirty or forty pounds, topped off with a large phone bill. CompuServe now have 'pay-as you go' pricing plans which help a little (GO BILLING) and if you can afford the service then it is unique and fascinating. But for those on a limited income it can seem expensive.

16

THE INTERNET

"Ignorant anticipation brings regrets"

16.1 The Internet

A network is a heap of computers connected together with signal cables. By networking computers together you increase their usefulness, and also the amount of esoteric knowledge needed to work and maintain them. Networks are for real computer users. A computer network allows users to share documents, applications, and electronic mail. If you go one step further and connect your network to another network you have created an inter-network, and once you have done that you can go on adding more networks and more computers to those inter-networks ad infinitum. The only things you need are increasingly large sums of money, and enough common sense to know when to stop spending it.

This is how The Internet started, as a ramshackle collection of scientific research computers, all hooked up together. It's now the largest coherent network in the world, with nearly a million separate computers connected to it. Only the telephone system is larger, but as we all know, the telephone system is an incoherent network.

The Internet was by and large created by the Pentagon's Advanced Research Projects Agency (ARPA) in the Kennedy era. The aim of ARPA was to bring together scientific minds to research and develop technology which would enable America to stay ahead in the Cold War between America and the rest of the world. This also happened to include the USSR. The guiding light in ARPA was Bob Taylor, a computer visionary who started trying to find better ways of working with computers, while he was at NASA. Taylor eventually moved to the Defense Department (spelt with an 's') and was one of the first funders/founders of ARPA.

ARPA-net

Taylor launched ARPA by setting up a number of research projects at American universities, and came up with the idea of ARPA-net, the very first transnational computer network. It's purpose was to link the scientists and researchers together. The technology used to transfer data between computers had been developed in the early sixties by Paul Baran, who was working on ways of preventing telephone systems from being destroyed by the electromagnetic pulse (EMP) effect during thermonuclear bomb blasts. Baran developed the first packet switching techniques, which were then incorporated into wide area network (WAN) technology by Mr. J.C. Licklider, who just happened to be a psychologist. JC Licklider was eventually to become the director of ARPA's information technology centre.

ARPAnet operated using DEC PDP-10 computers and the message and data handling was carried out using separate mini-computers known as TI's – (terminal interface processors). The TIPs were linked to other TIPs over leased phone connections and the first nodes connected were the University of California at Los Angeles, and also at Santa Barbara, the Stanford Research Institute, and the University of Utah.

By 1973 the ARPAnet had turned into a national network, but access to the system was limited to Universities, research establishments, and the odd private defence contractor. The network operated, like everything else in the sixties and early seventies, with a great sense of wonder that anything like this was at all possible, and there was no security anywhere on the system. Virtually any student (or friend of a student) who had access to a terminal connected to a TIP could log into any other computer, and spend hours or days cruising round its insides. Meanwhile, in the UK, computer enthusiasts were still trying to get elderly teletype printers to work with their HAM radio sets. Home computers were not to be unleashed to the masses in the UK until 1979.

Back in the USA changes were afoot. In 1975 the ARPAnet was turned over to the Defense Communications Agency, an organisation dedicated mainly to overseeing military and government radio and data traffic. If you study American history, and the relationship of that country with the rest of the world during the sixties and seventies, you'll see that America was becoming obsessed with national security, – although the reality of a threat from anyone other than a rebellious student population was highly unlikely. Security on the net was tightened somewhat, but to no great degree. The academics who ran and used the service had no great need for government intervention, apart from funding.

The ARPAnet was then limited to 8 bit addressing techniques, which meant that no more than 256 sites could be connected directly at any one time. A new network addressing scheme was introduced in 1982, which meant that thousands of networks could be connected to each other, and the true Internet was born.

The growth of the Internet was rapid, and spread not only to research establishments, but to the corporate sector. In the early days the ARPAnet was used mainly for communications and data generated and sustained by research projects but by the mid - 1980's the Internet was becoming saturated with electronic mail from all corners of the world, including private individuals. This was anathema to those involved at the start, mainly because costs of connecting to the Internet had dropped from the $250,000 to the sort of levels where small corporations could afford connection. Not only that, but the net was invaded by large numbers of journalists, whose editors had

forked out for corporate accounts and modems. By the start of the 1990's it was esti-
mated that the Internet carried over 2 million regular users, much to the chagrin of
the Universities and government departments who were directly funding the back-
bone of the service.

UNIX

In 1969 Ken Thompson, a worker at the Bell Laboratories Science Research Murray
Hill labs decided to invent UNIX, just as any normal person might experiment with
making an omelette. Thompson's idea was to write on operating system for his own
use, one which would multi-task, and eventually become virtually processor-indepen-
dent. Thompson's project quickly caught the enthusiasm of co-workers and UNIX
blossomed. Various universities also caught the bug, and many of the larger American
faculties eventually developed their own implementations of Thompson's work.

UNIX was tailor made for use on computer networks. Utilities such as ftp, finger and
sendmail became standards for accessing and using the computers connected to the
Internet. Even Bill Gates caught the UNIX bug, bought rights to the system and
released the Microsoft implementation (called XENIX), although sales were slow.

There are two types of UNIX user. There are those (mainly academics and programmers) who prefer the system above all else and are partisan about its qualities, and
those who see UNIX as the most dead-ended operating system in the world, next to
CP/M. The early UNIX implementations were often bug ridden, because anyone and
everyone had a hand its development and there was no central co-ordination of development amongst the academics who used and 'improved' UNIX. Authors of UNIX
books usually start their volumes with a introduction proclaiming that UNIX is the
world's most widely used operating system, but just which implementation of UNIX
this applies to is never stated. In fact there were so many implementations of UNIX
that it was possible to find different versions sitting on adjacent terminals, in most of
America's universities.

The combination of flaws in UNIX, the curious minds of students, an utter lack of
security on the Internet, and something called the 'hacker mentality' lead to huge
problems for the Internet on many occasions. Two notorious cases stand out, the
'Internet Worm' in which a student called Robert Morris brought much of the
Internet to a standstill with a self-replicating program (it exploited a flaw in the
UNIX sendmail program), and the case of a German hacker group who sold 'secrets'
to the Soviet KGB, obtained from American computers connected to the Internet.

Little real damage was done, although charges were brought to court in both cases.

16.2 Internet today

The Internet has continued to grow, and by the turn of this century and the end of the millennium, will boast over 1.5 million connected computers. The arrival of the personal computer and cheap telephone modem has meant that anyone can now connect to the Internet through the provision of a third party service provider (called Information Providers – IPs). Many recreational services now boast Internet connections, either purely for electronic mail use, as with CompuServe, or full interconnection to the Internet. Most of the computers connected to the Internet are hooked up via the National Packet Switch networks, or via the 'nodes' of commercial information providers.

Today there is so much information available on the Internet that tracking down whatever it is you are interested in is becoming increasingly difficult. To make matters worse there are few written standards or recommended procedures, and security on the Internet is still abysmal. Nevertheless, the Internet has recently achieved cult status in Britain, due mainly to the large numbers of IPs who are now selling network access. But one frequently overlooked fact about the Internet is that much of the incidental information therein is irrelevant or inaccurate, and exists purely for its own sake.

Getting onto the Internet

You can get access to the Internet in a variety of ways. The easiest method is to use the services of an Information Provider (IP) who will allow you access in Terminal Mode. This means that you use your existing computer, modem, and terminal software to dial into a host system that has an Internet feed attached. Your equipment then functions as a remote terminal connected to the host computer of the Information Provider. The Internet access node on the CIX (Compulink Information Exchange) dial-up Conferencing system is such an example.

Power users and Internet junkies often decide that they need a Network Connection. A Network Connection allows full access to the Internet. You get your own address for electronic mail (EMAIL), and it's possible to have your computer terminal provide multiple simultaneous connections (sessions) to different Internet nodes on the system. An example would be to have E-mail from CIX appear on your screen while you were connected to another computer somewhere on the system.

Network connections are expensive as they generally involve connections to the Packet Switch network and large payments to Information Providers, so companies like Demon Internet Services (DIS) (address in Appendix 5) provide a valuable service by leasing out network time on their own host computers. A subscription to DIS gives many of the facilities of a full network connection at a fraction of the cost, the only minor disadvantage is that specialist comms software has to be installed on your computer. This is supplied as part of the subscription to DIS. You can use your existing modem to dial into both CIX and DIS services.

Which connection type?

Terminal only connections such as those on CIX have the advantage of being easy to set up for the user – the only equipment you require is a computer with terminal emulation software. If you can already access CIX then you already have all the tools you need. If you just want occasional access to Internet E-mail, or some of the news feeder services on Internet (these are bundled together into a service called Usenet) then a terminal connection may be all you need. But for in-depth use you should consider a taking out a subscription to a Network Connection Provider such as DIS, as this may work out cheaper in the long run.

One small disadvantage with terminal connections such as those on CIX (apart from the single session limitation) is that files transferred over the Internet arrive in the in-tray of your Service Provider. They then have to be downloaded directly to you – a process which often takes three or four times as long as it did to get them from the other side of the world. Conversely a true Network Connection from DIS dumps the files directly onto the hard disk of your computer.

Internet jargon

You'll need to learn a little of the Internet jargon and command systems before you start spending your money on phone calls. These command systems are based on UNIX commands, and on UNIX system you would type these in lower case. On a personal computer system it may not matter whether you use upper or lower case, as programs like PC TCP/IP handle the translations for you.

Internet uses a couple of transport mechanisms to move data around the world. The first of these is FTP – File Transfer Protocol. FTP moves files from one site to another. Many remote sites offer 'Anonymous FTP' where files can be downloaded by anyone, often by using the password ANONYMOUS or FTP to get access to the system. FTP is also the way to gather information on the Internet itself. Many information-providing nodes have help files or entire books of compressed text which can be downloaded in this fashion.

TELNET is a command which allows you to connect to a remote site. You can TELNET to a site, log into the distant computer and use it as if you were attached locally. There are two further utilities which hunt across the Internet for information on your behalf. These are ARCHIE – interactive databases which keep lists of many of the files and utilities stored on the Internet, and GOPHER systems. GOPHER is a utility which networks services from around the Internet together into a menu-driven system. ARCHIE sites are a useful place to start looking for information and have the advantage of being menu-driven, for the most part.

UNIX-type commands such as PING allow you to check whether a site exists and whether it is alive or not before you TELNET or FTP to it and FINGER allows you to find out more details about a user or site.

Internet E-mail

One of the few consistent conventions on the Internet is the one used for allocating E-mail addresses. A CIX address for Fred Bloggs would translate to 'fbloggs@cix.compulink.co.uk.' (CIX is the host site, and its full name is Compulink Information Exchange) This structure is used across the Internet so that all computers can mail each other. 'co.uk' in this case means that Compulink is a UK Company, 'cd' would be an educational establishment, 'gov.' would be a government office, 'mil' would be a military establishment and so on.

Sending E-mail over the Internet is generally fast and reliable, but can sometimes take up to two days to reach its destination because of the amount of routing needed. There are reported delays of up to four days in some instances, especially where mail gets routed through the gateways of some of the smaller information providers.

Most of the commercial E-mail providers such as CompuServe, GEISCO, MCI MAIL and US Sprint now also recognise the Internet form of address, and it's usually possible to send mail from any system to any other system – as long as you know the full E-mail address format.

If you have an E-mail address it's useful to publish it on your letterhead, fax header or business card so others can find you easily. Your E-mail address is also the passport to many of the sites that allow anonymous FTP – you will generally be asked to present it as a password. It's therefore useful to assign a macro or function key in your comms package to hold all of the characters of your E-mail string for ease of use during log-ons.

Internet connections

You can get on to an Internet terminal connection via CIX, with little fuss other than payment of the CIX connection fee. If you have a CIX account already then there are no extra charges incurred by using the Internet gateway.

Many Internet computers use VT100 or derivatives for terminal emulation but not all sites use a full implementation. This makes setting up your terminal emulation software a hit and miss affair at first. VT100 or VT102 emulation is a good place to start, the most vital key sequence being ASCII 93,(i.e. hold down the CTRL key and press]) the TELNET escape key. CIX uses 8 bit data, no parity, 1 stop bit – you should set your software to this as CIX automatically manages any conversion from the 7 bit data format used by many of the Internet sites. If your comms software and modem supports it then ZMODEM is the best method of getting your files back from the Internet in-tray of CIX.

Finding out more

Paradoxically the best way to find out more about the Internet is to browse on the Internet or Usenet. There are some thousands of files scattered around the system which give advice on a multitude of related topics. Some of these information files have found their way onto CIX and the Internet Conference there carries some of the more useful. 'Zen and the Art of Internet' is one favourite file and contains much basic information about Internet and the technicalities of using it. 'Zen' is available from CIX in a variety of text formats, each with a different filename.

Other files on CIX give lists of available and interesting sites, and there is a 'Discoveries' section in the Internet Forum for users to share knowledge and site details. There are now several books on the Internet available but they tend to mirror a great deal of information which is already on the system. There is so much more which can be had for the price of a download.

Usenet, the Internet news service, carries much information of consequence – the conferences (or newsgroups) 'alt.internet.access.wanted' and 'news.newusers.questions' are a good place to start.

You can join the Usenet system on CIX and then get information simply by typing in the name of the newsgroup you wish to access. Alternatively type SHOW ALL for a full list – but turn your disk capture on first. Newsgroups are described by their prefix, ALT for alternative, BIZ for business, COMP for computer, etc. There's a full list of help commands available from the CIX Usenet prompt.

The Usenet feature on CIX is read only, but you can post mail to Usenet newsgroups by using a DIS or other network connection.

16.3 Internet example

This example uses the CIX internet gateway to connect you to the NASA/IPAC database of celestial objects in Denver, USA. You'll need a CIX subscription to try it out.

FIGURE 16.1

Connect to CIX and type 'run internet' at the Main: prompt…

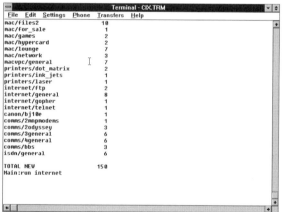

FIGURE 16.2

*...at the ip> prompt type
'telnet ned.ipac.caltech.edu'...*

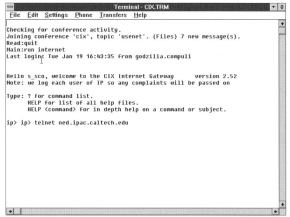

FIGURE 16.3

*...use 'ned' at the Login: prompt
for access. You should be connected
to the NASA database of celestial
objects in the USA...*

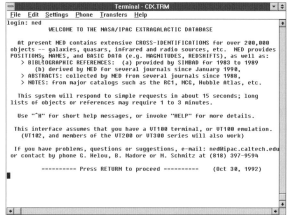

FIGURE 16.4

*...and press return to get to the
NED menu driven front screen.*

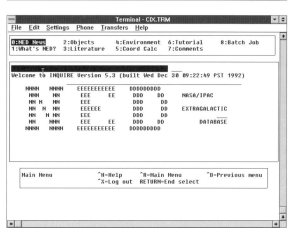

17
RADIO BASED TELECOMMUNICATIONS
"He changes the object of his pursuit and attains achievement"

17.1 Radio based telecommunications

One of the major problems in accessing dial-up services is not the cost of the equipment needed to get onto those services, but the constant call and access charges you have to pay. On most commercial services you are charged a registration fee, a regular set of monthly or weekly charges, and sometimes have to pay through-put fees related to the amount of data you transfer. All of these charges add up considerably and it's often the case the first flush of enthusiasm when using a service can result in some hefty fees. This is especially so in the UK where (in the main) all calls are charged on a time tariff basis. Contrast this with the free local call structure present over most of the USA and several other countries, and you'll see why modem sales in those countries are much higher per capita than in Britain.

One alternative to using the telephone network for communications is to use radio methods, and there are a multitude of different systems for transmitting and receiving computer data around the world. Two of the most useful are Radio Teletype (RTTY – pronounced as in 'gritty') and Packet Radio.

RTTY

RTTY is the sending of text based messages by radio. It's been established for many years – upgraded, downgraded and generally mucked around with in the name of technological advance, but the basics are the same as they were thirty years ago. RTTY uses a technique called frequency shift keying (FSK) to modulate radio waves. This is broadly similar to the techniques used in early data modems to send data over phone lines, and involves the use of two separate frequencies to denote mark and space, otherwise known as on and off. The equipment needed is very simple and you can have RTTY up and running for only a small outlay.

RTTY bits

Before we all had computers a teleprinter would be hooked up to a radio receiver by means of a 'terminal unit' (TU). The TU would take the warbling FSK tones from the audio output of the receiver and convert them to serial signals to directly drive the teleprinter solenoids and electro-mechanics. These signals were almost always at RS232 levels.

Rather than use ASCII (RTTY predates it) radio-teletype signals generally use the

BAUDOT code, now enshrined as International Telegraph Alphabet No. 2. This is still the case for modern RTTY, although many amateurs are now using ASCII with influx of personal computers into the radio shack.

The key words for personal computer users are the words 'serial' and 'RS232'. It's now possible to emulate all of the functions of a teleprinter in software, and there are many systems for all makes of personal computer which can not only decipher standard RTTY but can also read Morse code directly into the computer and display it on screen. Simply add a shortwave receiver and some means of turning the audio output into serial RS232 level input, and you have a working RTTY station. At least that's the theory. Morse is called CW – 'Carrier Wave' by radio enthusiasts.

What's on RTTY?

Unless you have a license to transmit over radio you can only sit and listen in to radio-teleteype traffic, but there is so much interesting information available that this is no great problem. You can read direct messages from news agencies, diplomatic embassies, navy broadcasts, weather forecasts, hurricane warnings and much else. What you won't find on the commercial RTTY stations is the low general level of conversation on many bulletin boards which deals mainly with equipment problems. RTTY is in altogether a different league.

As an example to whet your appetite you can read part of the text broadcast by TASS, the USSR news agency during the final days of the Gorbachev era at the end of this chapter. The text mirrors the great tensions in the country at that time and talks of states of emergency and such like. On the other hand it's often possible to receive oddball nationalistic propaganda from some of the less politically salubrious countries and much hilarity can ensue from pages of invective ranting on about 'running dogs of capitalism' and such like. There is banality too, many navy services carry messages from the crew home to loved ones, and if you have read one Voice of America weather forecast you have read them all. But in general RTTY watching is an absorbing pastime, almost to the extent of increasing the divorce rate amongst RTTY widows.

If you possess a Ham license you can also transmit your own RTTY, as well as receiving it. Much of this amateur RTTY is interesting for its own sake and is at the level of conversation found on recreational bulletin boards, except the level of problems aired is much broader. It's also rare for amateur RTTY operates to resort to 'flame wars' – bad tempered attempts to subvert the argument of others – and most of the banter is good humoured and suitable for family viewing. Unfortunately this cannot be said of some bulletin boards and conferencing systems.

Getting in to RTTY

You don't need to spend a lot of money to get a RTTY receive station set up and running. If you have a personal computer already then the only other equipment you will need will be a suitable radio receiver, and RTTY decoder (Terminal Unit).

The Receiver

Most commercial RTTY is broadcast on frequencies ranging from abut 500 kHz to 27817 kHz, so you need what is generally termed as a 'general coverage receiver' to pick them all up. Most general coverage receivers adequately cover this range. As with all radio equipment you generally get only as many features as you are prepared to pay for, and while almost all short-wave receivers will pickup some RTTY from the closer or more powerful transmitter, it takes a decent receiver to resolve the weaker stations.

Traditionally a short-wave receiver was the size of cabin trunk and stuffed with expensive thermionic tubes, but modern receivers suitable for general reception are the size of a transistor radio. Sony, and many other consumer electronics suppliers make a wide range, and there models on the market starting at under one hundred pounds.

The most important feature of any radio used for RTTY listening is that it must have the ability to resolve Upper and Lower Sideband transmissions. Single Sideband (SSB) working is a way of splitting up a radio frequency into two or more parts, so that the bandwidth and therefore the amount of traffic that can be carried, is increased. Short wave radio receivers resolve USB or LSB transmission by means of a gizmo called a Beat Frequency Oscillator (BFO). The BFO is used to fine tune the set to the incoming transmission, and is the beast responsible for most of those piercing whistles you hear coming from the back bedroom/radio shack.

If you are a computer user who has never been near a beat frequency oscillator or a short wave set, then fear not – as the technology is less intimidating to use than the DOS operating system. Modern radio sets have taken much of the mystery out of short-wave listening.

Once you have found a set with a BFO, look out for maximum frequency coverage. Ideally you should find a set with continuous AM (audio modulation) from 150 kHz to 30000 kHz. This is the minimum required for serious listening, and any other frequency coverage you get should be considered a bonus. Digital tuning is a great help too as you can punch in the required frequency instead of having to hunt for it with an analogue dial. Look out also for an external aerial connection – not all portable radios have them. Finally you should look for an audio out socket of some kind – either for an earphone/headphones, or for connection to a tape recorder.

For an example of suitable low price receiver look in the Maplin catalogue at their Multiband Receiver (order code GK85G). One of these was used to great effect during the preparation of this chapter. There are many other models around – you can pay up to eight hundred pounds for a receiver with coverage from DC to the speed of light, but these have many more features than are needed for general RTTY coverage. If you want to receive RTTY from local amateurs then you will need a slightly different radio which provides HF or VHF modes. These are more specialised, and its probably wise to consult specialist magazines such as Electronics and Wireless Worlds, Shortwave Magazine and Practical Wireless before spending money.

Aerials

The most important way to ensure good reception is to rig up a decent aerial system. Most modern solid state radios are sensitive enough to be used with a built-in telescopic whip antenna, but all radios will benefit from a proper aerial. Unfortunately, if you are listening on short wave then 'proper' means as long as piece of wire as you can reasonably manage. A 'long-wire' aerial is exactly that – a piece of copper wire running down the length of the garden up to about 30 meters long. But if you cannot manage this there are a number of active aerials around. These have sensitive amplifiers built in and can help in places where a long-wire would be impractical. Radio Hams will tell you (at great length) how to construct aerials of all shapes and sizes, but you can get good results with a piece of any old cable strung down the garden. As with all things you will get more ambitious as the bug bites, including building specialist aerial arrays, but it's better to start off small and cheap.

Earthing

If your radio is fitted a ground-post or earth screw then you should also pay attention to instructions for using a combined aerial/ground system – a good ground can dramatically improve the efficiency of most aerials. All radio shops supplying the amateur radio trade carry numerous books on building DIY aerials, but you should remember to insulate each end of the antenna wire from the building, tree or lamppost from which it is suspended. You can buy proper porcelain insulators to do this or use more prosaic materials such as PVC drainpipe. But if you intend to take up any sort of short-wave listening a good aerial/earth system is a must.

The Terminal Unit

The TU is traditionally a thing of mystery. It serves to convert the audio FSK tones from the receiver into digital representations of the BAUDOT or ASCII alphabet. Terminal Units come in many forms; the basic units offer options for setting the different modes of FSK shifts that are used by RTTY. TUs often have other radio-data related modes such as the ability to resolve weather fax and other data transmissions and one of the most feature laden (and expensive) is the Advanced Electronics PK 232-MBNX, which in addition to providing almost all known RTTY modes, includes the ability to decode radio based weather fax and navigation information. Terminal units in all sorts of shapes and sizes are available from Maplin or from your local Ham radio shop.

At the other end of the scale comes small passive filters. These often comprise a simple one chip circuit containing an op-amp and a few resistors, and serve to turn the audio into something approaching digital information. If you go for the simple filter method, then you will need correspondingly more intelligence built-in to the software you will use on your computer to decode the data.

Like all equipment based pastimes, it pays to start off small and then build your equipment collection towards the direction you want to go. There's no point forking out for a three hundred pound RTTY decoder before you have made up your mind whether RTTY watching is going to become an all absorbing hobby, or will be just something else to add to the pile of golf clubs, squash racquets and other deserted bits of kit in the garden shed. One good way of collecting shortwave bits is to exploit other peoples inability to resist the upgrade bug. Radio freaks can't keep equipment for more than six months before upgraditus sets in and they circulate used bits of equipment at frequent sales and Ham rallies. Details of these appear in the specialist radio ham press. You can pick up a RTTY TU for less than thirty pounds at some of these events, together with advice on hooking it up to your computer.

Computer software

There is great deal of RTTY software available for most makes of personal computer, although in the UK most of it seems to be for the IBM PC and its compatibles. In the States you can find RTTY software for virtually every computer, including old Coleco Adams, and ancient Commodore 64s. Even the tiny Tandy 100 has a machine code RTTY receive program written for it, as do most of the Atari range. In the UK your best place to rummage for oddball software is in the HAMNET conference on CompuServe or at any of the dozens of local Ham Radio User Group meetings.

The facilities you will need in your RTTY software will vary depending on the features you have built into your Terminal Unit. At best any old datacomms software will do if it goes down as low as 50 bps, at worst you will need highly intelligent terminal software to decode the digitised noise coming out of your home made filter. As a starting point you could do worse than download a programme called HAMCOM from the SIMTEL archive CD ROM on the HAYES UK BBS. (0252 77551) HAMCOM is intelligent RTTY and MORSE decoding software that works in connection with a small op-amp filter. Full details are enclosed in the program notes, along with construction details for the op-amp filter. The program supports most of the common RTTY modes, and has a built in spectrograph and tuning meter. HAMCOM works well if you have a relatively fast PC, that is, one that runs at least twice as fast as the original IBM PC. Most 286 and 386 based equipment will work with it. But bear in mind that the quality of the audio you feed into any RTTY TU or filter will decide the final quality of the textual output and that most computers emit large quantities of Radio Frequency Interference (RFI).

Getting rid of RFI

One of the problems of computers is that they emit large quantities of interference. This comes mainly from the motherboard and video display electronics inside the case and from the monitor or display scan electronics.

Cathode Ray tube (CRT) displays are worse than the liquid crystal or other displays found on some laptops, but it's true to say that most personal computers emit more electrical noise relatively speaking, than the distant RTTY stations you will want to receive on your radio. This is a perennial problem for radio hams, and some ingenuity is needed to alleviate the problem. The most popular method is to line the walls of a room with either metal foil or beer cans, and place the computer outside, but in modern homes this is likely to cause some friction with other members of the family. It's also true that PC clones are much better at emitting unwanted radiation than are Macs and the cheaper the clone the more radiation emitted.

One simple way around the problem with RTTY is to tape the station onto a cassette in a noise free environment, and play the tape back into the RTTY terminal unit. This has the advantage of time-shifting broadcasts, many of which tend to appear in the early hours of the morning, but it has the disadvantage of losing the spontaneity which is the great charm of RTTY listening. But in all cases you need to use screened serial leads (not ribbon cables) and screened audio cables at the very least. If you feed electrical noise into your terminal unit you can waste a lot of time in trying to resolve even the strongest of stations.

17.2 Getting going…

While you are nosing around your local ham radio store you should pick up a list of frequencies that broadcast RTTY. A good guide is Bill Laver's *'Pocket Guide to RTTY and FAX stations'* (ISBN 0 9512729 5 0) which lists the frequency of the station in kiloHerz, together with a brief note of the RTTY mode used, and transmitting times. The booklet also gives brief notes on the error corrected RTTY modes called SITOR and AMTOR, but to resolve these transmissions you will need a terminal unit with SITOR/AMTOR capability.

Setting up your receive RTTY system involves no more than plugging it all together, connecting the audio from the receiver into the Terminal Unit, and the RS232 or DATA OUT socket on the terminal unit to your computer. This assumes you have adequate aerial facilities. Load the software, punch in the frequency of your favourite station and off you go. Legible text should appear on your screen.

If it doesn't it is because of a variety of reasons: you could be set to the wrong baud rate, your radio BFO isn't tuned properly, you have too much RFI around, or the audio level is not loud enough to feed the terminal unit. All of these settings have to be checked and adjusted if need be, but if you are lucky it is possible to receive RTTY within minutes of plugging everything together. If you are unlucky you may have tuned into one of the many stations that broadcast Cyrillic or coded text, or may have your terminal software or unit set to the wrong shift or mode. Perseverance is needed but RTTY reception becomes easier as you start to recognise regular stations by their frequency and broadcast time.

If you want to discover just how much RTTY there is around before you commit yourself to buying equipment check out a shortwave radio fitted with a BFO. The best times are around dusk and after dark. Tune the receiver in until the BFO whistles as it finds a carrier, and then tune the BFO to resolve the signal. If you hear what sounds like continuous fast machine-driven Morse code then that is probably a RTTY station. If you hear what appears to be a cricket chirping regularly then that may be AMTOR/SITOR, (error corrected RTTY) and a more burbling sound might be weather fax. You can resolve weather fax with many combined RTTY/FAX terminal units, and the correct software. Bill Laver's guide lists over 2250 stations in the short wave range of 150-30000 kHz, so you should be able to find something...

If you should happen to tune to 9200 kHz you will be listening to the Interpol RTTY frequency, only a short hop away from the Met Office Bracknell weather fax transmissions, on 9203 kHz.

It pays to be patient in your first few days or evenings as a RTTY freak. Many of the embassy transmissions are encoded, as are some police and shipping services. If you see unresolved groups of letters or digits then you are almost certainly looking at confidential information but with practice you can pick out resolvable RTTY by ear, and then the world really starts to open up.

Finally, it pays to get another RTTY user to show you around and help get your set up working. If you already have access to dial-up services you can often find someone in your area who is a ham, or you can check-out the HAMNET conference on CompuServe, or the RADIO conference on CIX. If you don't then a great place to start is in the specialist magazines previously mentioned. You can also join BARTG, the British Amateur Radio Teleprinter Group. BARTG organise events and jumbles where RTTY bits are for sale at bargain prices, and where you can meet other red-eyed and bleary RTTY folk. RTTY is absorbing, and it doesn't cost a penny to access, once you have the necessary equipment. Their membership secretary is Peter Adams at 464 Whippendell Rd, Watford, Herts. WD1 7PT. Enclose an SAE when you write to him for more information about this absorbing method of computer/radio datacomms.

And if you want real excitement go to the library or your local ham radio shop and look up 'packet-radio'. The world, as they say, is literally at your feet.

17.3 RTTY received text

ZCZCKNA220 1 INF 0529 TASS EE066 E999 EN E999001

+MOSCOW-EMERGENCY +++

URGENT — MOSCOW UNDER STATE OF EMERGENCY.

19/8 TASS 58

MOSCOW AUGUST 19 TASS – A STATE OF EMERGENCY HAS BEEN DECLARED IN MOSCOW AS OF TODAY, IN KEEPING WITH A DECREE BY ACTING FEDERAL PRESIDENT GENNADY YANAYEV.

FOLLOWS THE FULL TEXT OF THE DECREE:

+IN VIEW OF THE AGGRAVATION OF THE SITUATION IN MOSCOW, CAPITAL OF THE UNION OF SOVIET SOCIALIST REPUBLICS, CAUSED BY FAILURES TO FULFIL RESOLUTION NO. 1 OF THE STATE COMMITTEE FOR THE STATE OF EMERGENCY IN THE USSR OF AUGUST 19, 1991, BY ATTEMPTS TO ORGANISE RALLIES, STREET PROCESSIONS AND MARCHES, AND BY INSTANCES OF INCITEMENT TO UNREST, AS WELL AS IN THE INTEREST OF PROTECTING CITIZENS AND THEIR SECURITY IN ACCORDANCE WITH ARTICLE 127, PARAGRAPH 3, OF THE USSR CONSTITUTION, I HEREBY RESOLVE:

+1. TO DECLARE A STATE OF EMERGENCY IN THE CITY OF MOSCOW AS OF AUGUST 19, 1991.

+2. TO APPOINT COLONEL-GENERAL N.V. KALININ, COMMANDER OF THE MOSCOW MILITARY DISTRICT'S FORCES, COMMANDANT OF THE CITY OF MOSCOW WITH THE RIGHTS TO ISSUE MANDATORY ORDER REGULATING ISSUES OF MAINTAINING THE STATE-OF-EMERGENCY REGIME.+

ITEM ENDS

MSK 18.56 19-08-1991

NNNN

ZCZCKNA224 1 INF 0543 TASS CE174 E999 N E999001

+NEWSPAPERS-SUSPENDED +++

URGENT — ALL BUT 9 MOSCOW-BASED NEWSPAPERS SUSPENDED.

9/8 TASS 59

MOSCOW AUGUST 19 TASS – THE PUBLICATION OF ALL BUT NINE MOSCOW-BASED NEWSPAPERS HAS BEEN SUSPENDED, UNDER THE STATE-OF- EMERGENCY COMMITTEE'S RESOLUTION NO. 2, WHICH WAS ISSUED HERE TODAY.

IT SAID: +IN VIEW OF THE DECLARATION OF A STATE OF EMERGENCY IN MOSCOW AND SOME OTHER TERRITORIES IN THE UNION OF SOVIET SOCIALIST REPUBLICS AS OF AUGUST 19, 1991, AND IN CONNECTION WITH CLAUSE 4, PARAGRAPH 14, OF THE USSR LAW 'ON THE LEGAL REGIME OF A STATE OF EMERGENCY', THE STAOZ COMMITTEE FOR THE STATE OF EMERGENCY IN THE USSR RESOLVES:

+1. TO TEMPORARILY LIMIT THE LIST OF PUBLISHED CENTRAL AND MOSCOW CITY AND REGIONAL SOCIO-POLITICAL PERIODICALS TO THE FOLLOWING NEWSPAPERS: TRUD, RABOCHAYA TRIBUNA, IZVESTIA, PRAVDA, KRASNAYA ZVEZDA, SOVETSKAYA ROSSIYA, MOSKOVSKAYA PRAVDA, LENINSKOYE ZNAMYA, AND SELSKAYA ZHIZN.

+2. THE ISSUE OF RESUMING THE PUBLICATION OF THE OTHER CENTRAL AND MOSCOW CITY AND REGIONAL NEWSPAPERS AND SOCIO- POLITICAL PERIODICALS WILL BE DECIDED BY A SPECIAL ORGAN OF THE STATE COMMITTEE FOR THE STATE OF EMERGENCY IN THE USSR.+

ITEM ENDS

APPENDICES

1

THE HAYES COMMAND SET

The Hayes Command Set 1

The Hayes Command Set

Courtesy: Hayes Microcomputer Products UK, Millenium House, Fleetwood Pk, Fleet, Hants, GU13 8UT – Tel 0252 77550

This Appendix lists the commands used on the Hayes Smartmodem 9600 + Quad. Many of these commands are used on non-Hayes products, but not all of non-Hayes products will use all of the codes. This Appendix will be useful if you have lost the manual for your modem, or are wondering just what some of those funny commands mean. Thanks to Hayes UK for providing the information.

When to use AT Commands

Aside from selected AT Commands in a setup or initialisation string within your software, most communications software does not require modem control with commands. Note that the use of AT Commands is not a substitute for the features provided by commercial software. On-line activities must be performed by software; no AT Commands are available, for example, for file transfers between connected systems.

IMPORTANT: To use the modem, even with AT Commands, communications software or some program that performs 'terminal emulation' is required. Commands cannot be issued from your computer's operating system prompt.

Command format

AT commands are issued from the modem's command state in the following format:

Command Prefix – AT.

The AT prefixes the command line to get the modem's attention, detect the speed at which the computer is sending information to the serial port, and recognise the character format (way the information is structured).

Commands and Parameters

The command tells the modem what action to take. AT Commands are either a single letter or a letter preceded by an ampersand(&). For example, the Q command determines whether the modem returns result codes in response to commands, and the &D command controls the modem's use of the DTR signal.

The parameter (0,1,2,etc.) follows a command to tell the modem which option to

THE PC PLUS MODEM AND COMMUNICATIONS GUIDE BOOK **263**

use. If a parameter is not specified, the modem assumes the 0 (zero) option. For example, E is the same as E0. Several commands can be issued on a single line as long as it does not exceed 255 characters. Although Q1 is one command, it counts as two characters in the command line.

End of Line Character

This character terminates the command line and sends the instructions from the computer to the modem. The particular character used to perform this function on your keyboard might be the Return key or the Enter key.

Escape Sequence – +++

The escape sequence returns the modem to the command state from the on-line state. The escape sequence is issued on a line by itself and is sent without the AT prefix and the command line terminator. The escape sequence includes a guard time bracketing the three characters. Both the character used and the duration of the guard time can be changed, if desired, by writing to S-Registers 2 and 12, respectively.

Issuing AT Commands

When the modem powers up, it enters the 'command state', ready to accept instructions (unless command recognition has been disabled by 'dumb mode' configuration). The modem also enters the command state when a connection is broken. When you use the D or A commands to make a connection, the modem enters the 'on-line state'. Anything you type is sent to the modem and computer on the other end of the line when the modem is in the on-line state.

To enter commands while still connected to another modem, issue the escape sequence (+++). The modem will enter the command state, ready to accept commands. When you are ready to go on-line again, simply issue the OO command.

AT Command Summary

Hayes V-series ULTRA Smartmodems 9600 supports the AT Commands listed . If you issue an AT Command not included in this listing, the modem will return an ERROR result code. Always precede the command option with the AT prefix and end the line with CR (except when issuing A/ and +++).

The most frequently used command is the D command and its dial modifiers (see below). The D command causes the modem to originate a telephone call and the dial modifiers initiate the desired features. For example, AT DT9 W 555-2369 CR instructs the modem to dial in the following way. The modem dials the access code 9 using the tone method (T), waits for a second dial tone (W), then dials the specified number (555-2368). The modem waits for a carrier tone from the modem at the other end of the line. If no carrier is detected within a given time (see S-Register 7; factory setting is 50 seconds), the modem automatically releases the line and sends the result code NO CARRIER. If a carrier signal is detected, the modem sends the result code CONNECT and goes on-line, thereby permitting communication with the remote modem.

MODIFIER	DESCRIPTION
0-9*#ABCD	SPECIFIES LETTERS, NUMBERS, AND SYMBOLS THE MODEM WILL USE WHEN DIALING
T	DIALS USING TONE METHOD
P	DIALS USING PULSE METHOD
'	PAUSES BEFORE CONTINUING
W	WAITS FOR SECOND DIAL TONE
@	WAITS FOR QUIET ANSWER
!	ISSUES TIMED BREAK RECALL (FLASH)
R	PLACES CALL IN REVERSE MODE (TO CALL AN ORIGINATE-ONLY MODEM)
;	RETURNS TO COMMAND STATE AFTER DIALING AND MAINTAINS THE CONNECTION
S=N	DIALS PHONE NUMBER N (0-3) STORED WITH &ZN=X

COMMAND	DESCRIPTION
A	ENTER ANSWER MODE; GO OFF HOOK, ATTEMPT TO ANSWER INCOMING CALL, AND GO ON-LINE WITH ANOTHER MODEM
A/	RE-EXECUTE PREVIOUS COMMAND LINE; NOT PRECEDED BY AT NOR FOLLOWED BY CR
B0	INITIATE CALLS USING V.22 AT 1200 BPS
B1	INITIATE CALLS USING 212A AT 1200 BPS
B2	IF ORIGINATING A CALL USING V.23, TRANSMIT AT 75 BPS AND RECEIVE AT 1200 BPS. IF ANSWERING AND NO SELECTED, TRANSMIT AT 1200 BPS AND RECEIVE AT 75 BPS.
B3	IF ORIGINATING A CALL USING V.23, TRANSMIT AT 1200 BPS AND RECEIVE AT 75 BPS. IF ANSWERING AND NO SELECTED, TRANSMIT AT 75 BPS AND RECEIVE AT 1200 BPS.
B15	INITIATE CALLS USING V.21 AT 300 BPS
B16	INITIATE CALLS USING 103 AT 300 BPS
B41	INITIATE A CALL USING V.32 AT 4800 BPS
B42	INITIATE A CALL USING PING PONG (HALF DUPLEX) AT 4800 BPS
B60	INITIATE A CALL USING V.32 AT 9600 BPS
B61	INITIATE A CALL USING PING PONG (HALF DUPLEX) AT 9600 BPS
D	ENTER ORIGINATE MODE; GO OFF HOOK AND ATTEMPT TO GO ON-LINE WITH ANOTHER

COMMAND	DESCRIPTION
	MODEM
E0	DO NOT ECHO CHARACTERS FROM THE KEYBOARD TO THE SCREEN IN COMMAND STATE
E1	ECHO CHARACTERS FROM THE KEYBOARD TO THE SCREEN IN COMMAND STATE
H0	HANG UP AND PLACE MODEM IN COMMAND STATE
H1	GO OFF HOOK AND OPERATE AUXILIARY RELAY
I0	DISPLAY PRODUCT CODE (3-DIGIT NUMBER)
I1	CALCULATE ROM CHECKSUM (3-DIGIT NUMBER)
I2	VERIFY ROM CHECKSUM OF MODEM (OK OR ERROR)
L0-L1	SET LOW SPEAKER VOLUME
L2	SET MEDIUM SPEAKER VOLUME
L3	SET HIGH SPEAKER VOLUME
M0	TURN SPEAKER OFF
M1	TURN SPEAKER ON UNTIL CARRIER DETECTED
M2	TURN SPEAKER ON
M3	TURN SPEAKER ON UNTIL CARRIER DETECTED, EXCEPT DURING DIALING
N0	WHEN ORIGINATING OR ANSWERING, HANDSHAKE ONLY AT SPEED SPECIFIED BY S37
N1	WHEN ORIGINATING, PERMIT NEGOTIATION OF A COMMON COMMUNICATION STANDARD AT HIGHEST ASSOCIATED LINE SPEED SUPPORTED BY BOTH MODEMS. BEGIN NEGOTIATIONS FROM THE DCE LINE SPEED SPECIFIED IN S37, FALLING BACK TO A LOWER SPEED IF NECESSARY. WHEN ANSWERING, FALL BACK FROM V.32 OR V.32 PING PONG (HALF DUPLEX) TO V.22/212A/V.22BIS, THEN V.21/103
N2	WHEN ORIGINATING, PERMIT NEGOTIATION OF A COMMON COMMUNICATION STANDARD AT HIGHEST ASSOCIATED LINE SPEED SUPPORTED BY BOTH MODEMS. BEGIN NEGOTIATIONS FROM THE DCE LINE SPEED SPECIFIED IN S37, FALLING BACK TO A LOWER SPEED IF NECESSARY. WHEN ANSWERING, FALL BACK FROM V.32 OR V.32 PING PONG (HALF DUPLEX) TO V.22/212A/V.22BIS, THEN V.23/V.21/103
N3	WHEN ORIGINATING, HANDSHAKE ONLY AT SPEED SPECIFIED BY S37. WHEN ANSWERING, FALL BACK FROM V.32 OR V.32 PING PONG (HALF DUPLEX) TO V.22/212A/V.22BIS, THEN V.21/103
N4	WHEN ORIGINATING, HANDSHAKE ONLY AT SPEED SPECIFIED BY S37. WHEN ANSWERING, FALL BACK FROM V.32 OR V.32 PING PONG (HALF DUPLEX) TO V.22/212A/V.22BIS, THEN V.23/V.21/103
N5	WHEN ORIGINATING, PERMIT NEGOTIATION OF A COMMON COMMUNICATION STANDARD AT HIGHEST ASSOCIATED LINE SPEED SUPPORTED BY BOTH MODEMS. BEGIN NEGOTIATIONS FROM DCE LINE SPEED SPECIFIED IN S37, FALLING BACK TO A LOWER SPEED IF NECESSARY. WHEN ANSWERING, HANDSHAKE ONLY AT SPEED SPECIFIED BY S37
O0	GO TO ON-LINE STATE
O1	GO TO ON-LINE STATE, INITIATE RETRAIN

COMMAND	DESCRIPTION
Q0	RETURN RESULT CODES
Q1	DO NOT RETURN RESULT CODES
Q2	RETURN RESULT CODES IN ORIGINATE MODE, DO NOT RETURN RESULT CODES IN ANSWER MODE
SR?	READ AND RESPOND WITH CURRENT VALUE OF REGISTER R (R=NUMBER OF REGISTER; ? REQUESTS VALUE)
SR=N	SET THE VALUE OF REGISTER R TO N (N=VALUE WITHIN RANGE OF REGISTER R)
V0	DISPLAY RESULT CODES AS NUMBERS
V1	DISPLAY RESULT CODES AS WORDS
W0	DO NOT RETURN NEGOTIATION PROGRESS MESSAGES
W1	RETURN NEGOTIATION PROGRESS MESSAGES
W2	DO NOT RETURN NEGOTIATION PROGRESS MESSAGES; RETURN CONNECT MESSAGES USING MODEM-TO-MODEM (DCE) SPEEDS INSTEAD OF MODEM-TO-DTE SPEEDS
X0	PROVIDE BASIC CALL PROGRESS FEATURES TO ENABLE CONNECTION, NO CARRIER, AND RING DETECTION
X1	PROVIDE BASIC CALL PROGRESS FEATURES AND CONNECTION SPEED WITH APPROPRIATE RESULT CODES
X2	PROVIDE BASIC CALL PROGRESS FEATURES, CONNECTION SPEED, AND DIAL TONE DETECTION
X3	PROVIDE BASIC CALL PROGRESS FEATURES, CONNECTION SPEED, AND BUSY SIGNAL DETECTION
X4	PROVIDE BASIC CALL PROGRESS FEATURES, CONNECTION SPEED, BUSY SIGNAL AND DIAL TONE DETECTION
Y0	DO NOT RESPOND TO LONGSPACE DISCONNECT
Y1	RESPOND TO LONGSPACE DISCONNECT
Z0	RESET AND RECALL STORED USER PROFILE 0
Z1	RESET AND RECALL STORED USER PROFILE 1
&C0	PRESUME PRESENCE OF CARRIER DETECT SIGNAL
&C1	TRACK THE STATUS OF CARRIER DETECT SIGNAL
&C2	PRESUME PRESENCE OF CARRIER DETECT SIGNAL UNTIL ON-LINE, THEN TRACK STATUS OF SIGNAL
&D0	IGNORE THE STATUS OF DTR SIGNAL
&D1	MONITOR DTR SIGNAL. WHEN AN ON-TO-OFF TRANSITION OF DTR SIGNAL OCCURS, THE MODEM ENTERS COMMAND STATE. RETURN TO THE ON-LINE STATE (IF THE CONNECTION HAS NOT BEEN BROKEN) WHEN THE 00 COMMAND IS ISSUED.
&D2	MONITOR DTR SIGNAL. WHEN AN ON-TO-OFF TRANSITION OF DTR SIGNAL OCCURS, HANG UP AND ENTER THE COMMAND STATE

COMMAND	DESCRIPTION
&D3	MONITOR DTR SIGNAL. WHEN AN ON-TO-OFF TRANSITION OF DTR SIGNAL OCCURS, HANG UP AND PERFORM A RESET
&F	RECALL FACTORY CONFIGURATION AS ACTIVE CONFIGURATION
&K0	DISABLE LOCAL FLOW CONTROL
&K1	ENABLE RTS/CTS LOCAL FLOW CONTROL
&K2	ENABLE XON/XOFF LOCAL FLOW CONTROL
&K3	ENABLE RTS/CTS LOCAL FLOW CONTROL
&K4	ENABLE XON/XOFF LOCAL FLOW CONTROL
&K5	ENABLE TRANSPARENT XON/XOFF LOCAL FLOW CONTROL
&L0	CONFIGURE FOR DIAL-UP OPERATION
L1	CONFIGURE FOR PRIVATE SPEECHBAND CIRCUIT (CONDITIONED LEASED LINE) OPERATION
&Q0	COMMUNICATE IN ASYNCHRONOUS MODE
&Q5	COMMUNICATE IN ERROR-CONTROL MODE
&Q6	COMMUNICATE IN ASYNCHRONOUS MODE WITH AUTOMATIC SPEED BUFFERING – FOR INTERFACES REQUIRING CONSTANT SPEED BETWEEN THE DTE (COMPUTER/TERMINAL) AND THE DCE (MODEM)
&R0	TRACK CTS ACCORDING TO RTS
&R1	IGNORE RTS; ASSUME PRESENCE OF CTS
&S0	ASSERT DSR SIGNAL ALWAYS
&S1	ASSERT DSR SIGNAL PRIOR TO HANDSHAKE OPERATION
&S2	ASSERT DSR SIGNAL AFTER HANDSHAKE NEGOTIATION, BUT BEFORE CONNECT XXXXX RESULT CODE SENT TO DTE
&T0	TERMINATE TEST IN PROGRESS
&T1	INITIATE LOCAL ANALOG LOOPBACK
&T3	INITIATE LOCAL DIGITAL LOOPBACK
&T4	GRANT REQUEST FROM REMOTE MODEM FOR REMOTE DIGITAL LOOPBACK
&T5	DENY REQUEST FROM REMOTE MODEM FOR REMOTE DIGITAL LOOPBACK
&T6	INITIATE REMOTE DIGITAL LOOPBACK
&T7	INITIATE REMOTE DIGITAL LOOPBACK WITH SELF TEST
&T8	INITIATE LOCAL ANALOG LOOPBACK WITH SELF TEST
	THE &T COMMANDS MUST BE ENTERED WHEN THE MODEM IS CONFIGURED FOR &Q0.
&U0	ENABLE TRELLIS CODING (V.32 9600 BPS ONLY)
&U1	DISABLE TRELLIS CODING
&V	VIEW ACTIVE CONFIGURATION, USER PROFILES, AND STORED TELEPHONE NUMBERS
&W0	WRITE STORABLE PARAMETERS OF CURRENT CONFIGURATION IN MEMORY AS PROFILE 0
&W1	WRITE STORABLE PARAMETERS OF CURRENT CONFIGURATION IN MEMORY AS PROFILE 1
&X0	DERIVE TRANSMIT CLOCK SIGNAL FROM MODEM'S INTERNAL OSCILLATOR (INTERNAL CLOCK SIGNAL ON PIN 15)

COMMAND	DESCRIPTION
&X1	DERIVE TRANSMIT CLOCK SIGNAL FROM ATTACHED COMPUTER (EXTERNAL CLOCK SIGNAL ON PIN 24)
&X2	DERIVE TRANSMIT CLOCK SIGNAL FROM RECEIVE CARRIER (SLAVE RECEIVE CLOCK SIGNAL ON PIN 15)
&Y0	SPECIFY STORED USER PROFILE 0 AS POWER-UP CONFIGURATION
&Y1	SPECIFY STORED USER PROFILE 1 AS POWER-UP CONFIGURATION
&ZN=X	STORE PHONE NUMBER X IN LOCATION N (0-3)

Result Code Summary

When you issue a command, the modem responds with a result code to indicate whether it understands and can act on the instructions (either OK or ERROR). In addition, result codes report the progress of a connection.

With the V command options, you can choose whether result codes are reported as words or numbers (see the chart below). The factory setting is as words (V1). You can also select the set of result codes you want reported during call progress with the X and W command options. If you prefer not to have the modem return result codes, or if the software you are using does not handle responses from the modem, you can turn off result codes with the Q1 command option.

Command response and call progress monitoring

The factory setting enables the extended set of result codes for call progress monitoring (X4). When set up in this way, the modem performs and reports full call progress monitoring (RING, NO CARRIER, NO DIALTONE, and BUSY). It also indicates the speed of the connection (CONNECT 1200 as opposed to simply CONNECT).

NUMBER	WORD	EXPLANATION
0	OK	COMMAND EXECUTED
1	CONNECT	CONNECTION AT 0 TO 300, 1200, 1200/75, 75/1200, 2400, 4800 9600, 19200, OR 38400 BPS IS X0 SELECTED; OTHERWISE, AT 0-300 BPS
2	RING	RING SIGNAL INDICATED
3	NO CARRIER	CARRIER SIGNAL NOT DETECTED, OR LOST
4	ERROR	INVALID COMMAND, CHECKSUM, ERROR IN COMMAND LINE OR COMMAND LINE EXCEEDS 255 CHARACTERS

NUMBER	WORD	EXPLANATION
5	CONNECT	1200 CONNECTION AT 1200 OR 1200/75, 75/1200, BPS (DISABLED BY X0)
6	NO DIALTONE	NO DIAL TONE DETECTED. ENABLED BY X2 OR X4, OR W DIAL MODIFIER
7	BUSY	ENGAGED (BUSY) SIGNAL DETECTED. ENABLED BY X3 OR X4
8	NO ANSWER	NO SILENCE DETECTED WHEN DIALING A SYSTEM NOT PROVIDING A DIAL TONE. ENABLED BY @ DIAL MODIFIER
10	CONNECT 2400	CONNECTION AT 2400 BPS (DISABLED BY X0)
11	CONNECT 4800	CONNECTION AT 4800 BPS (DISABLED BY X0)
12	CONNECT 9600	CONNECTION AT 9600 BPS (DISABLED BY X0)
14	CONNECT 19200	CONNECTION AT 19200 BPS (DISABLED BY X0)
22	CONNECT 1200/75	CONNECTION AT 1200 BPS WHEN TRANSMITTING AND 75 BPS WHEN RECEIVING
23	CONNECT 75/1200	CONNECTION AT 75 BPS WHEN TRANSMITTING AND 1200 BPS WHEN RECEIVING
28	CONNECT 38400	CONNECTION AT 38400 BPS (DISABLED BY X0)

Negotiation progress messages

Hayes V-series system products report special result codes during error-control negotiation. Whether or not these messages are displayed is selected with the W command. The factory setting is messages disabled (W0) to avoid conflict with software programs that do not support this additional level of call progress monitoring.

NUMBER	WORD	EXPLANATION
40	CARRIER 300	CARRIER DETECTED AT 300 BPS
44	CARRIER 1200/75	CARRIER DETECTED, AT 1200 BPS WHEN SENDING AND AT 75 BPS WHEN RECEIVING
45	CARRIER 75/1200	CARRIER DETECTED, AT 75 BPS WHEN SENDING AND AT 1200 BPS WHEN RECEIVING
46	CARRIER 1200	CARRIER DETECTED AT 1200 BPS
47	CARRIER 2400	CARRIER DETECTED AT 2400 BPS
48	CARRIER 4800	CARRIER DETECTED AT 4800 BPS
50	CARRIER 9600	CARRIER DETECTED AT 9600 BPS
66	COMPRESSION: CLASS 5	MNP5 COMPRESSION NEGOTIATED
67	COMPRESSION: V.42BIS	V.42BIS COMPRESSION NEGOTIATED

NUMBER	WORD	EXPLANATION
68	COMPRESSION: ADC	HAYES ADAPTIVE DATA COMPRESSION NEGOTIATED
69	COMPRESSION: NONE	NO COMPRESSION NEGOTIATED
70	PROTOCOL: NONE	ASYNCHRONOUS MODE
71	PROTOCOL:ERROR-CONTROL/LAP-B	ERROR-CONTROL MODE WITH LAPB PROTOCOL
72	PROTOCOL: CONTROL/LAP-B/HDX	ERROR-CONTROL MODE WITH EXTENDED PROTOCOL IN HALF-DUPLEX
73	PROTOCOL: ERROR-CONTROL/AFT	ERROR-CONTROL MODE WITH AFT
74	PROTOCOL: X.25/LAP-B	SYNCHRONOUS X.25 CONNECTION ESTABLISHED WITH A CARRIER SPEED OF 1200, 2400, 4800,OR 9600 BPS
75	PROTOCOL: X.25/LAP-B/HDX	SYNCHRONOUS X.25 HALF-DUPLEX CONNECTION ESTABLISHED WITH A CARRIER SPEED OF 4800OR 9600 BPS
76	PROTOCOL:X.25/ X.25/LAP-B/AFT	ASYNCHRONOUS X.25 CONNECTION ESTABLISHED; AFT USED
77	PROTOCOL: LAP-M	V.42 LAP-M
78	PROTOCOL: LAP-M/HDX	V.42 LAP-M WITH HALF-DUPLEX
79	PROTOCOL: LAP-M/AFT	V.42 LAP-M WITH AFT
80	PROTOCOL: ALT	ALTERNATIVE PROTOCOL (MNP COMPATIBLE)
91	AUTOSTREAM: LEVEL 1	MULTIPLEXING OF MULIPLE VIRTUAL CHANNELS
92	AUTOSTREAM: LEVEL 2	TRANSPARENT CONTROL OF ONE PAD (NON-SIMULTANEOUS)
93	AUTOSTREAM: LEVEL 3	TRANSPARENT CONTROL OF ALL PADS (SIMULTANEOUS)

S-Register Summary

S-Registers are special memory locations that hold values used by the modem for configuration and operating parameters. All V-series system products incorporate the group of S-Registers associated with Hayes Smartmodem product functions. These registers serve as counters, timers, and frequently used ASCII characters. A second group, associated with V-series functions, are used to configure the modem's feature negotiation options.

Changes to S-Register values can be made with the Sr=n command and read with the Sr? command. For a complete description of each S Register, see the V-series System Product User's Reference.

Smartmodem registers

These registers can be adjusted to suit the desired configuration of the modem within the range of values indicated in the Range/Units column below. A + in the Factory Setting column indicates the value of this register cannot be stored as part of a user-defined profile. When the modem is reset, the factory setting for this register will be recalled from memory.

REGISTER	DESCRIPTION	RANGE/UNITS	FACTORY SETTING
S0	SELECT RING TO ANSWER ON	0-255 RINGS	0
S1	RING COUNT (INCREMENTED WITH EACH RING)	0-255 RINGS	0+
S2	ESCAPE SEQUENCE CHARACTER	0-127 ASCII	43
S3	CARRIAGE RETURN CHARACTER	0-127 ASCII	13+
S4	LINE FEED CHARACTER	0-127 ASCII	10+
S5	BACK SPACE CHARACTER	0-32, 127 ASCII	8+
S6	WAIT BEFORE BLIND DIALING	2-255 SEC	2
S7	WAIT TIME FOR CARRIER	1-255 SEC	50
S8	DURATION OF DELAY FOR COMMA	0-255	2
S9	CARRIER DETECT RESPONSE TIME	1-255 1/10 SEC	6
S10	DELAY CARRIER LOSS TO HANG UP	1-255 1/10 SEC	14
S11	DURATION/SPACING OF TONES	50-255 MSEC	95
S12	ESCAPE SEQUENCE GUARD TIME	0-255 1/50 SEC	50
S18	SELECT TEST TIMER	0-255 SEC	0
S25	DTR CHANGE DETECT TIME	0-255 1/100 SECY	5
S26	RTS/CTS DELAY	0-255 1/100 SEC	1
S30	AUTOMATIC TIMEOUT. THIS REGISTER MONITORS THE ACTIVITY ON THE LINE	0-255 10 SEC	0 – TIMER DISABLED

When the modem is configured for synchronous operation, and until on-line, units are measured in seconds rather than in 1/100 seconds.

V-Series registers

The values held in the S-Registers described below select between several operating conditions. The values written to these registers (except the status response registers S85 and S86) can be stored in memory as part of a user-defined profile with the &W command options.

Register S36

Negotiation fallback – When the initial attempt to connect in error-control mode fails, this register specifies the subsequent action that should be taken.

VALUE	EXPLANATION
0	HANG UP
1	ATTEMPT A STANDARD ASYNCHRONOUS CONNECTION (&Q0)
3	ATTEMPT AN ASYNCHRONOUS CONNECTION USING AUTOMATIC SPEED BUFFERING (&Q6)
4	ATTEMPT A V.42 ALTERNATIVE PROTOCOL CONNECTION (MNP COMPATIBLE); IF NEGOTIATION FAILS, HANG UP
5	ATTEMPT A V.42 ALTERNATIVE PROTOCOL CONNECTION (MNP COMPATIBLE); IF NEGOTIATION FAILS, ATTEMPT A STANDARD ASYNCHRONOUS CONNECTION
7	ATTEMPT A V.42 ALTERNATIVE PROTOCOL CONNECTION (MNP COMPATIBLE); IF NEGOTIATION FAILS, ATTEMPT AN ASYNCHRONOUS CONNECTION USING AUTOMATIC SPEED BUFFERING

NOTE: The selected fallback option can be initiated immediately with Register S48. For example, a connection attempt using the Alternative Protocol can be forced by setting S48=128 and S36=5 or 7.

Register S37

Maximum DCE line speed – selects the speed (for all modes except V.25bis) at which the modem attempts to connect with a remote modem; speed will be the highest DCE speed supported by both modems not exceeding the speed specified by this register. (See S93 for V.25bis modes).

VALUE	EXPLANATION
0	SPEED OF LAST AT COMMAND ISSUED
1	75 BPS
2	110 BPS
3	300 BPS
5	1200 BPS
6	2400 BPS
7	4800 BPS
9	9600 BPS

Register S38   Delay before forced hang up – specifies the number of seconds the modem waits when in error-control mode (&Q5) before performing the disconnect operation after receiving the command to hang up or an on-to-off transition of DTR. The range of this register is 0-255 seconds; the factory setting is 20 seconds. If the register is set to a value between 0 and 254, the modem will wait that number of seconds, or until all data has been transferred, before hanging up. If the register is set to 255, the modem does not hang up until all data is transferred.

Register S46   Error-control protocol selection – specifies the error-control method used for subsequent connections

VALUE	EXPLANATION
0	EITHER LAPM OR FALLBACK TO LAPB
1	LAPB ONLY
2	LAPM OR FALLBACK TO LAPB; USE DATA COMPRESSION+
3	LAPB WITH DATA COMPRESSION+
6	X.25 OR FALLBACK TO LAPB; USE DATA COMPRESSION+
136	LAPM ONLY
138	LAPM WITH DATA COMPRESSION+
134	X.25

+ The technique negotiated is determined by capabilities and configuration of both modems. V.42bis is attempted first, then Hayes Adaptive Data Compression. If neither method is supported by both modems, or if either modem has compression disabled, no compression will be used.

Register S48   Feature negotiation action – selects how feature negotiation is used when making connections with the remote system. The negotiation process can be tailored to suit a connection or bypassed altogether. For example, when the capabilities of the remote modem are known, negotiation is unnecessary. The factory setting is 7, negotiation enabled.

VALUE	EXPLANATION
0	NEGOTIATION DISABLED; PRESUME THE REMOTE MODEM IS CONFIGURED FOR AND HAS THE CAPABILITIES NECESSARY FOR THE CONNECTION SELECTED WITH S46
3	NEGOTIATION ENABLED, BUT ORIGINATING MODEM REMAINS SILENT DURING DETECTION PHASE FOR CONNECTIONS WITH MNP MODEMS; DEFEATS CONNECTION SEQUENCE WITH OTHER V.42 MODEMS

VALUE	EXPLANATION
7	NEGOTIATION ENABLED
128	NEGOTIATION DISABLED; FORCES FALLBACK OPTIONS SPECIFIED IN S36 TO BE TAKEN IMMEDIATELY

Register S49 Buffer lower limit – specifies the minimum size of the buffer used in error-control or automatic speed buffering mode. The range is 1-249 bytes; the factory setting is 8.

Register S50 Buffer upper limit – specifies the maximum size of the buffer used in error-control or automatic speed buffering mode. The range is 2-250 bytes; the factory setting is 16.

Register S63 Leased line carrier level – selects the carrier power level in dBm for leased line operation. This register specifies a carrier level value that is not to be exceeded. The range for this register is 0-15 (0 dBm to -15 dBm). The factory setting is 0.

Register S69 Link layer window size – sets the number of frames (packets) sent between acknowledgements from the remote system. The range is 1-15 with a factory setting of 15. LAPM connections use a window size of 1-15; LAPB connections and X.25 connections use a window size of 1-8. If a LAPB or X.25 connection is made, any value greater than 8 is treated as 8.

Register S70 Maximum number of retransmissions – determines how many times the modem will retransmit a frame. The range is 0-255 retries with a factory setting of 10.

Register S71 Link layer timeout – sets the delay between retransmissions to the remote system. The range is 1-255 1/10 seconds, with a factory setting of 2 (200 milliseconds).

Register S72 Loss of "flag idle" timeout – specifies the interval between idle flags. The range is 1-255 seconds with a factory setting of 30.

Register S73 No activity timeout – specifies the period of inactivity (no data, only good carrier and flag idle received) before the modem sends a query (an "RR") to the remote modem to verify that it is operating properly. The range is 1-255 seconds with a factory setting of 5.

Register S82 Break signaling technique – selects a method of break signal handling for V.42 communications: in sequence, expedited, and destructive. Break signals provide a way for you to get the attention of the remote host. The break type used depends on your application.

VALUE	EXPLANATION
3	"EXPEDITED" SIGNALING REGARDLESS OF ITS SEQUENCE IN DATA SENT AND RECEIVED; DATA INTEGRITY MAINTAINED
7	"DESTRUCTIVE" SIGNALING REGARDLESS OF ITS SEQUENCE IN DATA SENT AND RECEIVED; DATA IN PROCESS AT TIME IS DESTROYED
128	"IN SEQUENCE" SIGNALING AS DATA IS SENT AND RECEIVED; DATA INTEGRITY MAINTAINED AHEAD OF AND AFTER BREAK.

Register S84 Adaptive start up negotiation (ASU) – selects the adaptive start up method to be negotiated for subsequent connections.

VALUE	EXPLANATION
0	DO NOT NEGOTIATE ASU CONNECTION
128	NEGOTIATE ASU WITH FIXED START UP
129	NEGOTIATE ASU WITH FAST START UP ON BOTH SIDES
130	NEGOTIATE ASU WITH SMOOTH START UP ON BOTH SIDES
131	NEGOTIATE ASU WITH CONFIGURING MODEM USING FAST START UP AND THE OTHER MODEM USING SMOOTH START UP
132	NEGOTIATE ASU WITH CONFIGURING MODEM USING SMOOTH START UP AND THE OTHER MODEM USING FAST START UP

Register S85 ASU negotiation report – indicates which adaptive start up method has negotiated for the current connection. To read this register, issue the escape sequence to place the modem in the command state, then issue ATS85?CR. The modem will report one of the values below.

CODE	EXPLANATION
0	ASU NOT NEGOTIATED; FIXED START UP IN USE
128	ASU NEGOTIATED WITH FIXED START UP
129	ASU NEGOTIATED WITH FAST START UP ON BOTH SIDES
130	ASU NEGOTIATED WITH SMOOTH START UP ON BOTH SIDES
131	ASU NEGOTIATED WITH REPORTING MODEM USING FAST START UP AND THE OTHER MODEM USING SMOOTH START
132	ASU NEGOTIATED WITH REPORTING MODEM USING SMOOTH START UP AND THE OTHER MODEM USING FAST START UP

Register S86   Connection failure cause code – helps determine the cause of a connection failure. When the modem issues a NO CARRIER result code, a value is written to this S-Register. To read this register following the connection failure, issue ATS86 CR. The modem will report one of the values below.

CODE	EXPLANATION
0	NORMAL HANG UP; NO ERROR OCCURRED
4	PHYSICAL CARRIER LOSS
5	FEATURE NEGOTIATION FAILED TO DETECT PRESENCE OF ANOTHER ERROR-CONTROL MODEM AT THE OTHER END
6	OTHER ERROR-CONTROL MODEM DID NOT RESPOND TO FEATURE NEGOTIATION MESSAGE SENT BY THIS MODEM
7	OTHER MODEM IS SYNCHRONOUS-ONLY; THIS MODEM IS ASYNCHRONOUS-ONLY
8	MODEMS COULD NOT FIND A COMMON FRAMING TECHNIQUE
9	MODEMS COULD NOT FIND A PROTOCOL IN COMMON
10	INCORRECT FEATURE NEGOTIATION MESSAGE SENT BY OTHER MODEM
11	SYNCHRONOUS INFORMATION (DATA OR FLAGS) NOT RECEIVED FROM OTHER MODEM. MODEM WAITED 30 SECONDS BEFORE HANGING UP
12	NORMAL DISCONNECT INITIATED BY OTHER MODEM
13	OTHER MODEM DID NOT RESPOND AFTER MANY TRANSMISSIONS OF THE SAME MESSAGE. MODEM MADE 10 ATTEMPTS THEN HUNG UP
14	PROTOCOL VIOLATION OCCURRED
15	COMPRESSION FAILURE

Register S92

Register S93   V.25bis DTE interface speed – selects the speed used when the modem is configured for V.25bis mode. When autobauding in any mode other than V.25bis, the modem uses the value held in S37.

VALUE	EXPLANATION
3	300 BPS
5	1200 BPS
6	2400 BPS
7	4800 BPS
9	9600 BPS

Register S94 Command mode selector – provides an alternative to setting internal DIP switches when choosing between the AT command mode (factory setting) and the various CCITT V.25bis command modes supported by the modem. To use this register, DIP switches 3 and 4 must both be in the UP position (factory setting).

VALUE	EXPLANATION
0	STANDARD AT COMMAND OPERATION (FACTORY SETTING)
1	ASYNCHRONOUS V.25BIS USING ADDRESSED ACCESS
2	SYNCHRONOUS V.25BIS (HDLC FRAMING) USING ADDRESSED ACCESS
3	SYNCHRONOUS V.25BIS (CHARACTER FRAMING) USING ADDRESSED ACCESS
5	ASYNCHRONOUS V.25BIS USING DIRECT ACCESS
6	SYNCHRONOUS V.25BIS (HDLC FRAMING) USING DIRECT ACCESS
7	SYNCHRONOUS V.25BIS (CHARACTER FRAMING) USING DIRECT ACCESS
9	ASYNCHRONOUS V.25BIS USING ADDRESSED ACCESS WITH EBCDIC CHARACTER SET OPTION
10	SYNCHRONOUS V.25BIS (DHLC FRAMING) USING ADDRESSED ACCESS WITH EBCDIC CHARACTER SET OPTION
11	SYNCHRONOUS V.25BIS (CHARACTER FRAMING) USING ADDRESSED ACCESS WITH EBCDIC CHARACTER SET OPTION
13	ASYNCHRONOUS V.25BIS USING DIRECT ACCESS WITH EBCDIC CHARACTER SET OPTION
14	SYNCHRONOUS V.25BIS (HDLC FRAMING) USING DIRECT ACCESS WITH EBCDIC CHARACTER SET OPTION
15	SYNCHRONOUS V.25BIS (CHARACTER FRAMING) USING DIRECT ACCESS WITH EBCDIC CHARACTER SET OPTION

Register S95 Negotiation message options – enables various result codes that indicate the sequence of events in the establishment of an error-control connection (these are listed under "Result Codes"). This register does not affect the way in which the modem negotiates the connection; it merely enables message options. The factory setting for this register is value 0, not bits selected. To enable any combinatin of the bits, add the values(s) to the right of the bit number and set the register to this sum. Note that changing the W command setting does not affect the value set for this register.

BIT	VALUE	EXPLANATION
0	1	USE SPEED OF DTE-TO-MODEM CONNECTION WHEN REPORTING DCE LINE SPEED (CARRIER MESSAGE).
1	2	APPEND "/ARQ" TO CONNECT RESULT CODE WHEN AN ERROR-CONTROL CONNECTION IS MADE

BIT	VALUE	EXPLANATION
2	4	ENABLE CARRIER MESSAGES
3	8	ENABLE PROTOCOL MESSAGES
4	16	ENABLE AUTOSTREAM MESSAGES
5	32	ENABLE COMPRESSION MESSAGES

DTE Interface Connection

Proper connections between the modem and the computer or other device on which it is installed are mandatory for establishing connections and maintaining data integrity during communications.

The chart below details the Data Terminal Equipment (DTE) interface connector pin assignments and circuit descriptions of each signal for the modem's DTE interface connection. Both the EIA (Electronic Industry of American) and the CCITT V.24 standard nomenclature are provided. This information should be used to determine the cabling requirements for your application. If you are unable to purchase a cable meeting your needs, contact Hayes Customer Service.

PIN	EIA	V.24	SIGNAL DIRECTION	DESCRIPTION
1	AA	101	N/A	PROTECTIVE GROUND
2	BA	103	TO MODEM	TRANSMIT DATA
3	BB	104	FROM MODEM	RECEIVE DATA
4	CA	105	TO MODEM	REQUEST TO SEND
5	CB	106	FROM MODEM	CLEAR TO SEND
6	CC	107	FROM MODEM	DATA SET READY
7	AB	102	N/A	SIGNAL GROUND
8	CF	109	FROM MODEM	DATA CARRIER DETECT
12	CI	112	FROM MODEM	DATA SIGNAL RATE
15	DB	114	FROM MODEM	TRANSMITTER CLOCK
17	DD	115	FROM MODEM	RECEIVER CLOCK
20	CD	108.2	TO MODEM	DATA TERMINAL READY
22	CE	125	FROM MODEM	RING INDICATOR
23	CI	112	FROM MODEM	DATA SIGNAL RATE
24	DA	113	TO MODEM	TRANSMITTER CLOCK

Experiencing Difficulties?

The following suggestions may answer your questions before you go to more technically detailed sources such as the V-series System Product User's Reference, or to your hardware manuals. Your first reference should always be your software's manual as the software controls the operation of the modem.

Check for proper use of communication signals

Refer to your computer and software manuals to determine whether the modem's response to signals needs to be adjusted with AT commands. For example, the requirements for Data Terminal Ready and Carrier Detect signaling (controlled by the &D2 and &C1 commands, respectively) vary between communication environments. The way in which the computer and the software use signals will determine how the modem should respond to or control them.

Verify the appropriate communication standard

The modem uses the B command options to select between various communication standards (see the B command listing on this card and the Installation Guide for communication standards supported by your modem). Some remote systems require that a particular communication standar and associated speed be selected.

Adjust modem's command response

Some computer and software combinations do not react as expected wh the modem responds to commands and/or provides call progress monitoring with result codes. Use the X,V,W, and Q commands to configure the modem's responses to meet these needs.

Verify adequate use of local flow-control

When using the modem in error-control mode (&Q5) or in asynchronous mode with speed buffering (&Q6), some method of flow-control is necessary. The method should be selected based on the capabilities of the software and the requirements of the attached device (see the &K command options).

2 MNP CLASS PERFORMANCE CHART

MNP Class Performance Chart

Class 1   Asynchronous half-duplex data exchange method. Not much used today.

Class 2   Asynchronous full-duplex data exchange method, often used on Z80 and 6800 cpu-based equipment.

Class 3   Full duplex Synchronous bit oriented data exchange. The synchronous data format eliminates the need for start/stop bits and thereby increases data throughput by approximately 8%.

Class 4   Full duplex Synchronous bit oriented data exchange as in MNP3 with Adaptive Packet Assembly (tm) and Data Phase Optimisation. Adaptive Packet Assembly assembles data into larger packets if the data channel is error-free and smallerpackets if the data channel generates errors. Data Phase Optimisation reduces modem administration of data packets. Data throughput is increased by around 20% with MNP 4.

Class 5   As MNP Class 4 with the addition of data compression. Uses a data compression algorythm to dynamically compress data coming from the DTE for transfer. Compression ratios varybetween 1.3:1 to 2:1 depending on the type of data being handled by the algorythm. MNP 5 provides an average increasein data throughput of around 60%.

Class 6   Introduces Universal Link Negotiation and Statistical Duplexing. Universal link Negotiation allows modems to begin operation at a common lower speed and negotiate the use of an alternate high speed modulation technique. The Statistical Duplexing algorithm monitors the user data pattern dynamically to allocate utilisation of the half-duplex modulation to deliver a full-duplex service.

Class 7   Adds Enhanced Data Compression to give increases in throughput of up to 300%.

Class 9   Adds CCITT V32 compliance plus Enhanced Data Compression to increase data throughput by up to 300% when compared to a standard V32 modem. Also includes Enhanced Universal Link negotiation to allow connection to non MNP modems at the optimum performance level.

3

COMPUSERVE FORUM INDEX

CompuServe Forum Index

KEY

Monthly membership gives free access to basic services

EXTENDED RATES

FREE	CONNECT CHARGES ONLY
+	HOURLY CONNECT CHARGES APPLY
$	EXTENDED SERVICE – PREMIUM SURCHARGES OVER HOURLY CONNECT CHARGES
E$	SERVICE IS ON THE EXECUTIVE OPTION AND CARRIES A SURCHARGE
W	INDICATES THAT THE SERVICE REQUIRES A WIDE (80 COLUMN) DISPLAY

ORGANISATION	TYPE GO:	ORGANISATION	TYPE GO:
ABC WORLDWIDE HOTEL GUIDE +	ABC	AMIGA TECH FORUM +	AMIGATECH
ACI US FORUM +	ACIUS	AMIGA USER'S FORUM +	AMIGAUSER,
AI EXPERT FORUM +	AIEXPERT	AMIGA VENDOR FORUM +	AMIGAVENDOR
ANZ COMPANY LIBRARY +	ANZCOLIB	APPLE DEVELOPER SOFTWARE +	DEVELOPER
AP SPORTS($)	SPORTS	APPLE II PROG. FORUM +	APPROG
APPC INFO EXCHANGE FORUM +	APPCFORUM	APPLE II USERS FORUM +	APPUSER
ASP/SHAREWARE FORUM +	ASPFORUM	APPLE II VENDOR FORUM +	APIIVEN
ACADEMIC AMERICAN ENCYCL.	ENCYCLOPEDIA	APPLE NEWS CLIPS($)	APPLENEWS
ACCESS PHONE NUMBERS(FREE)	PHONE	AQUARIA / FISH FORUM +	FISHNET
ADOBE FORUM +	ADOBE	ARTICULATE SYSTEMS +	MACAVEN
ADVENTURES IN FOOD (FREE)	AIF	ARTISOFT FORUM +	ARTISOFT
ADVENTURES IN TRAVEL +	AIT	ASK3COM +	THREECOM
AIR FRANCE(FREE)	AF	ASK3COM FORUM +	ASKFORUM
AIR TRAFFIC CONTROLLER +	ATCONTROL	ASSOCIATED PRESS($)	ENS
ALDUS CUSTOMER SERVICE FORUM +	ALDSVC	ASSOCIATED PRESS ONLINE	NWS-47
ALDUS DISPLAY +	ALDUS	ASTROLOGICAL CHARTING +	ASTROLOGY
ALDUS SPECIAL PROGRAMS FORUM +	ALDUSSP	ASTRONOMY FORUM +	ASTROFORUM
AMERICAN EXPRESS(FREE)	AE	ATARI 8-BIT FORUM +	ATARI8
AMERICAN HERITAGE DICTIONARY	DICTIONARY	ATARI FILE FINDER +	ATARIFF
AMERICANA CLOTHING(FREE)	AC	ATARI PORTFOLIO FORUM +	APORTFOLIO
AMIGA ARTS FORUM +	AMIGAARTS	ATARI ST ARTS FORUM +	ATARIARTS
AMIGA FILE FINDER +	AMIGAFF	ATARI ST PROD. FORUM +	ATARIPRO

ORGANISATION	TYPE GO:	ORGANISATION	TYPE GO:
ATARI USERS NETWORK +	ATARINET	BORLAND PARADOX/DOS FORUM +	PDOXDOS
ATARI VENDOR FORUM +	ATARIVEN	BORLAND PARADOX/WIN.	FORUM PDOXWIN
ATTN. DEFICIT DISORDER FORUM +	ADD	BORLAND PASCAL FORUM +	BPASCAL
AUDIO ENGINEERING SOCIETY +	AESNET	BORLAND QUATTRO PRO FORUM +	QUATTROPRO
AUTOQUOT-R(FREE)	AQ	BORLAND DBASE DISPLAY AREA +	ASHTON
AUTOVANTAGE ONLINE(FREE)	ATV	BORLAND DBASE FORUM +	DBASE
AUTODESK AUTOCAD FORUM +	ACAD	BOSE EXPRESS MUSIC(FREE)	BEM
AUTODESK RETAIL PRODUCTS FORUM	ARETAIL	BRETON HARBOR BASKET CO.(FREE)	BH
AUTODESK SOFTWARE FORUM +	ASOFT	BRITISH LEGENDS +	LEGENDS
AUTOMOBILE FORUM +	CARS	BRITISH TRADE MARKS($)	UKTRADEMARK
AUTOMOBILE INFO CENTER(FREE)	AI	BROADCAST PRO FORUM +	BPFORUM
AUTOMOTIVE INFORMATION +	AUTO	BRODERBUND SOFTWARE(FREE)	BB
AVIATION FORUM (AVSIG) +	AVSIG	BROOKS BROTHERS(FREE)	BR
AVIATION MENU +	AVIATION	BUICK MAGAZINE(FREE)	BUICK
AVIATION SAFETY INSTITUTE +	ASI	BUSINESS DATABASE PLUS($)	BUSDB
BASIS INTERNATIONAL FORUM +	BASIS	BUSINESS DATELINE($)	BUSDATE
BMG COMPACT DISC CLUB(FREE)	CD	BUSINESS DEMOGRAPHICS($)	BUSDEM
BACCHUS WINE FORUM +	WINEFORUM	BUSINESS INCORP. GUIDE(FREE)	INC
BANYAN FORUM +	BANFORUM	CA APP. DEVELOPMENT FORUM +	CAIDEV
BARNES & NOBLES BOOKS(FREE)	BN	CA MICRO GERMANY FORUM +	CAMICRO
BASIC CONVERSION AREA	NEWBASIC	CA PRO SOLUTIONS FORUM +	CAIPRO
BASIC SERVICES	BASIC	CA VAX/UNIX FORUM +	CAIMINI
BILLING INFORMATION(FREE)	BILLING	CA-CLIPPER GERMANY FORUM +	CLIPGER
BIORHYTHMS	BIORHYTHM	CADD/CAM/CAE VENDOR FORUM +	CADDVEN
BIZFILE($)	BIZFILE	CASE DCI FORUM +	CASEFORUM
BLACKDRAGON	BLACKDRAGON	CB CLUB +	CBCLUB
BLYTH FORUM +	BLYTH	CB FORUM +	CBFORUM
BONDS LISTING($)	BONDS	CB HANDLE +	HANDLE
BOOK REVIEW DIGEST($)	BOOKREVIEW	CB PROFILES +	CBPROFILES
BOOKS IN PRINT($)	BOOKS	CB SIMULATOR +	CB
BORLAND +	BORLAND	CB SOCIETY +	CUPCAKE
BORLAND APPL. FORUM +	BORAPP	CCML AIDS ARTICLES($)	AIDSNEWS
BORLAND C++ FOR WIN/OS2 FORUM	BCPPWIN	CD-ROM VENDOR FORUM +	CDVEN
BORLAND C++/DOS FORUM +	BCPPDOS	CDROM FORUM +	CDROM
BORLAND DB PRODUCTS FORUM +	BORDB	CIM SUPPORT FORUM(FREE)	CIMSUPPORT
BORLAND DEUTSCHLAND +	BORGER	CP/M USERS GROUP FORUM +	CPMFORUM
BORLAND DEVELOPER TOOL FORUM +	BDEVTOOLS	CTOS/OPEN FORUM +	CTOS
BORLAND GMBH FORUM +	BORGMBH	CABLETRON SYSTEM, INC. +	CTRON

ORGANISATION	TYPE GO:	ORGANISATION	TYPE GO:
CABLETRON SYSTEMS FORUM +	CTRONFORUM	COMPANY SCREENING($EW)	COSCREEN
CADENCE FORUM +	CADENCE	COMPAQ CONNECTION +	CPQFORUM
CALCULATE NET WORTH +	FINTOL	COMPENDEX ENGINEER INDEX($)	COMPENDEX
CALIFORNIA FORUM +	CALFORUM	COMPUADD EXPRESS(FREE)	EXPRESS
CANCER FORUM +	CANCER	COMPUADD FORUM +	COMPUADD
CANON SUPPORT +	CANON	COMPUBOOKS(FREE)	CBK
CANOPUS FORUM +	CANOPUS	COMPUSERVE EUROPE	EUROPE
CASTLEQUEST	CQUEST	COMPUSERVE HELP FORUM(FREE)	HELPFORUM
CENTRAL POINT DOS FORUM +	CPSDOS	COMPUSERVE MAGAZINE	OLI
CENTRAL POINT WIN/MAC FORUM +	CPSWIN	COMPUSERVE MAIL	MAIL
CHANGE YOUR PASSWORD PROGRAM	PASSWORD	COMPUSERVE MAIL HELP(FREE)	MAILHELP
CHECKFREE(FREE)	CF	COMPUSERVE MAIL HUB +	MHSADMIN
CHEF'S CATALOG(FREE)	CHEFS	COMPUSERVE NAVIGATOR	NAVIGATOR
CHESS FORUM +	CHESSFORUM	C'SERVE OPERATING RULES(FREE)	RULES
CITIZENS BAND SIMULATOR +	CB	COMPUSERVE PACIFIC FORUM +	PACFORUM
CLARION SOFTWARE FORUM +	CLARION	COMPUSERVE RATES(FREE)	RATES
CLARIS FORUM +	CLARIS	COMPUSERVE SOFTWARE	CISSOFT
CLASSIC ADVENTURE	CLADVENT	COMPUSERVE SUBJECT INDEX(FREE)	INDEX
CLASSIC QUOTES +	TMC-45	COMPUSERVE TOUR(FREE)	TOUR
CLASSIFIEDS	CLASSIFIEDS	COMPUTER ART FORUM +	COMART
CLIENT SERVER COMPUTING FORUM	MSNETWORKS	COMPUTER ASSOCIATES FORUMS +	CAI
CLIPPER FORUM +	CLIPPER	COMPUTER CLUB FORUM +	CLUB
COLLECTIBLES FORUM +	COLLECT	COMPUTER CONSULT. FORUM +	CONSULT
COLOR COMPUTER FORUM +	COCO	COMPUTER DATABASE PLUS($)	COMPDB
COLUMBIA HOUSE MUSIC CLUB(FREE)	FREECD	COMPUTER DIRECTORY($)	COMPDIR
COMICS/ANIMATION FORUM +	COMIC	COMPUTER EXPO PROMOTION(FREE)	CPE
COMMAND SUMMARY(FREE)	COMMAND	COMPUTER EXPRESS(FREE)	CE
COMMERCE BUSINESS DAILY($)	COMBUS	COMPUTER LANGUAGE FORUM +	CLMFORUM
COMMODITIES +	COMMODITIES	COMPUTER LIBRARY	COMPLIB
COMMODITY PRICING($)	CPRICE	COMPUTER PERIPHERAL, INC. +	VIVAMODEM
COMMODITY SYMBOL LOOKUP +	CSYMBOL	COMPUTER SHOPPER(FREE)	CS
COMMODORE APPLICATIONS FORUM +	CBMAPP	COMPUTER SHOPPER (UK) FORUM +	UKSHOPPER
COMMODORE ARTS/GAMES FORUM +	CBMART	COMPUTER TRAINING FORUM +	DPTRAIN
COMMODORE NEWSLETTER +	CBMNEWS	COMPUTING SUPPORT	COMPUTERS
COMMODORE SERVICE FORUM +	CBMSERVICE	CONNER FORUM +	CONNER
COMMODORE USERS NETWORK +	CBMNET	CONSUMER ELECT. FORUM +	CEFORUM
COMMONLY ASKED QUESTIONS(FREE)	QUESTIONS	CONSUMER REPORTS	CONSUMER
COMPANY ANALYZER($)	ANALYZER	CONSUMER REPORTS AUTO.	CRAUTO

ORGANISATION	TYPE GO:	ORGANISATION	TYPE GO:
CONSUMER REPORTS DRUG REF.	DRUGS	DIGITALK DATABASE +	DBDIGITALK
CONTACT LENS SUPPLY(FREE)	CL	DIGITALK FORUM +	DIGITALK
CONTINENTAL INSURANCE CENTER	CIC-12	DINOSAUR FORUM +	DINO
COOKS ONLINE FORUM +	COOKS	DIRECT MICRO(FREE)	DM
COREL FORUM +	COREL	DISABILITIES FORUM +	DISABILITIES
CORPORATE AFFILIATIONS($)	AFFILIATIONS	DISSERTATION ABSTRACTS($)	DISSERTATION
COSMETICS EXPRESS(FREE)	CM	DIVIDENDS AND SPLITS($)	DIVIDENDS
COURT REPORTERS FORUM +	CRFORUM	DOWNLOAD & SUPPORT FORUM +	DOWNTECH
CRAFTS FORUM +	CRAFTS	DOWNLOAD PRICING DATA +	IQINT
CREATIVE SOLUTIONS/FORTH FORUM	FORTH	DR. DOBB'S FORUM +	DDJFORUM
CROSSTALK FORUM +	XTALK	DR. NEUHAUS FORUM +	NEUHAUS
CURRENT DAY QUOTES($)	QQUOTE	DREYFUS CORPORATION(FREE)	DR
CURRENT MARKET SNAPSHOT +	SNAPSHOT	DUN'S CANADIAN MKT. IDENT($)	DBCAN
CYBERFORUM +	CYBERFORUM	DUN'S ELECT BUSINESS DIR($)	DYP
DATASTORM FORUM +	DATASTORM	DUN'S MARKET IDENTIFIERS($)	DMI
DBMS MAGAZINE FORUM +	DBMSFORUM	EMI AVIATION SERVICES($)	EMI
DEC PC FORUM +	DECPC	ERIC - EDUCATION RESEARCH($)	ERIC
DEC USERS NETWORK +	DECUNET	EARTH FORUM +	EARTH
DECPCI FORUM +	DECPCI	EDUCATION FORUM +	EDFORUM
DISCLOSURE II($E)	DISCLOSURE	EDUCATIONAL RES. FORUM +	EDRESEARCH
DTP VENDORS FORUM +	DTPVENDOR	EICON TECHNOLOGY FORUM +	EICON
DA VINCI FORUM +	DAVINCI	ELECTRONIC CONVENTION CTR +	CONVENTION
DATA ACCESS CORPORATION +	DAC	ELECTRONIC FRONTIER FOUNDATION	EFFSIG
DATA BASED ADVISOR(FREE)	DB	ELECTRONIC GAMER(TM) +	EGAMER
DATA BASED ADVISOR FORUM +	DBADVISOR	ENGINEERING AUTOMATION FORUM +	LEAP
DATA-PROCESS. NEWSLETTER($)	DPNEWS	ENHANCED ADVENTURE	ENADVENT
DATAEASE INTERNATIONAL FORUM +	DATAEASE	ENTERTAINMENT CENTER +	ECENTER
DATAQUEST ONLINE +	DATAQUEST	ENTREP. SMALL BUSINESS SQUARE	ENTMAGAZINE
DELL FORUM +	DELL	ENTREPRENEUR MAGAZINE(FREE)	ENT
DELRINA TECHNOLOGY FORUM +	DELRINA	EPSON FORUM +	EPSON
DEMOCRATIC FORUM +	DEMOCRATS	EUROPEAN COMPANY LIBRARY($)	EUROLIB
DEPARTMENT OF STATE	STATE	EUROPEAN FORUM +	EURFORUM
DESKTOP PUBLISHING FORUM +	DTPFORUM	EXAMINE DETAILED ISSUE($)	EXAMINE
DESKTOP/ELECTRONIC PUBL. +	DTP	EXECUTIVE NEWS SERVICE($)	ENS
DEUTSCHES COMPUTER FORUM +	GERNET	EXECUTIVE SERVICE OPTION(FREE)	EXECUTIVE
DEVELOPER RELATIONS FORUM +	MSDR	EXECUTIVE STAMPER(FREE)	EX
DIABETES FORUM +	DIABETES	FCC ACCESS CHARGE AREA(FREE)	FCC
DIGITAL'S PC STORE	DD	FANTASY/ROLE-PLAYING ADV.	ADVENT

ORGANISATION	TYPE GO:	ORGANISATION	TYPE GO:
FED. OF INT'L DISTRIBUTORS +	FEDERATION	GRAPHICS B VENDOR FORUM +	GRAPHBVEN
FEEDBACK TO CUSTOMER SERVICE	FEEDBACK	GRAPHICS CORNER FORUM +	CORNER
FIFTH GENERATION SYSTEMS FORUM	FIFTHGEN	GRAPHICS DEVELOPERS FORUM +	GRAPHDEV
FINANCIAL DOCUMENTATION +	FINHLP	GRAPHICS FILE FINDER +	GRAPHFF
FINANCIAL FILE TRANSFER +	FILTRN	GRAPHICS FORUMS +	GRAPHICS
FINANCIAL FILE/MQUOTE II +	MQUOTE	GRAPHICS GALLERY FORUM +	GALLERY
FINANCIAL FORECASTS +	EARNINGS	GRAPHICS PLUS FORUM +	GRAPHPLUS
FINANCIAL FORUMS +	FINFORUM	GRAPHICS SUPPORT FORUM +	GRAPHSUPPORT
FINANCIAL INTERFACES +	INTERFACES	GRAPHICS VENDOR FORUM +	GRAPHVEN
FINANCIAL SURCHARGE LIST	MMM-23	H&R BLOCK(FREE)	HRB
FINE ARTS FORUM +	FINEARTS	HOMEFINDER BY AMS(FREE)	HF
FINE JEWELRY OUTLET(FREE)	FJO	HP HANDHELD FORUM +	HPHAND
FLIGHT SIMULATION FORUM +	FSFORUM	HP OMNIBOOK FORUM +	HPOMNIBOOK
FLORIDA FORUM +	FLORIDA	HP PERIPHERALS FORUM +	HPPER
FLORIDA FRUIT SHIPPERS(FREE)	FFS	HP SYSTEMS FORUM +	HPSYS
FLORIDA TODAY FORUM +	FLATODAY	HSX ADULT FORUM +	HSX200
FLOWER STOP(FREE)	FS	HSX OPEN FORUM +	HSX100
FOCSERVICES FORUM +	FOCSERVICES	HAMMACHER SCHLEMMER(FREE)	HS
FOCWIZARD FORUM +	FOCWIZARD	HAMNET FORUM +	HAMNET
FONTBANK ONLINE +	FONTBANK	HANDICAPPED USER'S DATA	HANDICAPPED
FORD MOTOR COMPANY(FREE)	FORD	HANGMAN	HANGMAN
FOREIGN LANGUAGE FORUM +	FLEFO	HARDWARE FORUMS	HARDWARE
FORUMS	FORUMS	HAYES +	HAYES
FOX SOFTWARE FORUM +	FOXFORUM	HAYES FORUM +	HAYFORUM
FUNDWATCH BY MONEY MAG.	FUNDWATCH	HEALTH & FITNESS FORUM +	GOODHEALTH
GAME FORUMS AND NEWS +	GAMECON	HEALTH DATABASE PLUS($)	HLTDB
GAME PUBLISHERS A FORUM +	GAMAPUB	HEALTH/FITNESS +	FITNESS
GAME PUBLISHERS B FORUM +	GAMBPUB	HEALTHNET	HNT
GAMERS FORUM +	GAMERS	HOLLYWOOD HOTLINE	HOLLYWOOD
GARDENING FORUM +	GARDENING	HUMAN SEXUALITY DATABANK +	HUMAN
GARRETT WADE WOODWORKING(FREE)	GW	HUMANE SOCIETY FORUM +	HSUS
GENEALOGY FORUM +	ROOTS	IBES EARNINGS EST RPTS($E)	IBES
GENERAL COMPUTING FORUM +	GENCOM	IBM APPLICATIONS FORUM +	IBMAPP
GERMAN COMPANY LIBRARY($)	GERLIB	IBM BULLETIN BOARD FORUM +	IBMBBS
GIMMEE JIMMY'S COOKIES(FREE)	GIM	IBM COMMUNICATIONS FORUM +	IBMCOM
GLOBAL CRISES FORUM +	CRISIS	IBM FILE FINDER +	IBMFF
GLOBAL REPORT($)	GLOREP	IBM HARDWARE FORUM +	IBMHW
GOVERNMENT PUBLICATIONS +	GPO	IBM LMU2 FORUM +	LMU2FORUM

ORGANISATION	TYPE GO:	ORGANISATION	TYPE GO:
IBM NEW USERS FORUM +	IBMNEW	LDC SPREADSHEETS FORUM +	LOTUSA
IBM OS/2 DEVELOPER 1 FORUM +	OS2DF1	LDC WORD PROCESSING FORUM +	LOTUSWP
IBM OS/2 DEVELOPER 2 FORUM +	OS2DF2	LDC WORDS & PIXELS FORUM +	LOTUSB
IBM OS/2 SERVICE PAK +	OS2SERV	LDOS/TRSDOS6 USERS FORUM +	LDOS
IBM OS/2 SUPPORT FORUM +	OS2SUPPORT	LOGO FORUM +	LOGOFORUM
IBM OS/2 USERS FORUM +	OS2USER	LAN MAGAZINE FORUM +	LANMAG
IBM OS/2 VENDOR FORUM +	OS2AVEN	LAN TECHNOLOGY FORUM +	LANTECH
IBM PROGRAMMING FORUM +	IBMPRO	LEGAL FORUM +	LAWSIG
IBM SOFTWARE FORUM +	IBMDESK	LEGAL RESEARCH CENTER($)	LEGALRC
IBM SPECIAL NEEDS FORUM +	IBMSPEC	LINCOLN/MERCURY SHOWROOM(FREE)	LINCOLN
IBM SYSTEMS/UTIL. FORUM +	IBMSYS	LITERARY FORUM +	LITFORUM
IBM THINKPAD FORUM +	THINKPAD	LOGITECH FORUM +	LOGITECH
IBM USERS NETWORK	IBMNET	LOTUS 123 FOR WINDOWS UPGRADE	LOTUS123W
IQUEST($)	IQUEST	LOTUS GERMANY +	LOTGMBH
IT&T TENDERLINK/TRADELINK($)	TENDERLINK	LOTUS TECHNICAL LIBRARY +	LOTUSTECH
INCUE ONLINE +	INCUE	MECA SOFTWARE FORUM +	MECA
INDEPENDENT INVESTORS RESEARCH	IIR	MIDI A VENDOR FORUM +	MIDIAVEN
INFORMATION USA +	INFOUSA	MIDI B VENDOR FORUM +	MIDIBVEN
INT'L DUN'S MKT IDENTIFIER($)	DBINT	MIDI C VENDOR FORUM +	MIDICVEN
INTEL ACCESS IRUG FORUM	INTELACCESS	MIDI/MUSIC FORUM +	MIDIFORUM
INTEL CORPORATION +	INTEL	MMS INTERNATIONAL +	MMS
INTELLIGENCE TEST +	TMC-101	MMS/DAILY COMMENT($)	DC
INTERNATIONAL TRADE FORUM +	TRADE	MMS/FEDWATCH NEWSLETTER($)	FW
INTERSOLV FORUM +	INTERSOLV	MQDATA($)	MQDATA
INVESTEXT($)	INVTEXT	MS 32BIT LANGUAGES FORUM	MSLNG32
INVESTORS FORUM +	INVFORUM	MS APPLICATIONS FORUM +	MSAPP
ISLAND OF KESMAI +	ISLAND	MS BENELUX FORUM +	MSBF
ISSUE PRICING INTERFACE($)	MQINT	MS DOS FORUM +	MSDOS
ISSUES FORUM +	ISSUESFORUM	MS ITALY FORUM +	MSITA
JCPENNEY(FREE)	JCPENNEY	MS SQL SERVER FORUM +	MSSQL
JDR MICRODEVICES(FREE)	JDR	MS SOFTWARE LIBRARY +	MSL
JAVELIN/EXPRESS FORUM +	IRIFORUM	MS WINFUN FORUM +	WINFUN
JOHN WILEY BOOK STORE(FREE)	WILEY	MS WINDOWS EXTENSIONS FORUM +	WINEXT
JOURNALISM FORUM +	JFORUM	MS WINDOWS FORUM +	MSWIN
JUSTICE RECORDS	JR	MS WINDOWS OBJECTS FORUM +	WINOBJECTS
K&B CAMERA CENTER(FREE)	KB	MS WINDOWS SDK FORUM +	WINSDK
KNOWLEDGE INDEX +	KI	MS WINDOWS SHAREWARE FORUM +	WINSHARE
KODAK CD FORUM +	KODAK	MS WORKGROUPS +	MSWRKGRP

ORGANISATION	TYPE GO:	ORGANISATION	TYPE GO:
MTM CHALLENGE BOARD +	MTMCHALLENGE	MEGAWARS III +	MEGA3
MAC A VENDOR FORUM +	MACAVEN	MEMBER ASSISTANCE(FREE)	HELP
MAC APPLICATIONS FORUM +	MACAP	MEMBER DIRECTORY(FREE)	DIRECTORY
MAC B VENDOR FORUM +	MACBVEN	MEMBER RECOMMENDATION(FREE)	FRIEND
MAC C VENDOR FORUM +	MACCVEN	MEMBERS OF CONGRESS +	FCC-1
MAC CIM SUPPORT FORUM(FREE)	MCIMSUP	MENSA FORUM +	MENSA
MAC COMMUNICATIONS FORUM +	MACCOMM	MENTOR TECHNOLOGIES(FREE)	MENTOR
MAC COMMUNITY/CLUB FORUM +	MACCLUB	METRO SOFTWARE(FREE)	METRO
MAC D VENDOR FORUM +	MACDVEN	METROPOLITAN MUSEUM OF ART FRE	MMA
MAC DEVELOPERS FORUM +	MACDEV	MICROWAREHOUSE(FREE)	MCW
MAC ENTERTAINMENT FORUM +	MACFUN	MICROSOFT ACCESS FORUM +	MSACCESS
MAC HYPERTEXT FORUM +	MACHYPER	MICROSOFT BASIC FORUM +	MSBASIC
MAC NEW USERS HELP FORUM +	MACNEW	MICROSOFT CE SYSTEMS FORUM +	MSCESYSTEM
MACUSER (SUBSCRIPTIONS)(FREE)	MC	MICROSOFT CENTRAL EUROPE FORUM	MSCE
MACUSER FORUM +	MACUSER	MICROSOFT CONNECTION +	MICROSOFT
MACWAREHOUSE(FREE)	MW	MICROSOFT EXCEL FORUM +	MSEXCEL
MACWEEK FORUM +	MACWEEK	MICROSOFT KNOWLEDGE BASE +	MSKB
MACINTOSH FILE FINDER +	MACFF	MICROSOFT LANGUAGES FORUM +	MSLANG
MACINTOSH FORUMS	MACINTOSH	MICROSOFT PRESS(FREE)	MSP
MACINTOSH HARDWARE FORUM +	MACHW	MICROSOFT WIN32 FORUM +	MSWIN32
MACINTOSH MULTIMEDIA FORUM +	MACMULTI	MICROSOFT WORD FORUM +	MSWORD
MACINTOSH SYSTEMS FORUM +	MACSYS	MILITARY FORUM +	MILITARY
MACMILLAN PUBLISHING(FREE)	MMP	MIRROR TECHNOLOGIES +	MACCVEN
MACROMEDIA FORUM +	MACROMEDIA	MISSION CONTROL SOFTWARE(FREE)	MCS
MAGAZINE DATABASE PLUS($)	MAGDB	MODEL AVIATION FORUM +	MODELNET
MAGILL'S SURVEY OF CINEMA($W)	MAGILL	MODEM GAMES FORUM +	MODEMGAMES
MARKET HIGHLIGHTS($)	MARKET	MODEM VENDOR FORUM +	MODEMVENDOR
MARKET/INDEX LOOKUP(FREE)	INDICATORS	MODEM/MODEM GAME SUPPORT +	MTMGAMES
MARKET/MGT RESEARCH CENT.($)	MKTGRC	MORTGAGE CALCULATOR	HOM-17
MARKT & TECHNIK AG FORUM +	MUT	MOTOR SPORTS FORUM +	RACING
MARQUIS WHO'S WHO($)	BIOGRAPHY	MOVIE REVIEWS +	MOVIES
MASONRY FORUM +	MASONRY	MULTI ISSUE PRICE HISTORY($)	QSHEET
MAX ULE'S TICKERSCREEN(FREE)	TKR	MULTI-PLAYER GAMES FORUM +	MPGAMES
MCAFEE VIRUS FORUM +	VIRUSFORUM	MULTIMEDIA CONFERENCE FORUM +	MULTICON
MCGRAW-HILL BOOK COMPANY(FREE)	MH	MULTIMEDIA FORUM +	MULTIMEDIA
MEDIA NEWSLETTERS($)	MEDIANEWS	MULTIMEDIA VENDOR FORUM +	MULTIVEN
MEDSIG FORUM +	MEDSIG	MUSIC ALLEY ONLINE(FREE)	MAO
MEGAWARS I +	MEGA1	MUSIC/ARTS FORUM +	MUSICARTS

ORGANISATION	TYPE GO:	ORGANISATION	TYPE GO:
NAIC INVEST. ED. FORUM +	NAIC	OVERVIEW OF IBMNET +	OVERVIEW
NCAA COLLEGIATE SPORTS NETWORK	NCAA	PBS APPLICATIONS FORUM +	PBSAPPS
NTIS - GOV'T SPONSORED($)	NTIS	PBS ARCADE FORUM +	PBSARCADE
NWS AVIATION WEATHER	AWX	PC CATALOG(FREE)	PCA
NARADA PRODUCTIONS(FREE)	NARADA	PC COMPUTING	PCCOMP
NAT. COMPUTER SECURITY ASSOC	NCSA	PC COMPUTING (SUBSCRIBE)(FREE)	PCC
NEXT FORUM +	NEXTFORUM	PC COMPUTING(SUBSCRIBE)(FREE)	CMP
NEIGHBORHOOD DEMOGRAPHICS($)	NEIGHBOR	PC CONTACT FORUM +	PCCONTACT
NEW AGE FORUM +	NEWAGE	PC MAGNET +	PCMAGNET
NEW CAR SHOWROOM($)	NEWCAR	PC MAGNET AFTER HOURS FORUM +	AFTERHOURS
NEWS-A-TRON($W)	NAT	PC MAGNET EDITORIAL FORUM +	EDITORIAL
NEWSGRID +	NEWSGRID	PC MAGNET PROGRAMMING FORUM +	PROGRAMMING
NEWSNET(FREE)	NN	PC MAGNET UTILITIES/TIPS FORUM	TIPS
NEWTON/PIE FORUM +	NEWTON	PC MAGAZINE(SUBSCRIBE)(FREE)	PM
NIFTY-SERVE +	NIF-5	PC PLUG AND PLAY FORUM +	PLUGPLAY
NOVELL DSG FORUM +	DRFORUM	PC PLUS / PC ANSWERS +	PCPLUS
NOVELL DEV SUPPORT FORUM +	NDEVSUPPORT	PC PUBLICATIONS(FREE)	PCB
NOVELL FORUM A +	NOVA	PC VENDOR A FORUM +	PCVENA
NOVELL FORUM B +	NOVB	PC VENDOR B FORUM +	PCVENB
NOVELL FORUM C +	NOVC	PC VENDOR C FORUM +	PCVENC
NOVELL LIBRARY FORUM +	NOVLIB	PC VENDOR D FORUM +	PCVEND
NOVELL NETWARE 2.X FORUM +	NETW2X	PC VENDOR E FORUM +	PCVENE
NOVELL NETWARE 3.X FORUM +	NETW3X	PC VENDOR F FORUM +	PCVENF
NOVELL NETWIRE +	NOVELL	PC VENDOR G FORUM +	PCVENG
NOVELL NETWARE 4X FORUM +	NETW4X	PC VENDOR H FORUM +	PCVENH
NOVELL TECH BULLET. DBASE +	NTB	PC WEEK EXTRA FORUM +	PCWEEK
NOVELL VENDOR FORUM +	NOVVEN	PC WORLD ONLINE +	PCWORLD
OS-9 FORUM +	OS9	PCM FORUM +	PCMFORUM
OTC NEWSALERT($)	ENS	PCM ONLINE +	PCMONLINE
OZCIS DOWNLOAD AREA +	OZCISDL	PDP-11 FORUM +	PDP11
OFFICE AUTOMATION VENDOR FORUM	OAFORUM	PR AND MARKETING FORUM +	PRSIG
OFFICIAL AIRLINE GUIDE EE($)	OAG	PRC PUBLISHING(FREE)	PRC
OMAHA STEAKS INTL.(FREE)	OS	PSP BETA FORUM +	PSPBETA
OPTIONS PROFILE($W)	OPRICE	PACIFIC VENDOR FORUM +	PACVEN
ORACLE FORUM +	ORACLE	PACKARD BELL FORUM +	PACKARDBELL
ORDER FROM COMPUSERVE(FREE)	ORDER	PALMTOP FORUM +	PALMTOP
OUTDOOR FORUM +	OUTDOORFORUM	PAPERCHASE-MEDLINE($)	PAPERCHASE
OUTDOORS NEWS CLIPS($)	OUTNEWS	PARLOR AND TRIVIA GAMES +	TTGAMES

ORGANISATION	TYPE GO:	ORGANISATION	TYPE GO:
PARSONS TECHNOLOGY(FREE)	PA	REUTERS FINANCIAL REPORT($)	ENS
PARTICIPATE +	PARTI	REVELATION TECH FORUM +	REVELATION
PATENT RESEARCH CENTER($)	PATENT	REVIEW YOUR CHARGES(FREE)	CHARGES
PAUL FREDRICK SHIRTS(FREE)	PFS	ROCKNET FORUM +	ROCKNET
PEACHPIT PRESS(FREE)	PPP	ROGER EBERT'S MOVIE REVIEWS	EBERT
PEN TECHNOLOGY FORUM +	PENFORUM	ROLE-PLAYING GAMES FORUM +	RPGAMES
PENNY WISE CUSTOM PRINT SHOP	PWP	ROX +	ISDSUP
PENNY WISE OFFICE SUPPLY(FREE)	PW	S&P ONLINE($)	S&P
PERSONAL FILE AREA +	FILES	SAFEWARE COMPUTER INSURE(FREE)	SAF
PERSONAL MENU +	MENU	SHOPPERS ADVANTAGE CLUB(FREE)	SAC
PERSONALITY PROFILE +	TMC-90	SCIENCE/MATH ED. FORUM + V	SCIENCE
PERSONICS	PERSONICS	SCUBA FORUM +	DIVING
PETERSON'S COLLEGE DATABASE	PETERSONS	SECURITIES SCREENING($E)	SCREEN
PETS/ANIMAL FORUM +	PETS	SECURITIES SYMBOLS LOOKUP +	SYMBOLS
PHONE*FILE($)	PHONEFILE	SENIORS FORUM +	SENIORS
PHOTOGRAPHY FORUM +	PHOTOFORUM	SHAREWARE DEPOT(FREE)	SD
PHYSICIANS DATA QUERY($)	PDQ	SHAREWARE REGISTRATION +	SWREG
PLAY-BY-MAIL GAMES FORUM +	PBMGAMES	SHOP-AT-HOME	SHOPPING
POLITICAL DEBATE FORUM +	POLITICS	SHOWBIZ FORUM +	SHOWBIZ
PORTABLE PROG. FORUM +	CODEPORT	SIEMENS AUTOMATION +	SIEAUT
PORTFOLIO VALUATION($)	PORT	SIEMENS AUTOMATISIERUNGS	AUTFORUM
PRACTICAL PERIPH. FORUM +	PPIFORUM	SIERRA ONLINE(FREE)	SI
PRACTICE FORUM(FREE)	PRACTICE	SIGHT AND SOUND FORUM +	SSFORUM
PRES. CAMPAIGN NEWS CLIPS +	VOTENEWS	SINGLE ISSUE PRICE HIST.($)	PRICES
PRICE/VOL GRAPH($)	TREND	SMALL COMPUTER BOOK CLUB(FREE)	BK
PRICING STATISTICS +	PRISTATS	SOAP OPERA SUMMARIES	SOAPS
PRISMA DEUTSCHLAND FORUM +	PRISMA	SOCIETY OF BROADCAST ENG. +	SBENET
PROGRAMMING MS APPS +	PROGMSA	SOFTDISK PUBLISHING(FREE)	SP
PSYCHINFO ABSTRACTS($)	PSYCINFO	SOFTWARE FORUMS	SOFTWARE
QUARTERDECK FORUM +	QUARTERDEC	SOFTWARE PUB. ASSOC. FORUM +	SPAFORUM
QUICK PICTURE FORUM +	QPICS	SOFTWARE PUBLISHER ONLINE +	SPC
QUICK REFERENCE WORD LIST FREE	QUICK	SOFTWARE PUBLISHING FORUM +	SPCFORUM
READ USA ONLINE BOOKSTORE FREE	READ	SOLUTIONS AUSTRALIA FORUM +	SOLUTIONS
REHABILITATION DATABASE	REHAB	SPACE/ASTRONOMY FORUM +	SPACE
RELIGION FORUM +	RELIGION	SPECIALS/CONTESTS MENU(FREE)	SPECIAL
RENT MOTHER NATURE(FREE)	RM	SPINNAKER SOFTWARE FORUM +	SPINNAKER
RETURN ANALYSIS($E)	RETURN	SPORTS FORUM +	FANS
REUTER NEWS PICTURES FORUM +	NEWSPI	STAC ELECTRONICS FORUM +	STACKER

ORGANISATION	TYPE GO:	ORGANISATION	TYPE GO:
STANDARD INDUS. CLASS. +	SICCODE	THE MAC ZONE/PC ZONE(FREE)	MZ
STANDARD MICROSYSTEMS FORUM +	SMC	THE MULTIPLE CHOICE +	MULTIPLE
STATE CAPITOL QUIZ +	TMC-89	THE TANDY USERS NETWORK +	TANDYNET
STATE-COUNTY DEMOGRAPHICS($)	DEMOGRAPHICS	THE TRAVEL CLUB(FREE)	TTC
STUDENTS' FORUM +	STUFO	THE WHIZ QUIZ	WHIZ
SUNSELECT FORUM +	SUNSELECT	THE WORLD OF LOTUS +	LOTUS
SUNGLASSES/SHAVERS & MORE FREE	SN	THOMAS COMPANIES ONLINE($)	THOMAS
SUPPORT ON SITE +	ONSITE	THOMAS-CONRAD FORUM +	TCCFORUM
SYMANTEC ANTIVIRUS PROD. FORUM	SYMVIRUS	TICKER/SYMBOL LOOKUP	LOOKUP
SYMANTEC APPLICATIONS FORUM +	SYMAPPS	TIPS/TRICKS FROM PC/COMPUTING	TNT
SYMANTEC DEV. TOOLS FORUM +	SYMDEVTOOL	TOSHIBA FORUM +	TOSHIBA
SYMANTEC NORTON UTIL FORUM +	SYMUTIL	TOSHIBA GMBH FORUM +	TOSHGER
TAPCIS FORUM +	TAPCIS	TRAINNET FORUM +	TRAINNET
TICFIL +	TICFIL	TRAVEL BRITAIN ONLINE	TBONLINE
TRADEMARKSCAN($)	TRADERC	TRAVEL FORUM +	TRAVSIG
TRW BUS. CREDIT REPORTS($)	TRWREPORT	TWENTIETH CENTURY(FREE)	TC
TRW CREDENTIALS(FREE)	CRE	UK COMPANY LIBRARY($)	UKLIB
TANDY MODEL 100 FORUM +	M100SIG	UK COMPUTING FORUM +	UKCOMP
TANDY NEWSLETTER +	TANDY	UK FORUM +	UKFORUM
TANDY PROFESSIONAL FORUM +	TRS80PRO	UK HISTORICAL STOCK PRICING +	UKPRICE
TECHNET SERVICES +	TECHNET	UK MARKETING LIBRARY($)	UKMARKETING
TELECOMMUNICATIONS FORUM +	TELECOM	UK NEWS CLIPS	UKNEWS
TEXAS INSTRUMENTS FORUM +	TIFORUM	UK NEWSPAPER LIBRARY($)	UKPAPERS
TEXAS INSTRUMENTS NEWS +	TINEWS	UK SPORTS CLIPS	UKSPORTS
THE 'GO GRAPHICS' TUTORIAL +	PIC	UKSHARE FORUM +	UKSHARE
THE BUSINESS WIRE +	TBW	UNIX FORUM +	UNIXFORUM
THE CATALOG STORE(FREE)	CATALOGS	US NEWSPAPER LIBRARY($)	NEWSLIB
THE COMPANY CORPORATION(FREE)	CORP	ULTIMEDIA HARDWARE PLUS FORUM	ULTIHW
THE COURT PHARMACY(FREE)	RX	ULTIMEDIA TOOLS SERIES A FORUM	ULTIATOOLS
THE DISNEY CATALOG(FREE)	DISNEY	ULTIMEDIA TOOLS SERIES B FORUM	ULTIBTOOLS
THE ELECTRONIC MALL(FREE)	MALL	UNITED PRESS INT'L($)	ENS
THE ENTREPRENEUR'S FORUM +	USEN	UNIV OF PHOENIX(FREE)	UP
THE FOCUS CONNECTION +	FOCUS	UNIXWARE FORUM +	UNIXWARE
THE GIFT SENDER(FREE)	GS	USER PROFILE PROGRAM(FREE)	TERMINAL
THE HEATH COMPANY(FREE)	HEATH	USERLAND FORUM +	USERLAND
THE IBMLINK STORE(FREE)	IBMLINK	VAX FORUM +	VAXFORUM
THE INTEL FORUM +	INTELFORUM	VISA ADVISORS	VISA
THE LASER'S EDGE(FREE)	LE	VENTURA SOFTWARE FORUM +	VENTURA

ORGANISATION	TYPE GO:	ORGANISATION	TYPE GO:
VOLKSWAGEN(FREE)	VW	ZIFF EDITOR'S CHOICE +	EDCHOICE
WORLDSPAN TRAVELSHOPPER	PARS	ZIFF EXECUTIVES ONLINE FORUM +	EXEC
WORLDSPAN TRAVELSHOPPER (CIM)	WORLDCIM	ZIFF NEWSBYTES +	NEWSBYTES
WP CUSTOMER SUPPORT FORUM +	WPFILES	ZIFF SOFTWARE/UTILITY LIBRARY	SOFTLIB
WRQ/REFLECTION FORUM +	WRQFORUM	ZIFF WINDOWS DEUTSCHLAND	GERWIN
WUGNET FORUM +	WUGNET	ZIFF-DAVIS PRESS BOOKNET +	BOOKNET
WALDEN COMPUTER BOOKS(FREE)	WB	ZIFFNET DESIGNER TEMPLATES +	FORMS
WALTER KNOLL FLORIST(FREE)	WK	ZIFFNET FILE FINDER +	ZFILEFINDER
WANG SUPPORT AREA +	WANG	ZIFFNET POLLS(FREE)	ZPOLL
WAR GAMES +	WARGAMES	ZIFFNET REVIEWS INDEX +	ZIFFINDEX
WASHINGTON POST($)	ENS	ZIFFNET SUPPORT FORUM +	ZSUPPORT
WEATHER MAPS	MAPS	ZIFFNET UK - ZEUS +	ZEUS
WEATHER REPORTS	WEATHER	ZIFFNET/MAC +	ZMAC
WEST COAST TRAVEL +	WESTCOAST	ZIFFNET/MAC FILE FINDER +	ZMC:FILEFINDER
WHAT'S NEW	NEW	ZIFFNET/MAC ORDERING +	ZMACEDITION
WHITE HOUSE FORUM +	WHITEHOUSE	ZIFFNET/MAC REVIEWS INDEX +	ZMC:INDEX
WINCIM INFORMATION	WINCIM	ZIFFNET/MAC SEYBOLD NEWSLETTER	SEYBOLD
WINCIM SUPPORT FORUM(FREE)	WCIMSUPPORT	ZIFFNET SURVEYS(FREE)	ZSURVEYS
WINNT PRE-RELEASE FORUM +	WINNT		
WINDOWS 3RD PARTY A FORUM +	WINAPA		
WINDOWS 3RD PARTY APP. D FORUM	WINAPD		
WINDOWS 3RD PARTY B FORUM +	WINAPB		
WINDOWS 3RD PARTY C FORUM +	WINAPC		
WOLFRAM RESEARCH FORUM +	WOLFRAM		
WORDPERFECT CORPORATION +	WORDPERFECT		
WORDPERFECT USERS FORUM +	WPUSER		
WORDSTAR FORUM +	WORDSTAR		
WORKING-FROM-HOME FORUM +	WORK		
WORLDWIDE CAR NETWORK +	WWCAR		
YOU GUESSED IT! +	YGI		
Z BEST - DISCOUNT ELECTRONICS	ZBEST		
ZAGAT RESTAURANT GUIDE	ZAGAT		
ZENITH DATA SYSTEMS FORUM +	ZENITH		
ZIFF BUYERS' MARKET	BUYMARKET		
ZIFF COBB APPLICATIONS FORUM +	COBBAPP		
ZIFF COBB PROGRAMMING FORUM +	COBBPR		
ZIFF COMPUTER SHOPPER FORUM +	COMPSHOPPER		
ZIFF DEMOS SHOWCASE +	DEMOS		

4 GLOSSARY OF COMMUNICATIONS TERMINOLOGY

Glossary of Communications Terminology

A   ACOUSTIC COUPLER

Means of connecting external devices to a telephone handset avoiding direct electrical connection; most commonly used for low-speed data terminals.

ACK

The 'acknowledge' character in many data codes; used most commonly for an affirmative response of correct receipt. Compare to: NACK.

ADAPTIVE EQUALISATION

Equalisation of received digital signals capable of adjustment during actual transmission.

ADAPTIVE ROUTING

In data networks, routing algorythms capable of adjusting message routes in response to changes in traffic patterns or transmission channel failures.

ADDRESS

- In software, a location that can be specifically located in a program.

- In communications networks, the distinct identifier of a place, service or function to be reached.

ALGORYTHM

A prescribed set of steps for accomplishment of a function or task; equivalent to a mathematical solution.

AMERICAN NATIONAL STANDARDS INSTITUTE (ANSI)

Official repository of standards for the United States of America. Compare: British Standards Institute (BSI) for the United Kingdom. Example: ASCII data communications code is ANSI C.64 and CCITT International Telegraph Alphabet Number 5, with only the smallest variation in a few definitions.

AMPLITUDE

Magnitude or size; voltage or power of an electronic signal.

AMPLITUDE MODULATION (AM)

Modifying a 'carrier' signal by varying its instantaneous power to represent the information it carries; most commonly called 'AM'.

ANALOG LOOPBACK (ALB)
Connecting a received analog signal to the return transmitting path; a common test method for locating transmission problems in data transmission systems.

ANALOG SIGNAL
A signal in the form of a continuous varying in step with the actual transmitted information; attempts to transmit an exact replica of the inputed signal down a communications channel.

ANALOG TRANSMISSION
Communications by transmission of continuously varying representations of the input signal, as compared to coded words in digital transmission.

ANSWER BACK
An electrical and/or visual indication to the call originating end that the call terminating end is on the line. First associated with the International Telex network, answerbacks are also recommended in CCITT-standard fax machines and are provided in most PC data communications software packages.

ARCNET – A LAN
Architecture developed by Datapoint Corporation featuring low cost for connection of groups of (Async) terminals to a (mini) computer within a premises.

ARQ
Telegraphic code signal for 'Automatic Repeat Request', a time-honored method of telegraphic error correction upon which most data transmission error correction is based. ARQ receivers check for errors and initiate an order to retransmit data blocks determined to be corrupted in transmission. also proprietary error detecting system used on some asynch modems.

ASCII – AMERICAN (NATIONAL) STANDARD CODE FOR INFORMATION INTERCHANGE;
The most common code used for asynchronous data transmission by minicomputers and personal computers; derived from the TWX code of the Bell Model 28 teleprinter, expanded to use all possible character combinations; consists of 7 information bits with an 8th parity bit for error checking; numerous variations exist, for example use of the 8th bit in personal computers to extend the code with a number of graphics, special language characters and diacritical marks. Many common carrier data services cannot transmit the 8th bit needed to use that common PC extension of ASCII's alphabet.

ASYNCHRONOUS

Occurring without central control or in an unpredictable time interval between successive elements; the typical mode of telegraphy, minicomputers and personal computers; requires transmission of 'start' and 'stop' bits to provide decoding synchronisation at the receiver.

ATTENUATION

Term denoting a decrease in power between that transmitted and that received due to loss through equipment, lines, or other transmission devices. Usually expressed as a ratio in dB (decibels). Synonym: Loss; Antonym: Gain

AUTOMATIC ANSWER (AUTOANSWER; AUTO ANSWER)

A function providing for a transmission control unit or station to automatically detect being called and respond to an inbound call. Most commonly associated with telephone answering sets, voice mail, automated attendants and data sets (modems) for computer terminals.

AUTOMATIC NUMBER IDENTIFICATION (ANI)

On long distance calls, the process by which the local phone company passes a caller's local billing phone number to his/her long distance company when a '1+' or '10XXX' call is made. With ANI a caller's long distance carrier knows who (what phone number) to bill without requiring the caller to enter an Authorisation Code to be identified and billed. See: Caller Line Indication

AUTOMATIC REDIAL (AUTOMATIC RECALL)

A terminal function capable of detecting a busy signal and redialing the call until a connection is obtained; often called 'Demon Dialer' after an early add-on consumer unit made for telephones.

B

BABT

British Approvals Board for Telecommunications. An independent body responsible for approval procedures for UK telecomms equipment. Only BABT approved equipment may be connected to UK services, regardless of the supplier of these services.

BALUN

A form of impedance-matching transformer adapted by datacomms from radio antennas to connect unbalanced coaxially -interfaced data terminals to balanced twisted pair wiring in buildings.

BAND

In analog transmission, the range of frequencies between two defined limits. Synonym: Bandwidth.

BANDWIDTH

See: Band.

BATCH

- In data processing, the processing of data accumulated over a period of time.

- In telecommunications, the accumulation of messages for transmission in a single group.

BAUD

A unit of signaling speed. The speed in Baud is the number of discrete conditions or signal elements per second. If each signal event represents only one bit condition, then Baud is the same as bits per second. Baud does not otherwise equal bits per second.

BINARY CODED DECIMAL (BCD)

A binary-coded notation in which each decimal digit of a number is expressed in binary form. Example: 23 decimal is 10111 in binary, and 0010 0011 in BCD.

BINARY CODED DECIMAL INTERCHANGE CODE (BCDIC)

IBM's earlier 7-bit implementation of a code for synchronous data communications. Virtually completely replaced by EBCDIC at this point in time.

BIS

'Second Working' or 'Second Implementation' as used in CCITT recommendations.

BIT

The smallest unit of information in data processing; a contraction of the words, 'binary digit'.

BITS PER SECOND (BPS)

Basic unit of measurement for raw transmission throughput on a link. Often stated in kilobits, megabits, or gigabits.

BLOCK

In data communications, a string of data set into an 'envelope' of synchronizing, addressing, control and error- checking characters transmitted as an entity. Synonymous with 'packet' in X.25 packet networks. Equivalent to 'frames' in digital communications systems.

BOOTSTRAP LOADER

A computer input routine in which preset operations are placed into a computer that enable it to get into operation whenever a reset condition occurs; in electronic PBXs this may be called Automatic Program Loading or a similar term; in personal computers it is the sequence that searches predetermined disks for a Command Interpreter program, then a Configure System file; finally an Autoexecution Batch file.

BREAK

- In the sense of a transmission impairment, a momentary interruption of a circuit.

- In data transmission systems, a timed interruption of about 300 milliseconds, often intended to interrupt a distant transmitting station.

BREAKOUT BOX

A very common and low-cost data interface test adapter permitting physical access to the interface pins to view the status; sometimes force conditions on some pins or even connect the pins differently. When mounted in a larger device, often called a breakout panel. Used by exasperated comms engineers.

BRIDGE

- In WANs, a device to connect transmission circuits in parallel.

- In LANs, an electronic device providing a logical connection path between two LAN physical segments.

BROADBAND

- In analog transmission plant, a channel facility having a bandwidth of greater than nominal voice grade of about 3 khz.

- In LANs, an analog physical transport medium of very wide bandwidth, typically 300 megahertz or more.

BROADCAST

In telecommunications, a transmission mode in which every message is transmitted to all stations; only those authorised or addressed will record, read or display it, however.

BUFFER

A temporary storage medium to permit some difference in the capacity of two data devices to emit and accept data from each other.

BUG

Computer term for an error or mistake causing a processing delay or stoppage.

BULLETIN BOARD SYSTEM (BBS, EBBS)

A communicating computer equipped so as to provide informational messages, file storage and transfer and a degree of message exchange to dial-up data terminal or personal computer users.

BUS

A common physical conductor, to which several units of compatible type are connected in parallel, sharing use of the bus.

BYTE

In computers, a very specifically-sized unit containing 8 bits for the computer to operate on; frequently called a 'word' in computer systems.

C **CALLER LINE IDENTIFICATION**

A feature of digital telephone networks to pass the number of the caller to the recipient.

CARRIER

A signal of known characteristics that is modified (modulated) so it carries information. The receiver, knowing the expected characteristics of the carrier, can extract the information from it. However, noise or unintended changes to the carrier will, of course be also interpreted as part of the information. See: Common Carrier.

CARRIER SYSTEM

A transmission system capable of providing multiple communications channels over a single physical path.

CATHODE RAY TUBE (CRT)

A common form of visual display for data terminals, similar to a television picture tube.

CCIR

Comité Consultatif Internationale des Radio, a major constituent of the International

Telecommunications Union, issuing both Radio Regulations and Recommendations for all uses of radio transmission. See: ITU

CCITT

Comité Consultatif Internationale des Téléphones et Télégraphes, a major constituent of the International Telecommunications Union (ITU) that sets standards for the operation of telecommunications services across international boundaries. Many CCITT recommendations are adopted for use domestically.

CELLULAR MOBILE RADIO

A high capacity land mobile radio system in which radio channels are divided into clustered groups covering limited areas, with the radio units automatically switching channels as the user moves from cell to cell.

CHANNEL

A communications transmission path via any sort of transmission medium – wire, radio, optical fiber or otherwise.

CHARACTER

A unit of typographic information, usually variable as part of a language. Because data is handled and transferred as a series of characters, the term also can mean one bit pattern in a specific data code; frequently called a 'word' in the computer programming sense of the term.

CHARACTER ORIENTED

Descriptive of a communications protocol or transmission procedure that has control information transmitted in the form of special bytes called control characters. Implies by its nature limitation to a particular character code. Compare to: Bit oriented.

CIRCUIT SWITCHING

A switching system that completes a dedicated transmission path from sender to receiver at the time of transmission, then releases that path for another user when the transmission is completed.

CLOCKING

Repetitive, regularly timed signals used to control synchronous transmissions.

CLUSTER CONTROLLER

A device that handles remote communications control (and sometimes processing) for multiple data terminals or workstations.

COAXIAL CABLE

A cable in which one conductor surrounds the other. The electromagnetic wave travels between the grounded outer shield and the central conductor. Coaxials can carry much wider bandwidth and higher frequencies than twisted wire pair, while suffering less interference problems due to the grounded outer conductor. Where the maximum frequency capable on twisted pair wiring is about 16 megahertz and then only for short distances, coaxial cable readily carries several hundred megahertz for a thousand feet.

CDEC

Contraction of Coder-Decoder. Used to convert analog signals to digital pulses for transmission and back again to the original analog form for reception. Originally located in digital channel banks, codecs are now located within digital telephone sets.

COMPANDOR

Contraction of 'Compressor/Expandor'.

- In analog operations, used to transmit signals higher above noise with a restricted dynamic range, then restore that range by expansion at the receiver.

- In digital systems, used to restrict t he dynamic range of speech signals prior to digital transmission encoding, then expand them at the receiving terminal.

COMPATIBILITY

A property in data processing and telecommunications systems permitting exchange of information directly and in usable form; implies identical or interchangeable signals and methodologies. Achieving compatibility is a major function of standards organizations.

COMPRESSION

- In analog communications, restricting the range of volume levels of signals in order to transmit them at a higher average power above noise on the channel.

- In data communications, compacting the number of bits used to represent the information, losing the character structure while reducing the circuit time or capacity needed to transfer the data; decompression is then needed at the receiving end to again render the data useful.

CONCATENATION

Linking of transmission media by looping through devices; used in various ways by many data terminals, this term most closely associated with Burroughs data terminals. Other names: Daisy Chaining (NCR); Multiple Wiring (telephony); Paralleling; Looping.

CONCENTRATOR
Any communications device that allows a shared transmission medium to accommodate more terminals than channels available on the medium. Other names: Contention switches, Channel Contenders.

CONVERSATIONAL MODE (CHAT MODE)
Interactive data communications carried on between data terminals in a fashion emulating speech conversation.

CR (CARRIAGE RETURN)
A control character causing the print or display position to move to the first position on the line, drawn from the typewriter and teleprinter function with similar action.

CROSS TALK
Unwanted energy (speech, tone or digital pulses) transferred from one transmission path to another. Comprises part of the 'noise' observed on analog communications circuits.

CURRENT LOOP
A digital transmission method that recognizes current flows as compared to voltage changes; long used in telegraphy, some use is found in vendor proprietary terminal interfaces, most notably those of Digital Equipment Corporation.

CUSTOMER INFORMATION CONTROL SYSTEM (CICS)
An IBM computer system function to oversee and control the flow of information by means of software interfaces between application programs and the computer's operating system.

CYCLIC REDUNDANCY CHECK (CRC)
A powerful error checking method for data and digital communications. The transmitting terminal computes a numeric value representative of the number of marking bits in the associated block of data and sends that value to the receiver, where the number is recomputed to compare against the block as received. Depending on the number of bits in the CRC numeric value the error trapping efficiency ranges from about 97 % at CRC-6 to 99.997% at CRC-32. Values of CRC-8 and CRC-16 are adequate for most data message block sizes, while CRC-32 is needed mainly for very

long blocks of tens of thousands of characters.

D   **DATA**
Multiple units of information. Singular is 'datum'.

DATA COMMUNICATIONS EQUIPMENT (DCE)
Standards body term for devices that perform signal conversion at the extremities of a data circuit. A data set (modem) or a CSU are common examples of a DCE. Compare to: DTE.

DATA ENCRYPTION STANDARD (DES)
A cryptographic standard defined by the former National Bureau of Standards (NBS), now the National Institute of Science and Technology (NIST) for the general public to encrypt and decrypt digital and data transmissions.

DATA SET
A device converting data into signals suitable for transmission over telecommunications lines; the term 'modem' commonly used by computer communications personnel has a much broader sense and range of application in general telecommunications.

DATA TERMINAL
A station in a system capable of sending and/or receiving data signals.

DATA TERMINAL EQUIPMENT
The standards-body term for a computer, user terminal, workstation or personal computer used for data communications; abbreviated DTE. Compare to: DCE .

DECIBEL (dB)
A unit of measurement representing the logarithmic a ratio of two voltages, currents or power levels; used in telecommunications to express transmission loss or gain; defined as one-tenth of a Bel, hence the appropriate notation is dB, shown here.

DIAL UP
Using facilities of the PSTN to establish a connection.

DIGITAL DATA COMMUNICATIONS MESSAGE PROTOCOL (DDCMP)
Digital Equipment Corporation's (DEC) synchronous data transfer protocol.

DIGITAL LOOPBACK (DLB)
Testing method in which received data is fed back to the transmitting source without

processing; used to isolate circuit problems.

DIGITAL SIGNALING

Using techniques that transmit information as a series of discontinuous pulsed signals in a pattern representative of the inputted signals; requiring reconstitution at the receiver; capable of being regenerated to minimise noise contribution in transmission. Compare to: Analog.

DIGITAL SWITCHING

Establishing and maintaining a connection under stored program control, when information passed through the switching matrix is in the form of binary encoded information. The transmission medium through the matrix is assigned 'time slots' on a digital bus. Analog circuits may be switched digitally by providing codecs in the physical ports of the switch.

DISTORTION

Generally an unwanted, often unpredicted change in a transmission signal that renders the resulting output less than optimum.

DUAL TONE MULTI-FREQUENCY (DTMF)

Also known as Touch-Tone. A type of signaling which emits two distinct frequencies for each indicated digit. Also called ' Key Pulsing' at operator positions in toll networks.

DUMB TERMINAL

A data communications euphemism indicating a DTE with no processing capability. The data equivalent of a KSR teleprinter.

DUPLEX (DX)

Two-way transmission.

E
ECHO

A signal that has been reflected or otherwise returned with sufficient magnitude and delay to be perceived at the far end of the circuit. Both 'talker echo' and 'listener echo' are defined terms. 'Echo suppressors', now largely being replaced by 'echo cancellers', are designed into circuits requiring treatment for echoes.

ECHO CANCELLER

An echo removal device that operates by generating an exact opposite of any echo signal and injecting it into the transmission path to cancel echoes. Used in both speech telephony and in some higher-speed dial-up data modems, notably those compliant with CCITT V.32.

ECHO CHECK

One method of verifying accuracy of data transmission; functions by returning (echoing) received data back to the transmitter as verification; primarily used on async data links.

ECHOPLEX

An echo checking data accuracy method used rather commonly and specifically for async keyboard terminals; the received data at the computer port is echoed back to be used as the terminal operator's CRT screen copy; the operator is the error checker.

ECHO SUPPRESSOR

A speech-activated switch that detects echo conditions and cuts off the echo path momentarily when echo conditions exist; largely made obsolete by echo cancellers.

EIA RS-232

The most common DTE serial interface by far, in use for almost 30 years, with several revisions and additions; international equivalent: The suite of CCITT V.24 and V.28 combined with ISO 2110.

ELECTRONIC MAIL

- A common-carrier data communications service to transmit computer-generated messages between locations or cities.

- A feature of LANs for transmission of computer-generated messages within a closed community of users on the LAN. Note that the two forms of electronic mail may be used independently or they may be interfaced.

EMULATE/EMULATION

Imitating a system or device such that a connected device accepts the same information, executes the same computer programs and achieves the same results as if the emulator were one of its own kind. Most often, emulation is a downward step in capability of the device being used, as when a personal computer is used to emulate a mechanical teleprinter or a 'dumb' terminal on a computer network. While some degree of upward emulation is possible, it is less prevalent in the broad view of computer communications.

ENCRYPTION

The systematic encoding of a message or bit stream before transmission to prevent unauthorized recipients from understanding it. The process of again rendering the information readable is decryption.

ERLANG

A widely-used unit of telecommunications traffic intensity, named after work of the Danish statistician, D. K. Erlang. One Erlang is the intensity at which one traffic path would be continuously occupied, e.g. one call per hour; equivalent to 3600 call-seconds or 36 ccs in early Bell traffic engineering systems.

ERROR CONTROL

In data communications, methods used to detect and correct transmission channel errors.

ETHERNET

Originally the trade name for a LAN developed by Xerox Corporation; later supported by Digital Equipment Corporation, Intel Corporation and Hewlett-Packard; now standardized as IEEE specification 802.3.

EXTENDED BINARY CODED DECIMAL INTERCHANGE CODE (EBCDIC)

IBM's proprietary 8-bit code for synchronous data communications. Has numerous variations of control character meanings; is undergoing some standardisation as IBM moves SNA and SAA forward.

F ### FACSIMILE (FAX)

Graphic transmission of pictures, maps or documents via communications circuits using terminal devices that scan documents, transforming scanned images into coded data-like signals and reproduce likenesses of original documents at a distant point. Has a long history dating to the 1840's as a method of telegraphy; archaic press implementations of this century used the names Wirephoto and Telephoto for early, slow photographic transmissions.

FCC (FEDERAL COMMUNICATIONS COMMISSION) – USA

A board of Presidentially-appointed commissioners empowered to regulate interstate and international communications and all uses of radio in the United States. Operates under the Communications Act of 1934 and several more recent laws; promulgates its own regulations interpreting those laws, as Title 47 of the Code of Federal Regulations (CFR 47 , 47CFR).

FIBER OPTICS

A technology using light as a digital information bearer. Fiber optic cables light guides) are a direct replacement for conventional wire, coaxial cable and many forms of radio, including microwave. Fiber optic lines actually cost less, occupy less space and provided far more transmission capacity than earlier methods, while providing superior quality due to virtual immunity to electrical interference.

FIRMWARE

Permanent or semi-permanent control coding built into a software-operated computer device that operates an application program, instruction set, operating routine or other user-oriented instructions to a computer; often resident in a ROM (Read Only Memory) chip to simplify installation.

FLAG

In data transmission, an indicator of an expected event like the beginning or end of a block of data. In CCITT standards for X.25 networks, the 8-bit character 01111110 has been uniquely established with the name 'Flag' to be used at the beginning and end of a block; many other proprietary protocols have adopting it, even if the rest of their data block is not CCITT-compliant.

FLOW CONTROL

In data communications, the use of buffering and other mechanisms to avoid data loss in case the receiver cannot keep up with the transmitter. The ASCII control characters X-ON and X-OFF are frequently-used examples; they are returned in the reverse direction as an instruction for the sender to hold or restart held transmission.

FORWARD CHANNEL

The communications path from the originator of information toward the recipient; a path in the return direction (perhaps established for error checking and/or flow control) is called the 'reverse channel'.

FRAME

In digital communications, a group of bits or characters sent serially over a channel; generally a logical unit of information between data link layer entities that contains its own control information for addressing and error checking. Synonym: Block.

FRAMING

A control procedure used with digital transmission to permit the receiver to synchronise itself with the transmitter's sequence of bits or characters; framing bits in more recent systems also carry alarm and control messages in entities like T-1 carrier systems. This makes framing bits in communications carrier systems closely akin to control characters in data communications.

FREQUENCY

The number of complete cycles of an event (in communications typically an alternating current signal) per unit of time; usually expressed by means of the unit 'Hertz', named after Heinrich Hertz an early German investigator of the properties of high-frequency alternating current waves.

FREQUENCY SHIFT KEYING (FSK)

One of the more basic and durable forms of transmitting binary information; in FSK, one of the binary states is represented by one known frequency and the other by another known frequency. The receiver produces outputs only when one of the two known frequencies is received in the absence of the other. Applications of FSK abound in every form of telecommunications; computer data modems used FSK exclusively for speeds up to 120 bps for years, and the classic FDM of telegraphers was 24 FSK channels on a voice channel to produce what was called 'carrier telegraph' and variations on that name.

FULL DUPLEX (FDX)

A circuit which allows independent transmission information in both directions simultaneously. Synonym: In wire telephony, 4 wire circuit.

G GATEWAY

A conceptual, logical or physical connection between two different networks; the term implies a need for conversion of some aspect of the information or communication in order to operate through a function named a gateway. Compare to 'port', which implies a point not requiring significant conversion of the message or information.

H HALF DUPLEX (HDX)

A circuit capable of transmitting or receiving information both ways, but only one direction at a time; a function of both computer protocols and transmission channels. Many computers operate only half duplex on transmission channels capable of full duplex operation.

HAMMING CODE

In data transmission, a code with added redundant bits for error detection purposes.

HANDOFF

In cellular radiotelephony, the protocol by which a call in progress is transferred from one cell to another as the mobile unit moves.

HANDSHAKE

The exchange of control sequences between two locations to set up needed conditions for communications. In the strictest sense, even the steps of dialling a telephone call can be thought of as a 'handshake sequence'.

HARDWIRE

Using physical wire or cable directly between units of hardware equipment.

HDLC (HIGH LEVEL DATA LINK CONTROL)

A bit-oriented international standard data link protocol used in CCITT X.25 packet network links and influencing many others such as SDLC, BDLC and DDCMP; also Honeywell Data Link Control, Honeywell Corporation's bit-oriented protocol for its computer networks.

HEADER

That portion of a message containing information for routing, handling and delivering a message, such as address, size, priority, intermediate routing and synchronisation signals.

HERTZ (HZ)

International standard unit of frequency. Replaces, and is identical to, the older unit 'Cycles-per-second. '

HEXADECIMAL

A number system based on 16, providing convenient notation of the 16 possible combinations of half an 8-bit data processing byte; uses digits 0 through 9 followed by letters A through F to count to 16, thus two 'hex' digits can describe one byte in software. Example: ASCII letter capital 'A' has the decimal value 65 but is written as 41 in hex software code, while small 'z' has the decimal value 122 but is noted as 7A in hex, still requiring only two digits instead of three. Using only two hex digits from 00 to FF, a code of 256 different characters can be described as is done with the adaptation of ASCII used by personal computers; the added characters beyond 128 are often called 'Extended ASCII' or 'IBM graphics characters'.

HYBRID

A very common communications electronics circuit performs the wire conversions necessary for the connection of a 2 wire local loop with a 4 wire long-haul facility; sometimes called a 'two wire / four wire converter'. The classic source of echo problems in long-distance telephony, hybrids were once made of expensive, bulky, specially-built transformers; today they are an IC chip full of microelectronics that is even self-adjusting.

INPUT/OUTPUT (I/O) CHANNEL/PORT

- In computers, the hardware function, usually a bus of parallel wires, hence 'channel', that transports data in parallel form between the CPU and peripherals like storage, printers or communications.

- In communications, usually a serial data port to a computer, then often with controls per RS-232.

INTELLIGENT TERMINAL

A terminal containing a programmable processor capable of some degree of local processing; the range of functions and degree of capability is not standardized and subject to wide discussion of what constitutes 'intelligence'.

INTERFACE

The junction or point of interconnection between two systems or equipment having different characteristics; has both hardware and software implications.

INTERFERENCE

Any unwanted noise, crosstalk or spurious signals on a communications circuit that acts to reduce the intelligibility of the desired information signal or speech.

INTERNATIONAL STANDARDS ORGANISATION (ISO)

A world standards body that generally sets standards for any fabricated or manufactured; thus ISO standards apply to physical aspects of the '25-pin connector' of CCITT V.24/28 data interfaces (RS-232), definitions of the several layers of data networks for which different hardware units may be required, and such diverse things as the exposure speeds of photographic film and definitions of units of measurement. ISO is an Anglicised form of the proper French name of l'Organisme pour le Standardisation Internationale, resident in Geneva, Switzerland.

INTERNATIONAL TELECOMMUNICATIONS UNION (ITU)

Anglicisation of the proper French name of the Union Internationale des Télécommunications (UIT), resident in Geneva, Switzerland. ITU is the treaty-established world center for agreements on telecommunications technical and operating standards and is a constituent body of the United Nations, engaging also in international development and education concerning telecommunications.

INTERNATIONAL TELEGRAPH ALPHABET #1 (ITA 1)

World-standard CCITT version of the manual telegrapher's code. Colloquial name: International Morse Code.

INTERNATIONAL TELEGRAPH ALPHABET #2 (ITA 2)

World-standard CCITT version of the 5-unit (also called 7.5 unit) teleprinter code used for Telex, international telegrams and most general telegraphy by wirelines; Colloquial name: Baudot code.

INTERNATIONAL TELEGRAPH ALPHABET #3 (ITA 3)

World-standard CCITT version of a 6-unit extended set of ITA 2 to include characters needed for automatic typesetting directly from telegraph circuits. Colloquial names: Teletypesetter code, press code, extended Baudot code, and others.

INTERNATIONAL TELEGRAPH ALPHABET #4 (ITA 4)

World-standard CCITT version of a 7-unit code in which only the combinations using 4 marking bits are valid; receiving any character with more or less than 4 marking bits is its error checking feature. Colloquial names: 7-unit ARQ Code, Moore ARQ Code, Moore Code, RCA Code, and others.

INTERNATIONAL TELEGRAPH ALPHABET #5 (ITA 5)

World-standard CCITT version of a 7-unit teleprinter code with an 8th parity bit also used for asynchronous data terminals such as minicomputers or PCs. Colloquial name: ASCII code.

INTERRUPT

Data processing term for a processing stoppage made in such a way as to be resumable. Compare to a 'halt', typically meaning a stoppage that requires initialising the machine to restart processing.

ISDN (INTEGRATED SERVICES DIGITAL NETWORK)

A global plan under auspices of the CCITT to provide any information service users may desire on a single worldwide public switched network. The ultimate ISDN has as its goal the elimination of need for discrete telephone, telegraph, data, packet and other networks.

J   ### JACK

Any of a range of hardware devices on which the permanent wiring of telecommunications circuits or apparatus is terminated to provide a physical access point by the insertion of a plug.

JUMP SCROLLING

Characteristic of a terminal with vertical motions of a whole line of characters at a time in discrete steps of one line, much as a teleprinter terminal might do. Contrast with: 'smooth scrolling' as done by graphics terminals.

L   **LEASED LINES**

Any circuit or combination of circuits designated to be at the exclusive disposal of a given user. Synonym: Private line; Full Period Line; Dedicated Line, Tie Line (colloquial).

LED (LIGHT EMITTING DIODE)

A semiconductor device that emits light under proper electrical conditions. Used both for simple indicators on electronic equipment and (with proper selection and use) as the source of signals for short-range (multimode) fiber optic transmission systems.

LINE PRINTER

Descriptive of computer printers that set and print an entire line of data at a time; often indicative of a high-speed, high volume printer.

LOCAL LOOP

The local circuit connection between the end user and the user's nearest telephone exchange office; notorious for being the poorest, weakest link in data circuits.

LONG HAUL (LONG-HAUL)

Descriptive of communications circuits spanning considerable distances; ranging from inter- LATA to intercontinental.

M   **MAINFRAME**

- One of the telephony synonyms for Main Distributing Frame;

- Data processing term descriptive of very large computers.

MARK

The signal state on a binary channel representing a '1'. Corresponds to current on, hole in paper tape, and (usually) negative voltage, as in EIA RS-232. Antonym: Space, current off, 0, no hole, positive voltage. Telegraphic circuits (with the notable exception of Telex trunks) hold a mark state when idle as a form of circuit assurance alarm technique.

MEGAHERTZ (MHZ)
A unit of a million Hertz; meaning millions of cycles per second of AC current.

MODEM
Contraction of the term Modulator/Demodulator; device that modulates and demodulates signals on and off a 'carrier' frequency; not limited to computer data use, thus the telco- specific term 'data set' for data modems.

MODULATION
Alterations in the characteristics of analog carrier waves, impressed on the amplitude, phase and/or the frequency of the wave.

MONITORING
Listening in on telephone calls in progress. Subject to severe restrictions as to the purpose and use of information obtained in doing so.

MSU (MODEM SHARING UNIT)
A hardware device, most often a simple contention switch operating on RTS (Request to Send) leads of DTE interfaces, that permits only one terminal at a time to use the modem.

MULTIPLEX/MULTIPLEXING
Transmitting more than a single message simultaneously on a physical transmission path; if analog, the technique is FDM, but if digital it is TDM.

N **NACK/NAK**
'Negative Acknowledge' character in many data codes; typically used to indicate receipt of a corrupted message, ordering re-transmission; compare to 'REJect ' character in IBM data systems.

NOISE
Unplanned energy introduced into a communications channel, resulting in transmission errors.

NON-VOLATILE (NONVOLATILE) STORAGE
A storage medium that does not lose its contents when power is removed.

P **PACKET**
In the sense of communications, a structured group of binary digits in a prearranged sequence containing synchronism, address, control an error-checking data.

Specialized synonym for a 'block' of data in CCITT Packet Data Network standards. Packet Switched Network – A network dedicated to the routing and delivery of data put in the form of standardized 'packets'.

PACKET SWITCHING
The technique in which a stream of data is broken into standardized units called 'packets', each of which contains address, sequence, control, size and error checking information in addition to the user data. Specialized packet switches operate on this added information to move the packets to their destination in the proper sequence and again present them in a contiguous stream. Compare: Circuit Switching; Message Switching.

PAD
An attenuator deliberately placed in a transmission channel to cause transmission loss; contraction of the term Packet Assembler/Disassembler in Packet Switched networks, the instrumentality that converts user data between steady streams and packets.

PAD CHARACTER/FILL CHARACTER
A control character inserted into data fields when insufficient characters are supplied to fill the data block or the block is incomplete. Interesting to note that a common 'pad' character is hex 7F, equating to ASCII 'Delete', the same as TWX 'rubout' and Baudot 'Letter Shift', all essentially the same in every generation of data communications.

PARALLEL TRANSMISSION
Simultaneous transmission of all parts of a signal at one time; in data transmission, requiring a separate signal path for each of the bits of a character; internal to computers, this is called a 'parallel bus'.

PARITY
A constant state of equality; one of the oldest and simplest methods of error checking data transmission. Characters are forced into parity (total number of marking bits odd or even as selected by choice) by adding a one or zero bit as appropriate when transmitted; parity is then checked as odd or even at the receiver.

PARITY BIT
A check bit appended to an array of binary digits to make the sum of all the digits always odd or always even.

PARITY CHECK

A checking method that determines if the sum of all the digits in an array is odd or even.

POINT-TO-POINT

A communications circuit between two terminations only.

PORT

Entrance or access point to a computer, multiplexor device or network where signals may be supplied, extracted or observed.

POST TELEPHONE AND TELEGRAPH (PTT)

Government agencies responsible for regulating communications, having the voting status of 'Administrations' in the ITU charter. In the UK PTT's are now called PTO's – Public Telephone Operators.

PROTOCOL

A set of procedures for establishing and controlling the transmission of information. Examples: SDLC; Bisync.

PROTOCOL CONVERSION/PROTOCOL CONVERTER

Generic name and name of the devices that perform a widely variable set of conversions of code, speed, electrical interface and/or block formatting and error checking/correction in data circuits. Example: a packet network PAD operating between an ASCII terminal and a packet network is a form of protocol converter. When the function is to make the line signals of a particular terminal appear like another, the protocol converter is a type called a Terminal Emulator.

PULSE

In communications, typically a signal characterized by a constant amplitude and duration; the line signal representation of a binary digit.

PUSH BUTTON DIALLING

Synonyms: Dual Tone Multi-Frequency; Touch-Tone (an AT&T service mark); Key Pulsing (on long distance operator positions).

Q **QUAD STANDARD**

Modem providing four CCITT modes, usually V21, V22/V22Bis, V23.

QUIN STANDARD

Modem providing five CCITT modes, usually V21, V22/V22Bis, V23, V32.

R   **RS-232**

The most common technical specification for interconnection of DTEs to DCEs; extremely close equivalent to the suite of CCITT V.24/V.28 and ISO-2110.

S   **SERIAL TRANSMISSION**

Transmitting data characters or bytes one bit at a time, in sequence. Contrast with: Parallel Transmission.

SEXTUPLE STANDARD

Modem providing six CCITT modes, usually V21, V22/V22Bis, V32/V32 bis.

SHANNON'S LAW

A statement defining the theoretical maximum at which error-free digits can be transmitted over a bandwidth-limited channel in the presence of noise; the rough equation works out to about 10 bits per hertz of bandwidth in practical analogue circuits, making the Shannon limit about 30,000 bps for voice-grade lines: 'I=F LOG2 (1+Sn)' where F is the bandwidth and SN the signal to noise ratio.

SIGNAL

Energy intentionally introduced into a transmission path for the purpose of transmitting information. Contrast with: Noise.

SIGNALING

In telephony, the process of transferring information between two parts of a network to control the establishment of communications between long distance carrier terminal points, and customer equipment required for voice grade dedicated circuits.

SIGNAL TO NOISE RATIO

Ratio of the signal power to the noise power in a specified bandwidth, usually expressed in decibels; the smaller the ratio, the poorer the channel. Generally speaking, a ratio of 20 dB or more is a channel subjectively 'excellent' for telephony, while broadcast television video requires 30 dB or more, but 1200 bps modems can function with only 12 dB, requiring more as the data speed increases.

SMART TERMINAL

A data terminal capable of operating in either a conversational or a block mode; containing a full set of local editing capabilities without reliance on a controlling external computer.

SPACE

The communications signal state corresponding to binary zero. Variously represented as no current, no hole in paper tape, (usually) positive voltage. A very 'long space' is used in telegraphy as a circuit failure alarm and a disconnect signal for Telex lines. Contrast with: Mark.

START BIT

The leading bit of every asynchronous character, needed to trigger the receiver that a new character is starting; must intrinsically be a space (0) bit.

START-STOP TRANSMISSION

Telegraphic and IBM synonym for asynchronous transmission.

STOP BIT

A mandatory mark bit that must follow the information bits of an asynchronous character to inform the receiver the character has ended; it can be a single bit when sent to electronic receivers, but mechanical printers have classically required a stop bit in excess of 1 bit time. The CCITT long ago standardized it at 1.42 bit times for teleprinters.

SYNCHRONISATION

The function of getting a receiver into step with a transmitter, preparatory to starting transmission.

T **TELECOMMUNICATIONS**

The transmission of voice and/or data through a medium by means of electrical impulses and includes all aspects of transmitting information.

TELEGRAPH

A system employing the interruption of, or change in, the polarity of DC current signaling to convey coded information. Many techniques of data communications follow precepts first established in telegraphy.

TELEMETRY

Technology of measuring a quantity or quantities, transmitting the results to a distant point and there interpreting, indicating or recording the quantities measured; with so many elements common to classic public communications, it can be seen to fit under the umbrella of telecommunications.

TELEPHONE

A device converting acoustical (sound) energy into electrical energy for transmission to a distant point.

TELEPROCESSING

Remote access data processing; use of data link communications to accomplish a computer-based task; distinguished from Distributed Data Processing in that an application processor is not required at each and every node as in DDP.

TELETEXT

Generic term for essentially one-way broadcast of graphics and text for display on user television sets or low cost CRT's. Many forms simply transmit frame after frame of video repeatedly and the user selects the desire frame(s) at the receiver. Rather long-established and highly evolved in Europe, all North American efforts have been rather ineffective to date, with a number of commercial failures. Typical transmission medium is as a data signal hidden in the blank space of broadcast television vertical synchronizing pulses, although other means are possible on TV broadcast signals as well. Videotex is the interactive form of Teletext.

TELETYPEWRITER

A machine used to transmit and/or receive communications on printed page and/or tape.

TELEX

A communications service enabling textual correspondence service based on 50 bps transmission of Baudot code. While archaic in view of recent advances, Telex remains the most conveniently widespread telecommunications service to any corner of the world, reaching more places than the telephone.

TER

Means 'third working' or third implementation, as used in CCITT recommendations.

TERMINAL

- A point at which information can enter or leave a communications network;

- Any device capable of sending or receiving information over a communications channel.

TERMINAL EQUIPMENT

Devices, apparatus and their associated interfaces used to forward information to a local customer or distant terminal.

TTY (TELETYPE)

The registered trade name for teleprinters and data terminals of the Teletype Corporation; used generically in the telecommunications industry for teleprinters or data terminals that emulate teleprinter operations.

TURNAROUND TIME

Time required to reverse the direction on a half-duplex communications channel; somewhat misapplied if used in data communications to describe the total response time, including processor time, for interactive data transactions.

V **VALUE-ADDED NETWORK SERVICE (VANS)**

A data transmission network routing transmissions according to available paths, assures that the message will be received as it was sent, provides for user security, high speed transmission and conferencing among terminals. Closely akin to courier services or shipping forwarders in physical commerce.

VIDEOTEX

Interactive version of teletext.

VIRTUAL CIRCUIT

In packet switching, network facilities with the appearance of a dedicated private line, even though individual packets may constantly be taking variable routes.

W **WINDOWING**

A technique in (mostly PC) data communications protocols that permits the sender to run ahead in transmission, backing up to re-send if the receiver signals an error in a recently-sent block. As in the 'Sliding Window KERMIT' file transfer protocol.

PC PLUS MODEM AND COMMUNICATIONS GUIDE BOOK SOFTWARE OFFER

NO COMMS SOFTWARE?

Send for a low cost shareware comms program to 'get you going'. All disks are £2.50 each, including VAT and First Class P&P. All disks are virus checked before despatch and include shareware antivirus software. A 'get-you-going' instruction sheet is enclosed with each package.

DISK 1 – ODYSSEY – SHAREWARE VERSION – FOR THE PC

Powerful shareware program with ZMODEM and MNP5. UART and other utilities included.

☐ **3.5" 720k disk**
☐ **5.25" 1.2Mb disk**

DISK 2 – ZTERM FOR THE MAC

Shareware comms program with ZMODEM and scripting. 'Terminal' and other utilities included.

☐ **3.5" 800k disk**

DISK 3 – TERM FOR THE AMIGA

With ZMODEM and voice synthesis. 'Baudbandit' is included. Requires Kickstart 2.04 and Workbench 2.04.

☐ **3.5" 700k disk**

Cheques and Postal Orders should be made out to **Connect Ltd**
and sent to the address overleaf. Allow 14 days for delivery.

EXCLUSIVE DISCOUNTS ON COMMS SOFTWARE

AS A SPECIAL OFFER TO READERS OF THE PC PLUS MODEM AND COMMUNICATIONS GUIDE BOOK THE FOLLOWING DISCOUNTS ARE AVAILABLE

RENCOM PLUS – SAVE OVER £20

For those who want to access European services this package is a must. Its supports BTX and Minitel emulation, needed for some large European services. It is multilingual, mouse and Network aware.   ORDER CODE R2910PCP

Normal price	£79 + P&P + VAT
Special Readers Price	£59 + £4 P&P + VAT
	Total £74.02

☐ **3.5" 720k disk**   ☐ **5.25" 360k disk**

ODYSSEY – FULL VERSION – SAVE OVER £30

With MNP5 software emulation, Viewdata (for Prestel) and a sophisticated script language; this well known package is all you will need.

          ORDER CODE R2404PCP

Normal price	£89 + P&P + VAT
Special Readers Price	£59 + £4 P&P + VAT
	Total £74.02

☐ **3.5" 720k disk**   ☐ **5.25" 360k disk**

Name _____

Address _____   Post Code _____

Method of Payment: ☐ Cheque   ☐ Postal Order   ☐ Access   ☐ Visa

Credit Card No ☐☐☐☐ ☐☐☐☐ ☐☐☐☐ ☐☐☐☐   Expiry Date ☐☐☐☐☐☐

Signature _____

Cheques and Postal Orders should be made out to **Shareware Publishing** and sent with this coupon to the address overleaf.

COMMS BOOK DISK OFFER
PO BOX 190
EAST GRINSTEAD
WEST SUSSEX
RH19 3GT

SHAREWARE PUBLISHING
3A QUEEN STREET
SEATON
DEVON

COMPUSERVE SPECIAL INTRODUCTORY OFFER

FREE CompuServe Introductory Membership Kit

- Access telephone numbers and a Personal ID and Password
- CompuServe Information Manager software for Windows
- A CompuServe Mini User's Guide
- A month's FREE membership to CompuServe allowing access FREE of connect charges to CompuServe's basic services (communication surcharges may apply)
- $15 credit to explore CompuServe's Extended and Premium services

Name _____

Address _____

_____

Post Code _____ Date _____

Please complete your name and address details on coupon and return to the FREEPOST address overleaf

THIS OFFER EXPIRES 1ST AUGUST 1994

SAVE 10% OFF MODEMS

EXCLUSIVE TO READERS OF THE PC PLUS MODEM AND COMMUNICATIONS GUIDE BOOK

SEG COMMUNICATIONS have arranged a special deal exclusive to purchasers of the **PCPLUS MODEM AND COMMUNICATIONS GUIDE BOOK**. SEG supply a complete range of quality modems and accessories, from low cost 'get-you-going' type modems to high specification top of the range models.

SEG already offer very competitive prices, but with this voucher, you can save a further **10%** off their published prices. All modems are fully BABT approved. SEG are happy to discuss your requirements prior to ordering.

HOW TO CLAIM

Simply phone or send a fax to SEG to obtain their latest catalogue. To claim your 10% discount return this coupon with your order to to the address overleaf.

Name _____ Date of Claim _____ Model Ordered _____

Tel: 081 959 3377 – Fax: 081 959 2137

Offer subject to SEG's normal terms and conditions. Offer prices exclude carriage charges.

THIS OFFER EXPIRES 1ST AUGUST 1994

COMPUSERVE INFORMATION SERVICES (UK) LTD
FREEPOST (BS6971)
PO BOX 676
BRISTOL
BS99 1NZ

SEG COMMUNICATIONS
137 HALE LANE
EDGEWARE
MIDDX
HA8 9QP

5
USEFUL CONTACTS

Useful contacts

ACTION COMPUTER SUPPLIES

TEL: 0800 333 333

Suppliers of PC related hardware/software, and modems. An excellent free catalogue can be had for the asking on the above number, next day delivery services are usually impeccable, as is their customer service.

APPLE COMPUTER UK

TEL: FREEFONE APPLE

UK distributor of Apple Products

AT&T

TEL: 0527 64274

Pan-global telecomms supplier, everything from managed networks to Viewdata systems provision.

AUTHOR

You can contact the Author on CompuServe 100113,2132, or as S_SCO @ CIX.

BRITISH APPROVALS BOARD FOR TELECOMMUNICATIONS (BABT)

TEL: 0932 222 2289

BRITISH TELECOM:

GNS DIALPLUS MARKETING – TEL: 0800 181555

ISDN MARKETING – TEL: 071 356 7401

CIX – COMPULINK INFORMATION EXCHANGE

VOICE – TEL: 081 390 8446

DATA – TEL: 081 390 1244

New users with credit cards can join on-line by typing CIX at the LOGIN: prompt followed by NEW at the NICKNAME prompt.

COMMODORE BUSINESS MACHINES UK

TEL: 0628 770088

Distributor of Amiga computers.

COMPUSERVE
VOICE – TEL: 0800 289458

Global Value Added Service and messaging provider. Ask for membership details and a log-on ID.

DATAFLEX DESIGN
TEL: 081 543 6417

Manufacturers of telecomms products including ISDN adaptors.

DEMON INTERNET SERVICES (DIS)
TEL: 081-349-0063

Providers of dial-up Internet services for around £10 per month. Help desk staffed by human beings.

GPT LTD
TEL: 0628 77200

Provider of telecomms equipment.

HAYES UK
TEL: 0252 775500

Definitive communications products.Online With Hayes BBS on 0252 775599 has CD-ROM of BBS software, International BBS lists, etc.

IBM UK
TEL: 0962 844433

Provider of ISDN terminal adaptors and telecomms equipment.

ILI
TEL: 0344 874343

Provider of CCITT recommendations, with a document update service.

IP NETWORKING
TEL: 0734 333496

Supplier of Internet training, workshops etc.

JAGUAR COMMUNICATIONS LTD
TEL: 0727 41311

ISDN and comms equipment manufacturers.

MAC CONNECT
TEL: 091 230 5596
Suppliers of Macintosh-aware ISDN products.

MAPLIN ELECTRONICS
TEL: 081 523 4879
Mail order supplier of computer and electronic components. Catalogue available. Nationwide chain of electronics shops now open.

MERCURY COMMUNICATIONS
0500 500194
UK Public Telephone Operator (PTO). Useful helpline number for all Mercury queries.

MINITEL COMMUNICATIONS DUBLIN
TEL: DUBLIN 01- 768233
Joint French-Irish venture. Viewdata services.

OFFICE OF TELECOMMUNICATIONS (OFTEL)
TEL: 071 634 8700
Non-ministerial government office which regulates the UK telecomms industry.

PAN TECHNOLOGY
TEL: 0892 667022
Specialist PC hardware/software designers.

RACAL DATACOM
TEL: 0256 763911
Providers of telecomms equipment

RENCOMM PLUS (BY DORTEC)
DISTRIBUTED BY: SHAREWARE MARKETING, 3A, QUEEN STREET, SEATON, DEVON EX12 2NY
TECHNICAL SUPPORT – TEL: 0297 24 089
DORTEC'S UK SUPPORT BBS – TEL: 0297 24469
DORTEC EUROPEAN OFFICE BRUSSELS – TEL: +32 2 375 2579
DORTEC HEAD OFFICE – TEL: COPENHAGEN +45 45 87 87 58

S/E/G COMMUNICATIONS

TEL: 081 959 3377

Retail suppliers of modems and telecommunications products, also provide cables, fast PC serial ports etc.

TELECOMMS USERS ASSOCIATION

TEL: 081 445 0996

Represents the interests of small business and domestic users of telecomms services.

TRANSPAC

TEL: 071 379 4747

Global telecomms provider, also Minitel provider.

USEFUL ISDN HELP

ISDN SUPPORT GROUP – TEL: 0473 645498

ISDN HELPDESK – TEL: 0800 181514

VIKING OFFICE SUPPLIES

TEL: 0800 424444

Mail order suppliers of office and computer consumables, good delivery service.

6
DIALPLUS NETWORK ACCESS POINTS

GNS Dialplus Network Access Points

Dialplus is the BT service which provides access to the packet switching network. These numbers allow Dialplus subscribers to access any other computer system connected to the International Packet Switching Service, including CompuServe. They are especially useful where there is no local telephone number for the service required. (See Chapter 10). To access Dialplus you'll need an account. Call the Dialplus Sales Office on 0800 282 444 for details.

Reproduced by permission of BT – with thanks to Rod Hillen and Bill Kirkwood for their help.

THESE NODES SUPPORT ACCESS TO 2400 BPS

ABERDEEN	0224 210701	DUNDEE	0382 22452
ABERDEEN	0224 210701	DUNOON	0369 2210
AYR	0292 611822	EDINBURGH	031-313 2137
BALLYMENA	0266 654284	ELGIN	0343 543890
BANGOR	0247 274284	ENNISKILLEN	0365 328284
BELFAST	0232 331284	EXETER	0392 421565
BENBECULA	0870 602657	FIONNPHORT	0681 7203
BIRMINGHAM	021-633 3474	GLASGOW	041-204 1722
BRECHIN	0356 625782	GOLSPIE	0408 633021
BRECON	0874 623151	GRIMSBY	0472 353550
BRIGHTON	0273 550045	GUILDFORD	0483 38632
BRISTOL	0272 211545	HALIFAX	0422 349224
BRODICK	0770 2031	HASTINGS	0424 722788
CAMBRIDGE	0223 460127	HUNTLY	0466 793653
CAMPBELTOWN	0586 552298	INVERGARRY	08093 406
CANTERBURY	0227 762950	INVERNESS	0463 711940
CARDIFF	0222 344184	IPSWICH	0473 210212
CARLISLE	0228 512621	KINGS LYNN	0553 691090
CHELMSFORD	0245 491323	KINGUSSIE	05402 661078
CHELTENHAM	0242 227547	KINROSS	0577 863111
COLERAINE	0265 56284	KIRKWALL	0856 876004
COLONSAY	09512 351	LEAMINGTON	0926 451419
CREWE	0270 588531	LEEDS	0532 440024
DALMALLY	08382 410	LEICESTER	0533 628092
DOWNPATRICK	0396 616284	LERWICK	0595 6211

LINCOLN	0522 532398	OBAN	0631 63111
LIVERPOOL	051-255 0230	OMAGH	0662 240284
LLANDRINDOD-WELLS	0597 825881	OXFORD	0865 798949
LLANDUDNO	0492 860500	PETERSFIELD	0730 265098
LOCHCARRON	05202 598	PETERBOROUGH	0733 555705
LOCHGILPHEAD	0546 603717	PLYMOUTH	0752 603302
LOCHINVER	05714 548	POOLE	0202 666461
LONDON:		PORT ELLEN	0496 2143
CLERKENWELL	071-490 2200	PORTADOWN	0762 351284
COLINDALE	081-905 9099	PORTREE	0478 3208
CROYDON	081-681 5040	PRESTON	0772 204405
MONUMENT	071-283 9123	READING	0734 500722
LONDONDERRY	0504 370284	ROTHERHAM	0709 820402
LUTON	0582 481818	RUGELEY	0889 576610
MACHYNLLETH	0654 703560	SEDGWICK	0539 561263
MAGHERAFELT	0648 34284	SEVENOAKS	0732 740966
MALLAIG	0687 2728	SHREWSBURY	0743 231027
MANCHESTER	061-834 5533	SOUTHAMPTON	0703 634530
MELVICH	06413 364	STORNOWAY	0851 706111
MIDDLESBROUGH	0642 245464	STRATHDON	09756 51396
MINTLAW	0771 24560	SWINDON	0793 541620
NEATH	0639 641650	TAUNTON	0823 335667
NEWCASTLE	091 261 6858	TOBERMORY	0688 2060
NEWRY	0693 64284	TRURO	0872 223864
NORTHAMPTON	0604 33395	WARMINSTER	0985 846091
NORWICH	0603 763165	WICK	0955 4537
NOTTINGHAM	0602 506005	YORK	0904 625625

CELLNET (V42)	2250 0860 321321(VOICE)
VODAFONE GATEWAY	970970 0635 33251(VOICE)
TELECOM GOLD DIRECT ACCESS	081 203 3033

THESE NODES SUPPORT A V32 (9600BPS) CONNECTION

ABERDEEN	0224 211230	CARDIFF	0222 223874
BELFAST	0232 241035	CHELMSFORD	0245 347317
BIRMINGHAM	021 6439911	EDINBURGH	031 3133361
BRIGHTON	0273 562724	GLASGOW	041 2216442
BRISTOL	0272 294149	GUILDFORD	0483 452273

IPSWICH	0473 288573	NEWCASTLE	091 2331146
LEEDS	0532 341058	NOTTINGHAM	0602 417498
LEICESTER	0533 532983	PLYMOUTH	0752 255912
LIVERPOOL	051 2364057	READING	0734 393958
LONDON (COLINDALE)	081 2056519	SHEFFIELD	0742 757903
LUTON	0582 415606	SOUTHAMPTON	0703 339241
MAIDSTONE	0622 685447		

Any enquiries relating to Dialplus should be directed to the GNS Front Office on 0800 181555.

INDEX